C000277196

The Open University

MST209 Mathema and models

Block 5

Contents

The Open University, Walton Hall, Milton Keynes, MK7 6AA.

First published 2005. Second edition 2008.

Edited, designed and typeset by The Open University, using the Open University TeX System.

Printed and bound in the United Kingdom by Charlesworth Press, Wakefield.

ISBN 978 0 7492 5285 4

1.1

UNIT 17   Damping, forcing and resonance

Study guide for Unit 17

This mechanics unit refers back to the contents of several earlier units. In particular, it builds upon and extends the model of simple harmonic motion which was introduced in *Unit 7*. In so doing, it uses the approach to analysing one-dimensional motion which was put forward in *Unit 6*, and also returns to the concept from that unit of a resistance force proportional to the velocity of a particle. The models which are developed here feature linear constant-coefficient second-order differential equations, whose solution was included in *Unit 3*.

The sections may be studied in their numerical order, with the computer work grouped together in Section 5. However, if you have ready access to your computer at other times, then you may wish to try some of the computer-based activities at the points indicated earlier in the text. Sections 1 and 4 both contain video sequences. It is best for these to be viewed as referred to in the text, though if necessary they could be viewed beforehand.

Introduction

In *Unit 7* you studied a model of vibrating systems based upon the concept of a model spring. This model predicted simple harmonic motion. In particular we looked at a simple experiment with a home-made oscillating system, as shown in Figure 0.1. In *Unit 7* certain qualitative features of the motion of the bag of coins were satisfactorily modelled by the assumption that the elastic string could be modelled as a model spring. There was one feature of the motion that was not satisfactorily modelled in *Unit 7* — the fact that the oscillations die away until the bag is at its equilibrium position. This feature is known as *damping* and is the first topic studied in this unit.

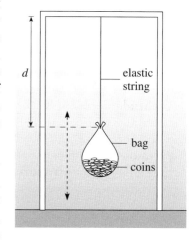

Figure 0.1

Rather than continue to model this experiment, you will meet four new oscillating system experiments in Section 1, which we shall attempt to model in this unit. Section 1 then introduces a linear model for damping. Section 2 introduces the *model damper*, which provides a convenient diagrammatic and algebraic representation of linear damping just as the model spring provides a convenient representation of a linear restoring force. After application to some everyday examples, the various types of motion brought about by the damping of an oscillatory system are summarized mathematically.

Section 3 looks at models of systems which undergo sinusoidal *forcing*, that is, an additional sinusoidal force is applied to the system. Forcing is needed to keep a system vibrating, in spite of any damping. For example, a pendulum clock may have a wound spring to force its oscillations, and a wave machine in a swimming pool is designed to keep the water vibrating. A vehicle driving over a bumpy surface, formed perhaps by cobbles or a cattle grid, is forced to vibrate by the bumps which its wheels encounter.

Resonance refers to the fact that the amplitude of the vibrations with which a system responds to periodic forcing may be much greater at some frequencies of the forcing than at others. This effect may be desired, as in the tuning of a radio. However, resonant oscillations can be unwanted and even destructive in mechanical systems, bridges and tall buildings. For this reason, platoons of soldiers are often ordered not to march in step over bridges. Designers try to choose spring stiffnesses and damping devices within system components so as to eliminate unwanted resonant behaviour over the range of frequencies likely to be encountered. The amplitude of the forced oscillations of a vehicle going over a set of bumps depends very much on the speed or frequency with which it encounters the bumps. Rumble strips on roads are therefore designed to take this into account, so that resonant vibrations are likely to occur at higher speeds and drivers are encouraged to slow down. Section 4 shows that resonance is predicted under certain circumstances by the model developed earlier for forced oscillations, and that the experimental particle–spring system also exhibits resonance.

Section 5 consists of related activities to be carried out with the computer algebra package. The results of some of these activities are referred to earlier in the text.

1 *Damping and vibrations*

The model of vibrating systems which was developed in *Unit 7* led to the prediction of *simple harmonic motion*. For a particle with position $x\mathbf{i}$ at time t, the corresponding graph of $x(t)$ is shown in Figure 1.1. The motion, about an equilibrium position $x = x_{\text{eq}}$, has amplitude A and period τ. However, in the real world no system when left to its own devices maintains oscillations of constant amplitude as predicted by this model. In reality the amplitude *decreases* with time, as illustrated in Figure 1.2, and the motion eventually dies away. This section therefore introduces a new ingredient whose inclusion in a revised model leads to predictions which match better the observed behaviour of *damped vibration*. This ingredient is a resistive force which depends upon the velocity of the particle.

This behaviour was noted for the home-made oscillating system described in *Unit 7*, Section 1.

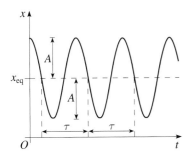

Figure 1.1

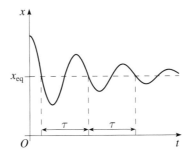

Figure 1.2

Subsection 1.1 introduces a linear model for resistance, which is applied in Subsection 1.2 to an experiment on video which involves a magnet falling down tubes with differing resistance properties. Subsection 1.3 then models a damped particle–spring system. The model is tested experimentally in the video sequence in Subsection 1.4.

1.1 *A linear damping model*

The reason for the decreasing amplitude of vibrations shown in Figure 1.2 is the effect of some form of *resistance* due either to the air in which the system is vibrating or to some other form of friction. In the context of vibrations, such frictional effects are commonly referred to as **damping** and the corresponding motion is spoken of as a **damped vibration**.

Damping can be due to a number of physical causes and there is a variety of mathematical models. As you saw in *Unit 6*, air resistance is commonly modelled as a force opposed to the motion and of magnitude proportional to some power of the speed of the body, as for example on an object falling from the Clifton Suspension Bridge. The emphasis here is not to model one particular physical cause of resistance, but to set up a general mathematical model that could apply in many situations.

In *Unit 6* linear and quadratic models for air resistance were investigated: the magnitude of the resistance force was assumed to be proportional either to the magnitude of the velocity, or to its square, where in each case the resistance force opposes the motion. In mathematical modelling it is a good principle to start with the *simplest* available mathematical model which appears reasonable, and not to complicate matters unless this initial model turns out to be inadequate. Consequently we shall begin here by assuming that a linear model applies, so we model the resistance to motion as being proportional to the velocity, but in the opposite direction.

If the velocity of the particle is $\dot{x}\mathbf{i}$, then the resistance force is assumed to be $\mathbf{R} = -r\dot{x}\mathbf{i}$, where r is a positive constant, and the minus sign shows that the direction of $\mathbf{R}$ opposes the motion. This model is called *linear damping*, and the constant r is called the *damping constant*. The model has the virtue of simplicity in that it is mathematically easy to handle, which is such an advantage that the model is sometimes used even in situations where it may not be strictly appropriate. In such circumstances you would not expect the model to give results which were accurate in detail, but it could still show the effects of resistance and friction in general terms.

In *Unit 6* when air resistance was considered, r was taken to be Dc_1, where D was the effective diameter of the object and c_1 was a constant.

The SI units of the damping constant r are $\mathrm{N\,s\,m^{-1}}$ (force divided by speed), or $\mathrm{kg\,s^{-1}}$.

Definition

The **linear damping** model assumes that the resistance force acting on a particle is proportional to the velocity, but in the opposite direction. If the velocity is $\dot{x}\mathbf{i}$, then the resistance force is modelled by

$$\mathbf{R} = -r\dot{x}\mathbf{i},$$

where r is a positive constant, called the **damping constant**.

The following example should help you recall from *Unit 6* how the linear damping model applies to motion with air resistance. It also provides some revision of the methods for solving second-order differential equations from *Unit 3*. The result obtained will be of use in Subsection 1.2.

Example 1.1

An object of mass m falls vertically under gravity. The object is to be modelled by a particle which experiences linear damping, with damping constant r, due to air resistance. Suppose that the particle has fallen a distance x after time t.

(a) Derive the equation of motion for the particle.

(b) Find the particular solution of the equation of motion for which the particle is dropped from the origin at time $t = 0$.

Solution

(a) The choice of direction for the x-axis (downwards) is determined by the fact that x is the distance fallen. The force diagram is shown in Figure 1.3. The weight of the particle is $\mathbf{W} = mg\mathbf{i}$ (acting vertically downwards). According to the linear damping model, the air resistance force is given by $\mathbf{R} = -r\dot{x}\mathbf{i}$, which opposes the motion as required.

By Newton's second law,

$$m\ddot{x}\mathbf{i} = \mathbf{W} + \mathbf{R} = mg\mathbf{i} - r\dot{x}\mathbf{i}.$$

Resolving in the $\mathbf{i}$-direction gives

$$m\ddot{x} + r\dot{x} = mg.$$

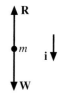

Figure 1.3

(b) This differential equation may be solved in several different ways. Since it is linear, of second order and with constant coefficients, the methods of *Unit 3* may be applied.

The differential equation is inhomogeneous, so the solution will be the sum of the complementary function (the general solution of the associated homogeneous differential equation) and a particular integral.

Another approach was adopted in Example 4.2(a) of *Unit 6*, giving a solution which agrees with that obtained here.

The associated homogeneous differential equation is

$$m\ddot{x} + r\dot{x} = 0,$$

whose auxiliary equation is

$$m\lambda^2 + r\lambda = 0.$$

This has solutions $\lambda = -r/m$ and $\lambda = 0$. The complementary function is therefore

$$x_c = Ae^{-(r/m)t} + Be^{0t} = Ae^{-rt/m} + B,$$

where A and B are arbitrary constants.

The right-hand side of the original differential equation is mg. Since this is a constant, we might think of trying a constant for the particular integral. However, there is already a constant term, B, in the complementary function, so we need here to use a trial solution of the form $x_p = pt$, where p is a constant to be determined. Substituting this into the differential equation gives $0 + rp = mg$, so $p = mg/r$. Thus $x_p = mgt/r$ is a particular integral. On adding the complementary function to this, we obtain the general solution of the equation of motion as

$$x = x_c + x_p = Ae^{-rt/m} + B + \frac{mgt}{r},$$

where A and B are arbitrary constants.

In order to find the appropriate particular solution, we need to refer to the initial conditions. Since the object is dropped from the origin at time $t = 0$, these conditions are $x(0) = 0$ and $\dot{x}(0) = 0$. Substituting the first of these into the general solution gives $0 = A + B + 0$, so $B = -A$. The derivative of the general solution is

$$\dot{x} = -\left(\frac{r}{m}\right)Ae^{-rt/m} + \frac{mg}{r},$$

from which the second initial condition gives $0 = -(r/m)A + mg/r$. Hence we obtain $A = m^2g/r^2$ and $B = -m^2g/r^2$. We conclude that

$$x = \frac{mgt}{r} - \frac{m^2g}{r^2}\left(1 - e^{-rt/m}\right) \tag{1.1}$$

is the required particular solution. ∎

Look at the form of the particular solution obtained in this example, and think about its interpretation. What does the model predict will happen?

The second term contains a negative exponential. As t increases, this exponential becomes negligibly small, and so the second term in the solution tends to a constant. The first term is linear in t. In the absence of any other significant term involving t, this represents motion at the constant speed mg/r. The model predicts, for large values of t, that the motion will be at the constant velocity $(mg/r)\mathbf{i}$, which is the terminal velocity of the object.

Terminal velocity was defined in *Unit 6*.

1.2   An experiment with damping

When a magnet moves inside a copper tube, an electromagnetic effect causes its motion to be damped. The level of damping depends upon the thickness and diameter of the tube. The video sequence associated with this subsection looks initially at the motion of a magnet falling down three different copper tubes under gravity, and also down a glass tube where only air resistance counteracts the descent. In each case, the resistive force may be modelled by linear damping as in Subsection 1.1.

Phenomena like this electromagnetic damping are beyond the scope of this course. For current purposes, you do not need to understand how this effect comes about.

The equation of motion which arises is that of Example 1.1(a), and the appropriate particular solution is given by Equation (1.1). It is possible to determine, using this equation and other measurements made, an estimate for the damping constant r for each tube.

The magnet is then attached to a particle–spring system, like those which you met in *Unit 7*, and the system is set in motion. The model of motion of an undamped system is modified in order to take the damping into account. A more detailed account of this modelling is provided in Subsection 1.3.

Note that the video uses the notation $\mathbf{x}$ in place of $\mathbf{r}$ for the position vector, and similarly $\dot{\mathbf{x}}$ for $\dot{\mathbf{r}}$ and $\ddot{\mathbf{x}}$ for $\ddot{\mathbf{r}}$. This avoids confusion between $\mathbf{r}$ and the damping constant r, and is used because bold font is hard to distinguish on a video screen. Since the motion is one-dimensional, we have $\mathbf{x} = x\mathbf{i}$, $\dot{\mathbf{x}} = \dot{x}\mathbf{i}$ and $\ddot{\mathbf{x}} = \ddot{x}\mathbf{i}$. Thus the model for linear damping appears as

$$\mathbf{R} = -r\dot{\mathbf{x}}.$$

Watch Part 1 of the video for this unit now.

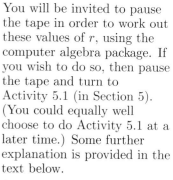

You will be invited to pause the tape in order to work out these values of r, using the computer algebra package. If you wish to do so, then pause the tape and turn to Activity 5.1 (in Section 5). (You could equally well choose to do Activity 5.1 at a later time.) Some further explanation is provided in the text below.

Alternative names for a particle–spring system, used in the video, are mass–spring system and spring–mass system.

In the first part of the video, the motion of the magnet down a tube is modelled with the origin at the top of the tube and the x-direction down the tube. This leads to the equation of motion

$$m\ddot{x} + r\dot{x} = mg,$$

which you met in Example 1.1(a). Since the magnet is dropped from the origin, the initial conditions are also the same as in Example 1.1. Hence the particular solution is, once more,

$$x = \frac{mgt}{r} - \frac{m^2 g}{r^2}\left(1 - e^{-rt/m}\right). \tag{1.1}$$

In the video the time t for the magnet to fall the length of each tube was measured. The length of each tube was $x = 1\,\mathrm{m}$. The magnet's mass was found to be $m = 0.038\,\mathrm{kg}$, and the acceleration due to gravity is $g = 9.81\,\mathrm{m\,s^{-2}}$. Using these values, Equation (1.1) can be solved numerically, to find the value of r for each tube. The results are in Table 1.1.

This is the task which you are asked to complete in Activity 5.1.

Table 1.1

Tube	Material	Time of descent (s)	Damping constant r ($\mathrm{N\,s\,m^{-1}}$)
A	Glass	0.64	0.15
B	Copper	2.52	0.92
C	Copper	3.60	1.33
D	Copper	22.60	8.42

These values for the damping constant r will be used to predict the motion of the magnet in each tube when it is attached, as in the second part of the video, to a particle–spring system.

1.3 Damping the spring motion

As you saw described in the first part of the video, the next set of experiments with the magnet and tubes involves the magnet being attached to a particle–spring system. The model of *Unit 7* is modified by the inclusion of a linear damping force $\mathbf{R}$ as well as the model spring force $\mathbf{H}$ and the weight $\mathbf{W}$ of the particle, to give the equation

$$m\ddot{x}\mathbf{i} = \mathbf{W} + \mathbf{H} + \mathbf{R}. \tag{1.2}$$

The video claimed that, with an appropriate choice of origin for x, the equation of motion could be written in the homogeneous form

$$m\ddot{x} + r\dot{x} + kx = 0,$$

where m is the mass of the particle, r is the damping constant and k is the spring stiffness. However, it was not explained how the origin should be chosen in order to achieve this, and in the current subsection we pursue this question while looking again at the modelling involved.

An alternative name for the spring stiffness, used in the video, is *spring constant*.

The experimental apparatus is shown in Figure 1.4(a), and the corresponding force diagram is Figure 1.4(b). This diagram corresponds to the situation in which the spring is extended and the particle descending, at which time both the spring force $\mathbf{H}$, and the damping force $\mathbf{R}$ will be directed upwards.

As before, we take the x-axis to be directed downwards, but for the moment leave open the choice of origin. Regardless of this choice, the acceleration of the particle is $\ddot{x}\mathbf{i}$ and its velocity is $\dot{x}\mathbf{i}$, so the linear damping force is $\mathbf{R} = -r\dot{x}\mathbf{i}$. The weight of the particle, $\mathbf{W} = mg\mathbf{i}$, is independent of where the origin is chosen. In fact, only the expression for the spring force $\mathbf{H}$ in terms of x will depend upon the choice of origin.

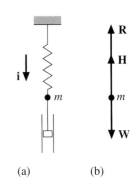

(a)   (b)

Figure 1.4

Hooke's law states that the force exerted by a model spring

$$\mathbf{H} = -k(l - l_0)\widehat{\mathbf{s}},$$

Hooke's law was introduced in *Unit 7*.

where k, l and l_0 are respectively the stiffness, length and natural length of the spring, and $\widehat{\mathbf{s}}$ is a unit vector in the direction from the centre of the spring towards the end where the particle is attached. Here we have $\widehat{\mathbf{s}} = \mathbf{i}$, so $\mathbf{H} = -k(l - l_0)\mathbf{i}$. Newton's second law (Equation (1.2)) therefore gives

$$m\ddot{x}\mathbf{i} = \mathbf{W} + \mathbf{H} + \mathbf{R} = mg\mathbf{i} - k(l - l_0)\mathbf{i} - r\dot{x}\mathbf{i},$$

which after resolution in the $\mathbf{i}$-direction leads to

$$m\ddot{x} + r\dot{x} + kl = mg + kl_0. \tag{1.3}$$

When the system is in equilibrium, we have $\dot{x} = 0$ and $\ddot{x} = 0$, so the equilibrium length l_{eq} of the spring is given by

$$0 + 0 + kl_{\text{eq}} = mg + kl_0, \quad \text{that is,} \quad l_{\text{eq}} = l_0 + \frac{mg}{k}.$$

This is the same expression for the equilibrium spring length that was derived in *Unit 7*. It is the sum of the natural length of the spring, l_0, and its equilibrium extension mg/k.

Hence Equation (1.3) can be written as

$$m\ddot{x} + r\dot{x} + kl = kl_{\text{eq}}.$$

It follows that if we take $x = l - l_{\text{eq}}$, then the equation of motion takes the homogeneous form

$$m\ddot{x} + r\dot{x} + kx = 0. \tag{1.4}$$

This choice for x corresponds to taking $x = 0$ at the point where $l = l_{\text{eq}}$, that is, choosing the origin to be *at the equilibrium position* of the particle.

Exercise 1.1

In the next set of experiments on the video, the total mass suspended from a spring of stiffness $k = 23\,\text{N}\,\text{m}^{-1}$ is $m = 0.711\,\text{kg}$. Find the equilibrium extension of the spring, taking $g = 9.81\,\text{m}\,\text{s}^{-2}$.

Exercise 1.2

Use Equation (1.3) to write down the equation of motion for the case in which the origin for x is chosen to be at the fixed upper end of the spring.

You saw in the case of the simpler model derived in *Unit 7* that the equation of motion took its simplest (homogeneous) form when the origin was chosen at the equilibrium position of the particle, and we have now shown that this continues to be true even when linear damping is incorporated in the model. Also the equilibrium position remains the same as it was without damping. This is perhaps not surprising, since when the particle is in equilibrium (at rest), the magnitude of the resistance force **R** is zero.

Whatever the choice of origin made for x, the equation of motion takes the form

$$m\ddot{x} + r\dot{x} + kx = kx_{\text{eq}}, \tag{1.5}$$

where x_{eq} is the equilibrium displacement of the particle relative to the chosen origin. We shall normally use the simplest form, Equation (1.4), for which $x_{\text{eq}} = 0$.

Notice that all the terms on the left-hand side of Equation (1.4) (or Equation (1.5)) have the same sign, and that if damping were to be removed (by putting r equal to zero), then the resulting equation would revert to that of simple harmonic motion, as derived in *Unit 7*.

In order to use our model to predict the motion of the damped particle–spring system described in the video, we need first to solve the equation of motion

$$m\ddot{x} + r\dot{x} + kx = 0. \tag{1.4}$$

This is a linear constant-coefficient second-order differential equation, so once again the methods of *Unit 3* may be applied to find the form of its solution. The auxiliary equation is

$$m\lambda^2 + r\lambda + k = 0,$$

whose roots are

$$\lambda_1 = \frac{-r + \sqrt{r^2 - 4mk}}{2m} \quad \text{and} \quad \lambda_2 = \frac{-r - \sqrt{r^2 - 4mk}}{2m}.$$

Provided that $\lambda_1 \neq \lambda_2$, the solution will then be

$$x(t) = Be^{\lambda_1 t} + Ce^{\lambda_2 t},$$

where B and C are arbitrary constants which depend on the initial conditions. If λ_1 and λ_2 are real, which they will be if $r^2 - 4mk$ is positive, then the solution is the sum of two real exponential terms. As you may recall from *Unit 3*, if the roots of the auxiliary equation are complex (in this case, when $r^2 - 4mk$ is negative), then the solution can be written in real form as an exponential times a sinusoid, that is, as

$$x(t) = e^{-\rho t}\left(B\cos(\nu t) + C\sin(\nu t)\right),$$

where $\rho = r/(2m)$, $\nu = \sqrt{4mk - r^2}/(2m)$, and B and C are arbitrary constants which depend on the initial conditions. As in *Unit 7*, the sine and cosine terms can be combined to write this solution in the form

$$x(t) = Ae^{-\rho t}\cos(\nu t + \phi), \tag{1.6}$$

where A and ϕ are arbitrary constants.

It can be seen that, under certain circumstances, the model predicts oscillations (due to the sinusoidal factor) of decreasing amplitude (since the exponential term has a negative exponent).

This equation was investigated in *Unit 3*.

The process of solving Equation (1.4) will be revisited in Section 2, so do not dwell upon the mathematical details here. The main point is that both graphical (Figure 1.5 below) and numerical (Table 1.2 below) predictions of the behaviour of the damped particle–spring system on the video can be obtained from the model.

Algebraic manipulation reveals that $B = A\cos\phi$ and $C = -A\sin\phi$. (See *Unit 7*.)

The computer algebra package can be used to produce the appropriate particular solution of Equation (1.4) and to plot the corresponding graph for each of the four tubes in the video experiments. The results are shown in Figure 1.5. Note here that the x-axis points downwards in each case, to match the direction specified in our model.

If you would like to verify these results at this stage, then turn to Activity 5.1, which also provides the numerical predictions summarized in Table 1.2 below.

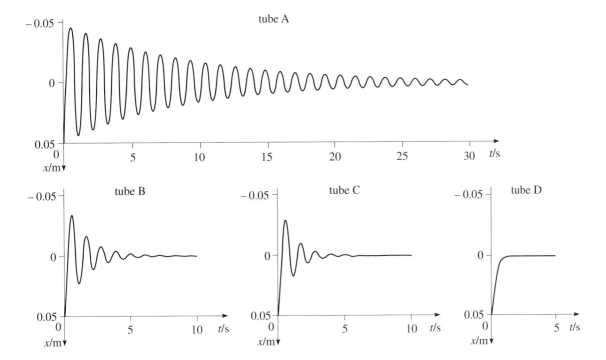

Figure 1.5   Predictions from model for each tube

These are computer-generated graphical predictions for each of the four tubes. What are the most significant features in each case?

Tube A: The graph of the solution clearly shows the amplitude of the oscillations decreasing exponentially. The amplitude corresponds to the exponential factor $Ae^{-\rho t}$ identified earlier, while the sinusoidal factor gives oscillations of constant frequency. The model predicts that the oscillations die away relatively slowly.

See Equation (1.6).

Tube B: The model again predicts decaying oscillations, though these die down more quickly than for tube A.

Tube C: The model predicts very similar motion to that for tube B.

Tube D: The model predicts no oscillations at all and a rapid return directly to the equilibrium position.

Note that for tube D, with $r = 8.42\,\mathrm{N\,s\,m^{-1}}$, the expression $4mk - r^2$ is negative, that is, $r^2 - 4mk$ is positive. In this case the auxiliary equation has two negative real roots and the solution is purely exponential (see page 12). Hence there are no oscillations in this case, as confirmed by the corresponding graph in Figure 1.5.

The model also permits us to make numerical predictions, in the cases of tubes A–C, for the period of each oscillation and the rate at which the oscillations decay. For these three tubes we have, from Equation (1.6), that the period of oscillations (in seconds) is

$$\tau = \frac{2\pi}{\nu} = \frac{4\pi m}{\sqrt{4mk - r^2}},$$

and that, over each complete oscillation, the amplitude decays by a factor $e^{-\rho\tau}$, where $\rho = r/(2m)$. With $m = 0.711\,\mathrm{kg}$ and $k = 23\,\mathrm{N\,m^{-1}}$ (as for the system on the video), we can therefore calculate the predicted values given in the last two columns of Table 1.2.

13

Table 1.2

Tube	Damping constant, r $(\mathrm{N\,s\,m^{-1}})$	Period, τ (s)	Amplitude decay factor per cycle, $e^{-\rho\tau}$
A	0.15	1.10	0.89
B	0.92	1.11	0.49
C	1.33	1.12	0.35

In the video sequence associated with the next subsection, you will be able to see how these various predictions compare with the actual experimental behaviour.

1.4 Comparing predictions with reality

Figure 1.5 provides predictions for the behaviour of the damped particle–spring system for each of the tubes. You can now see whether these predictions bear any relationship to reality.

Watch Part 2 of the video for this unit now.

As you watched the video, you probably noticed that qualitatively at least the model predicted the actual motion well. The match between the model's graphical predictions in Figure 1.5 and the video traces from the experiment in Figure 1.6 is striking.

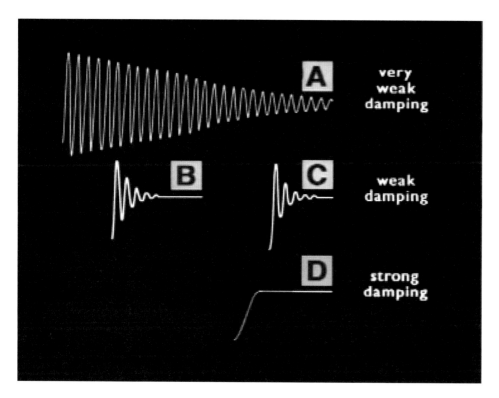

Figure 1.6   Video traces of experimental results for each tube

These traces do not give an indication of the timescale involved. Timings taken directly from the video provide an estimate of 1.1 seconds for the period of oscillations for tube A. The corresponding periods for tubes B and C are very similar, but harder to measure due to the few oscillations which occur. This period estimate is in agreement with those given in Table 1.2.

You might like to check this yourself, using a stopwatch. Time (say) 5 oscillations, then divide your reading by 5. Take the average of several readings for greater accuracy.

The tabulated predictions for the amplitude decay factor also appear to be borne out by the experiments, to the accuracy with which measurements can be made from the video traces. For example, the prediction for tube A is that the amplitude should halve over about six cycles (since $0.89^6 \simeq 0.5$), whereas for tube B the amplitude is predicted to halve approximately every cycle.

We conclude that, both qualitatively and quantitatively, the model is validated quite well by the experimental results. (There are nevertheless some discrepancies. For example, the actual decay of the amplitude in tube A does not look exponential throughout the range shown.)

When the magnet is in tube A, the damping is very light. With the magnet in either tube B or tube C, the damping level is higher but there are still some oscillations. The even higher level of damping in tube D prevents oscillations altogether. Damping like this, for which there are no oscillations, is called **strong damping**. Damping where there are decaying oscillations, as for the other three tubes, is called **weak damping**. For a system in which the level of damping can be varied continuously, there will be a cross-over point between weak and strong damping, and the corresponding level of damping is called **critical damping**. In the case of the video experiments, critical damping lies between the damping levels of tubes C and D. Critical damping gives the most rapid return to the equilibrium position, given an initial displacement, whereas very strong damping can cause a significant delay in the return to equilibrium.

In terms of the mass m, spring stiffness k and damping constant r, we have weak damping if $r^2 - 4mk < 0$, strong damping if $r^2 - 4mk > 0$ and critical damping if $r^2 - 4mk = 0$. More is said about the mathematical aspects of damping in Section 2. To conclude this section, we ask you to consider briefly what type of damping might be required in various real-world systems.

For the particle–spring system discussed in Subsection 1.3, critical damping occurs when $r = 8.09 \, \mathrm{N \, s \, m^{-1}}$.

Different levels of damping are appropriate in different situations. The baby bouncer, which you saw on the video, is more fun for the child the longer its oscillations continue, following an initial displacement, so here very weak damping is desirable.

For kitchen scales to be useful, any oscillations should die down quickly, so that readings may be taken. In this case the damping should be close to critical damping. For given kitchen scales, the values of r and k are fixed. There is then only one value m of the mass placed on the scales for which critical damping can be achieved exactly, since in this case $r^2 = 4mk$. Scales are usually designed to give a speedy return to the equilibrium position for a specified range of values of mass, and since a few small oscillations initially are acceptable, damping which is weak but close to critical is preferred. Strong damping would result in the scales taking a longer time to return to the equilibrium position, and hence hold up the taking of a reading.

Vehicle suspension systems are designed to smooth out the ride and so here strong damping is better. However, the damping should not be too strong. The spring needs to be returned close to its equilibrium position in order to be able to absorb the next jolt from the road. The time between jolts will obviously depend upon the road surface and the speed at which the vehicle is travelling. When the vehicle is carrying a heavy load, m will be larger. Designers must aim to include a level of damping which is appropriate for both the heaviest and lightest loads envisaged, as well for the different terrains and speeds likely to be encountered.

The sit-ski suspension shown in the video must similarly be strongly damped, but not so strongly that it prevents the spring from returning to near equilibrium in time to absorb the next jolt. Thus the terrain and the speed of the sit-ski are relevant factors in choosing the appropriate level of damping, as is the mass of the sit-skier. For a sit-skier who is heavier than average, a higher level of damping is required, and the sit-ski has a mechanism which permits the level of damping to be adjusted.

*Exercise 1.3

What level of damping would be appropriate for each of the following mechanisms?

(a) Buffers at the end of a railway line, which are intended to halt a train which comes into the station too fast.

(b) A device which prevents a door from slamming shut.

(c) A mechanism linking the fuel gauge of a vehicle and a float in the fuel tank, which is designed to damp fluctuations in the gauge reading caused by travel over an uneven surface.

(d) A tow-bar mechanism, which is designed to minimize the transfer of jolts from the towing to the towed vehicle or vice versa.

(e) Bathroom scales.

2 Spring–damper models of motion

This section is designed to give you practice in modelling systems where both model spring forces and linear damping forces act. As earlier in the course, this involves drawing appropriate diagrams and deriving the equation of motion. The emphasis is on setting up the model, including appropriate initial conditions, and on interpreting solutions in terms of the physical system concerned.

In order to represent linear damping diagrammatically, we introduce in Subsection 2.1 the concept of a *model damper*. This is applied to the various modelling examples which are described in Subsection 2.2. A mathematical summary of the various types of motion which can be caused by model springs and dampers is given in Subsection 2.3.

2.1   The model damper

In *Unit 7* we introduced the concept of a *model spring*. This is a convenient means of indicating diagrammatically and describing algebraically the presence of a force which depends linearly on the length l of the spring. The force exerted on a particle connected to an end of the model spring is given by

$$\mathbf{H} = -k(l - l_0)\,\widehat{\mathbf{s}}, \tag{2.1}$$

where k is the stiffness and l_0 is the natural length of the spring. The vector $\widehat{\mathbf{s}}$ is a unit vector in the direction from the centre of the model spring towards the particle (see Figure 2.1). In *Unit 7* you saw this force specification applied to model springs which had one end attached to a particle and the other kept fixed. However, the same expression for the force on the particle

Unit 7, Subsection 2.1

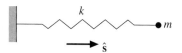

Figure 2.1

applies even when the other end of the model spring is in motion. You will see applications of this type in Section 3 and in *Unit 18*.

We now define a *model damper*. Like the model spring, this is a hypothetical one-dimensional system component which can be included in diagrams and with which a certain vector expression for force is associated. When one end of the damper is fixed, it embodies the linear damping model defined in Subsection 1.1.

Definition

A **model damper**, with a particle attached to one of its ends, provides a force on the particle which opposes its motion relative to the other end. The magnitude of this resistance force is proportional to the rate of change of length of the model damper. The force provided by the model damper (when compressing or extending) is therefore

$$\mathbf{R} = -r\dot{l}\,\widehat{\mathbf{s}}, \tag{2.2}$$

where $\dot{l}$ is the rate of change of length of the model damper, r is a positive constant (called the **damping constant**), and $\widehat{\mathbf{s}}$ is a unit vector in the direction from the centre of the model damper towards the particle. A model damper has zero mass. It is represented diagrammatically in Figure 2.2.

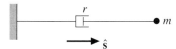

Figure 2.2

The diagrammatic representation of a model damper, as shown in Figure 2.2, is a cross-sectional picture of an actual physical device known as a **dashpot**, which involves the motion of a piston within a circular cylinder. However, you could also think of it as a picture of the magnet within a copper tube from the Section 1 video sequence, where the resistance was electromagnetic.

One form of dashpot is used as the shock-absorber on a car, where the cylinder is full of oil and the relative motion of the piston causes oil to flow through the small annular gap between piston and cylinder. This provides resistance to the relative motion.

When used in a diagram, the model damper simply indicates the presence of a force of the type described by Equation (2.2), just as a model spring on a diagram stands for a force of the type given by Equation (2.1). Thus we could represent the modelling of the damped particle–spring system on the video as shown in Figure 2.3. This is a more abstract form of Figure 1.4(a), but it indicates clearly the assumed presence of linear damping, which the former diagram does not do.

Although we represent a model spring and a model damper as independent elements, they may correspond to a single physical entity (a real spring, say) which exhibits to some extent both types of force behaviour. For example, the elastic string from which a bag of coins was hung in *Unit 7* shows spring-like behaviour but also seems to exhibit considerable 'internal friction', which may be a more significant factor than air resistance in reducing the amplitude of oscillations. If we were to model this internal friction as being linear, then Figure 2.3 as it stands would suffice to represent our model for the bag plus elastic string.

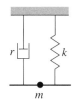

Figure 2.3

Exercise 2.1

(a) Suppose that a model damper is attached to a particle at one end and to a fixed point at the other, where the damper lies along the direction of motion of the particle (described by an x-axis). Show that Equation (2.2) leads in this case to the expression

$$\mathbf{R} = -r\dot{x}\mathbf{i}$$

(as in the definition of linear damping in Subsection 1.1, page 8) for either of the possible choices of x-direction.

(b) Suppose now that the end of the model damper not attached to the particle is made to move in such a way that its position on the x-axis is given at time t by $y(t)\mathbf{i}$. Show that Equation (2.2) now leads to

$$\mathbf{R} = -r(\dot{x} - \dot{y})\mathbf{i}.$$

Note that the model damper is very much a first model of damping effects, and may not describe accurately what occurs in real systems except over small ranges of the relative velocity. However, its simplicity makes it convenient to use, and it is capable (as you saw in Section 1) of providing reasonable representations of certain damped systems.

2.2   Applying model dampers

The examples and exercises in this subsection present a number of situations where there is some damping. In each case you are invited to consider carefully the setting up of the model, by drawing diagrams and then using Newton's second law to obtain the equation of motion. Do not focus too much here on how to solve the differential equations which arise. Concentrate rather on the modelling, including the specification of initial conditions and the way in which they enable values for the arbitrary constants to be found. Think also about the interpretation of the solutions.

The methods required to solve these differential equations are from Unit 3.

Example 2.1

A toy train of mass $2\,\mathrm{kg}$, travelling on a straight horizontal track, freewheels into buffers at a speed of $0.25\,\mathrm{m\,s^{-1}}$. The buffers are to be modelled by a model spring, with stiffness $25\,\mathrm{N\,m^{-1}}$, together with a model damper with damping constant $15\,\mathrm{N\,s\,m^{-1}}$. Use this model to predict the subsequent motion. In particular, by how much will the buffers be compressed, and what happens to the train thereafter? Comment on the validity of the model.

Solution

The model of the buffers is shown in Figure 2.4(a). The train is represented by a particle, and the model spring and model damper are assumed to be joined at their non-fixed ends. The origin is taken to be where the free end of the spring is situated when the length of the spring is equal to its natural length. This is the point at which the front of the train will first come into contact with the buffers. The train's initial direction of travel is taken to be the positive x-direction.

The corresponding force diagram is Figure 2.4(b). Since the weight $\mathbf{W}$ of the train and normal reaction $\mathbf{N}$ on it from the track are vertical forces which balance each other, they have been omitted from the analysis below. As with model springs, there is in general no single choice of direction for the model damper force which is correct at all times, but for the purposes of the force diagram, *either of the possible choices will do*. The directions for $\mathbf{H}$ and $\mathbf{R}$ in Figure 2.4(b) correspond to the model spring being compressed and the model damper shortening.

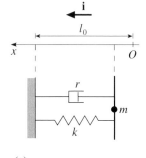

(a)

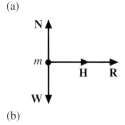

(b)

Figure 2.4

From Equation (2.1), the model spring force is

$$\mathbf{H} = -k(l - l_0)\,\widehat{\mathbf{s}} = -k(l_0 - x - l_0)(-\mathbf{i}) = -kx\mathbf{i}$$

and, from Equation (2.2) and Exercise 2.1(a), the resistance force is

$$\mathbf{R} = -r\dot{l}\,\widehat{\mathbf{s}} = -r\dot{x}\mathbf{i}.$$

The equation of motion is therefore

$$m\ddot{x}\mathbf{i} = \mathbf{H} + \mathbf{R} = -kx\mathbf{i} - r\dot{x}\mathbf{i},$$

which after resolution in the **i**-direction gives

$$m\ddot{x} + r\dot{x} + kx = 0.$$

This is Equation (1.4) once more.

Substituting the given values $m = 2\,\text{kg}$, $k = 25\,\text{N}\,\text{m}^{-1}$ and $r = 15\,\text{N}\,\text{s}\,\text{m}^{-1}$, we have

$$2\ddot{x} + 15\dot{x} + 25x = 0.$$

The corresponding auxiliary equation is $2\lambda^2 + 15\lambda + 25 = 0$, which has roots $\lambda = -5$ and $\lambda = -2.5$. Hence the general solution of the differential equation is

$$x = Ae^{-5t} + Be^{-2.5t},$$

where A and B are arbitrary constants which depend upon the initial conditions. In order to find the appropriate particular solution, we need to formulate these initial conditions.

Note that in this case $r^2 - 4mk = 25$, which is positive. According to the criterion obtained in Section 1 (see page 15), this confirms that the buffers will provide strong damping, with real exponential terms in the solution, rather than decaying oscillations.

Choose the origin of time as the instant at which the particle representing the train makes contact with the buffers. The initial conditions are then $x(0) = 0$ and $\dot{x}(0) = 0.25$. Substituting the first of these into the general solution gives $0 = A + B$, so we have $B = -A$. To apply the second initial condition, we need first to differentiate the general solution, obtaining

$$\dot{x} = -5Ae^{-5t} - 2.5Be^{-2.5t}.$$

Substituting $\dot{x}(0) = 0.25$ and $B = -A$ here gives $0.25 = -5A + 2.5A$, so $A = -0.1$ and $B = 0.1$. Putting these values for A and B into the general solution gives the required particular solution as

$$x = 0.1\left(e^{-2.5t} - e^{-5t}\right).$$

The graph of this position function is shown in Figure 2.5.

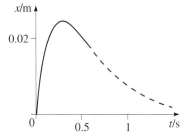

Figure 2.5

We now need to interpret this solution in order to predict the motion of the train after it meets the buffers. Clearly, the buffers will be compressed. The maximum compression is achieved when x is a maximum, for which $\dot{x} = 0$ (the train's velocity is zero). This occurs when

$$\dot{x} = -0.25e^{-2.5t} + 0.5e^{-5t} = 0, \quad \text{that is, when} \quad 1 = 2e^{-2.5t}.$$

Here we have divided through by $e^{-2.5t}$ and noted that
$$e^{-5t} = \left(e^{-2.5t}\right)^2.$$

The corresponding time is $t = 0.4\ln 2 \simeq 0.28$ seconds, and (putting this time into the particular solution) the maximum compression is $x = 0.1(\frac{1}{2} - \frac{1}{4}) = 0.025$ metres. The model predicts that the buffers will be compressed by 0.025 metres (2.5 cm). For this to be reasonable, the spring must have a natural length longer than this! Otherwise, the model predicts that the train will compress the spring to zero length without being brought to a halt, which might result in the train breaking through the buffers or becoming derailed.

It remains to consider what happens to the train after it has been instantaneously brought to rest at the point of maximum compression for the model spring. As expected, and as the graph in Figure 2.5 indicates, it then starts to move back in the direction from which it arrived. However, the spring–damper is not attached to the train and so can only 'push' it, not 'pull' it. If at some time the model predicts a total force on the particle which is in the positive x-direction, then the model has become invalid. This will correspond to a moment at which the train has lost contact with the buffers.

According to Newton's second law, the total force on the particle is equal to $m\ddot{x}\mathbf{i}$, so the train leaves the buffers where $\ddot{x}$ becomes positive. This is where the graph in Figure 2.5 changes to a broken line. Differentiation of the expression above for $\dot{x}$ gives

$$\ddot{x} = 0.625e^{-2.5t} - 2.5e^{-5t} = 0.625e^{-2.5t}\left(1 - 4e^{-2.5t}\right).$$

This expression becomes positive when $4e^{-2.5t}$ is less than 1, which happens after $t = 0.4\ln 4 \simeq 0.55$ seconds. Therefore the corresponding position of the particle is $x = 0.1(\frac{1}{4} - \frac{1}{16}) \simeq 0.019$ metres, which is $0.6\,\text{cm}$ back from the point of maximum compression. The velocity at this time is $\dot{x}\mathbf{i}$, where $\dot{x} = -0.25 \times \frac{1}{4} + 0.5 \times \frac{1}{16} \simeq -0.031\,\text{m s}^{-1}$.

We conclude that provided the buffers are long enough to sustain the maximum compression, they are predicted to turn an incoming speed of $0.25\,\text{m s}^{-1}$ into an outgoing speed of $0.031\,\text{m s}^{-1}$. This is the sort of effect which buffers are intended to have! ■

In the example above, we chose the x-axis to be directed from the track towards the buffers, with origin at the point where the train first comes into contact with the buffers. If the opposite direction were to be chosen for the x-axis, with the same origin, then the equation of motion would not be altered. The initial condition $x(0) = 0$ is unchanged, while that for $\dot{x}$ has the opposite sign, that is, $\dot{x}(0) = -0.25$. The solution for x, correspondingly, has its sign reversed.

If, on the other hand, we selected a different point for the origin (with either direction for the x-axis), the equation of motion would become

$$m\ddot{x} + r\dot{x} + kx = kx_{\text{eq}},$$

where x_{eq} is the value of x where the train meets the buffers. The initial conditions are now $x(0) = x_{\text{eq}}$, $\dot{x}(0) = \pm 0.25$, where the sign for $\dot{x}(0)$ depends on the choice of x-direction, as discussed above. The solution for x is altered by the addition of x_{eq} to the expression obtained previously (when the origin is at the point where the train meets the buffers).

As you would expect, the eventual answers to the problem in Example 2.1 do not depend on the choices of origin or direction for the x-axis. The interpretation is the same in each case.

Exercise 2.2

A miniature train of mass $40\,\text{kg}$, travelling on a straight horizontal track, freewheels into buffers at a speed of $1\,\text{m s}^{-1}$. The buffers are to be modelled by a model spring, with stiffness $140\,\text{N m}^{-1}$, together with a model damper with damping constant $180\,\text{N s m}^{-1}$. The x-axis is chosen directed away from the buffers down the track (in the direction opposite to the incoming train), with origin at the fixed end of the model spring. The natural length of the model spring is 0.5 metres.

(a) Show that the equation of motion can be written as

$$4\ddot{x} + 18\dot{x} + 14x = 7,$$

and use the $r^2 - 4mk$ criterion to say if the damping is strong or weak.

(b) Write down a pair of initial conditions for the motion of the train while in contact with the buffers.

(c) The solution of the equation of motion which satisfies the initial conditions of part (b) is

$$x = 0.5 - 0.4e^{-t} + 0.4e^{-3.5t}.$$

What is the maximum compression of the buffers? At what point, and with what speed, does the train leave the buffers?

Notice that the curvature of the graph reverses where the graph changes to a broken line; there is a point of inflection, where $\ddot{x}$ changes sign.

The speed decrease is also evidence of a very significant decrease in the train's kinetic energy. There is not space in this unit to focus further on the topic of energy, beyond pointing out that the presence of damping in a system will always entail loss of energy, and that heavier damping means a greater rate of loss of energy.

This is Equation (1.5) once more.

(d) Suppose that the damping constant were altered to $120 \, \text{N} \, \text{s} \, \text{m}^{-1}$, with other parameters of the system as before. Without solving the differential equation, say how you would expect the nature of the predictions to be altered.

Example 2.2

A baby bouncer suspension (see Figure 2.6) is modelled by a model spring, with stiffness $200 \, \text{N} \, \text{m}^{-1}$. There is some internal damping in the suspension and there is some air resistance, which together can be modelled by a model damper with damping constant $0.2 \, \text{N} \, \text{s} \, \text{m}^{-1}$. The bouncer is designed for a baby whose mass is about $10 \, \text{kg}$.

Set up the equation of motion for the model, and find the particular solution for the case in which the baby is released from rest when 0.3 metres above its equilibrium position. Use the model to predict how long it takes before the amplitude of the oscillations drops below 0.05 metres, if the baby is not pushed in any way.

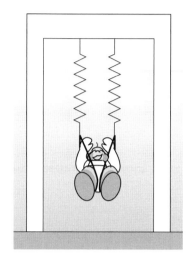

Figure 2.6

Solution

The system and force diagram are shown in Figure 2.7. We model the baby as a particle. Assume that the mass of the baby (plus the parts of the baby bouncer suspended from the spring) is $m = 10 \, \text{kg}$. Take the origin at the top of the spring, with the x-axis pointing downwards. The forces acting on the baby are the weight $\mathbf{W} = mg\mathbf{i}$, the model spring force $\mathbf{H} = -k(x - l_0)\mathbf{i}$ and the resistance force $\mathbf{R} = -r\dot{x}\mathbf{i}$. Newton's second law gives

$$m\ddot{x}\mathbf{i} = \mathbf{W} + \mathbf{H} + \mathbf{R}$$
$$= mg\mathbf{i} - k(x - l_0)\mathbf{i} - r\dot{x}\mathbf{i},$$

which leads, after resolution in the $\mathbf{i}$-direction, to the equation of motion

$$m\ddot{x} + r\dot{x} + kx = mg + kl_0.$$

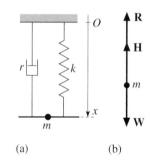

Figure 2.7

The right-hand side can be written as kx_{eq}, where $x_{\text{eq}} = mg/k + l_0$ is the equilibrium position of the baby. Hence $x = x_{\text{eq}}$ is a particular integral of the differential equation. After substituting the given values for m, k and r, the associated homogeneous differential equation has auxiliary equation

$$10\lambda^2 + 0.2\lambda + 200 = 0,$$

which has solutions $\lambda = -0.01 \pm 4.5i$ (to two significant figures). This leads to the complementary function

$$Ae^{-0.01t} \cos(4.5t + \phi),$$

where A and ϕ are arbitrary constants, so the general solution is

$$x = Ae^{-0.01t} \cos(4.5t + \phi) + x_{\text{eq}}.$$

This represents decaying oscillations about the equilibrium position.

In order to find the particular solution, we need the initial conditions. Since the baby is released from rest at 0.3 metres above the equilibrium position, these are $x(0) = x_{\text{eq}} - 0.3$ and $\dot{x}(0) = 0$. These give

$$-0.3 = Ae^0 \cos\phi \quad \text{and} \quad 0 = Ae^0(-0.01 \cos\phi - 4.5 \sin\phi).$$

Solving these leads to $A \simeq 0.30$ metres, so the amplitude of the decaying oscillations is about $0.30e^{-0.01t}$ metres. This reduces to 0.05 metres when $0.30e^{-0.01t} = 0.05$, or $t = 100 \ln 6 \simeq 180$ seconds (about 3 minutes). ∎

Exercise 2.3

As you may recall from the video, a sit-ski is a seat attached above a ski, with a spring–damper suspension. The spring is chosen according to the weight of the skier. The damper can be adjusted according to the skier's weight and the terrain. Suppose that a particular sit-ski suspension is modelled as a model spring–damper system, with spring natural length 0.2 metres, stiffness $30\,000\,\mathrm{N\,m^{-1}}$, damping constant $6300\,\mathrm{N\,s\,m^{-1}}$ and the skier (plus seat) as a single particle of mass 60 kg. Take the acceleration due to gravity as $g = 9.81\,\mathrm{m\,s^{-2}}$. Figure 2.8 represents the sit-ski with skier.

Figure 2.8

(a) Draw the diagram for the forces acting on the skier. Take the x-axis to be directed upwards, with origin at ground level, and obtain the corresponding equation of motion.

(b) Suppose that the skier is lowered onto the seat and then released from rest when the spring has its natural length. Write down the corresponding initial conditions for the skier's subsequent motion.

(c) Given that the required particular solution of the equation of motion is $x = x_{\mathrm{eq}} + 0.021e^{-5t} - 0.001e^{-100t}$ (in metres), find approximately how long the model predicts that it will take before the skier's displacement is within 0.001 metres (1 mm) of the equilibrium position.

We look next at a different type of situation, which however leads to an equation of motion very similar to those seen already. The fuel gauge for a vehicle is connected to a mechanism which monitors the level of fuel in the tank. This mechanism is designed to damp oscillations in the gauge reading after disturbances such as those caused by travel over bumps on the road. The mechanism includes a float on the surface of the liquid in the fuel tank, and the buoyancy force of the liquid on this float acts in an analogous way to a spring. A buoyancy force, sometimes called an *upthrust*, is experienced by any object which is wholly or partly immersed in a liquid. If the object floats in equilibrium on the surface of a liquid, then the upthrust from the liquid balances the weight of the object (see Figure 2.9). If you push the object down further into the liquid, then there is a greater upthrust pushing it back up. When you lift the object up a little from its equilibrium position, the upthrust is less and the weight of the object pulls it down again.

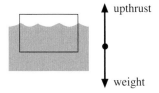

Figure 2.9

According to Archimedes' principle, the upthrust is directed vertically upward and is equal in magnitude to the weight of liquid displaced by the object. It follows that if the object has a constant horizontal cross-section, then the magnitude of the upthrust on it is proportional to the depth of its base below the surface of the liquid. In fact, if the displacement of the base (measured downwards from the surface of the liquid) is $x\mathbf{i}$, then the upthrust is $-kx\mathbf{i}$, where k is a constant that depends upon the density of the liquid and the cross-sectional area of the floating object. (For this model to be valid, the object must be at least partly immersed in the liquid, but not wholly submerged.) Hence the float system in a vehicle's fuel tank can be modelled by a model spring–damper system, provided that the length of the spring is regarded as being equal to its natural length when its non-fixed

Archimedes' principle was quoted in *Unit 7*, Exercise 4.9, in the context of simple harmonic motion.

In fact, $k = \rho A g$, where ρ is the liquid density, A is the cross-sectional area and g is the acceleration due to gravity.

end is at the level specified by the liquid surface. However, it may be more straightforward to write down the upthrust force directly, as in Example 2.3 below. The return to equilibrium should be rapid, for ease of reading the fuel gauge, and hence the system requires near-critical damping.

Example 2.3

The mechanism in a particular fuel tank is to be modelled by a model spring–damper system. The upthrust from the liquid fuel on the float is equal in magnitude to twice the weight of the float times the proportion of the float below the surface. The mass of the float is $m = 0.1$ kg, its vertical height is $d = 0.01$ metres, and the damping constant is $r = 21\,\mathrm{N\,s\,m^{-1}}$. Take $g = 9.81\,\mathrm{m\,s^{-2}}$. Find the equation of motion, and solve it for the case in which the motion begins with the base of the float 0.01 metres below the surface with zero velocity. Hence predict when the float will be less than 0.001 metres (1 mm) from its equilibrium position, assuming that there is no further disturbance.

> This formula for the upthrust is specific to this example. It corresponds to the equilibrium position of the float being half in and half out of the fuel.

Solution

Take x as the downward displacement of the bottom of the float from the surface of the liquid (see Figure 2.10). Then the unit vector $\mathbf{i}$ points downwards.

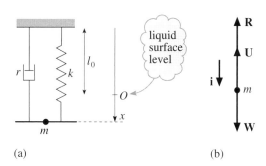

(a)   (b)

Figure 2.10

The upthrust from the fluid is $\mathbf{U} = -2mg(x/d)\mathbf{i}$, the weight is $\mathbf{W} = mg\mathbf{i}$ and the damping resistance force is $\mathbf{R} = -r\dot{x}\mathbf{i}$. Hence, using Newton's second law, we obtain

> In other words, the stiffness of the model spring equivalent to the upthrust is $k = 2mg/d$.

$$m\ddot{x}\mathbf{i} = \mathbf{W} + \mathbf{U} + \mathbf{R} = mg\mathbf{i} - (2mg/d)x\mathbf{i} - r\dot{x}\mathbf{i},$$

which leads to the equation of motion

$$m\ddot{x} + r\dot{x} + (2mg/d)x = mg.$$

Once the parameter values have been substituted, the general solution is found to be

$$x = Ae^{-200t} + Be^{-9.80t} + 0.005.$$

The initial conditions are $x(0) = 0.01$ and $\dot{x}(0) = 0$, which give the particular solution

$$x = 0.005\,26e^{-9.80t} - 0.000\,257e^{-200t} + 0.005 \text{ (metres)}.$$

There are three terms in the solution. The last represents the equilibrium position of 0.005 metres. The second involves e^{-200t}, which dies away very quickly, and the other term is the dominant term in the variable part of the solution, namely $0.005\,26e^{-9.80t}$. This will reduce to 0.001 metres when $e^{-9.80t} = 0.190$, that is, when $t = -(\ln 0.190)/9.80 \simeq 0.17$ seconds. Hence the model predicts that the displacement of the float will be within 1 mm of its equilibrium position in less than a fifth of a second. ∎

Exercise 2.4

Modify the model from Example 2.3 for a mechanism where the upthrust from the fluid fuel is again equal in magnitude to that of twice the weight of the float times the proportion of the float below the surface level, and the mass of the float is again $m = 0.1\,\mathrm{kg}$, but now the vertical height of the float is $d = 0.02$ metres and the damping constant is $r = 11\,\mathrm{N\,s\,m^{-1}}$. Take $g = 9.81\,\mathrm{m\,s^{-2}}$.

(a) Derive the equation of motion, and write down the initial conditions for the case in which the motion begins with the base of the float at the liquid surface with zero velocity.

(b) Given that the particular solution for the initial conditions described in part (a) is $x = 0.001\,08e^{-100.2t} - 0.0111e^{-9.79t} + 0.01$ (metres) predict when the float will be less than 0.001 metres (1 mm) from its equilibrium position, assuming that there is no further disturbance.

Exercise 2.5

Bathroom scales can be modelled by a model spring–damper system, as shown in Figure 2.11. If the stiffness of the spring is $k = 50\,000\,\mathrm{N\,m^{-1}}$ and the damping constant is $r = 5000\,\mathrm{N\,s\,m^{-1}}$, what mass of person standing on the scales will give critical damping? What would you expect to happen if a slightly heavier or lighter person stood on the scales?

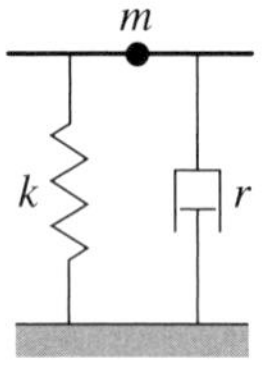

Figure 2.11

All the models encountered in this subsection have led to equations of motion of the form

$$m\ddot{x} + r\dot{x} + kx = kx_{\mathrm{eq}}, \tag{2.3}$$

where x_{eq} is the equilibrium position of the particle. The following points should now be apparent.

- In Equation (2.3), only the expression for x_{eq} depends upon the choices of origin and direction for the x-axis.

- If the origin is chosen to be the equilibrium position of the particle, then Equation (2.3) reduces to its homogeneous form

$$m\ddot{x} + r\dot{x} + kx = 0. \tag{2.4}$$

- Given any solution to Equation (2.4), there is a corresponding solution to Equation (2.3) obtainable by adding the constant x_{eq}.

In fact, x_{eq} is a particular integral for Equation (2.3).

Hence Equation (2.4) always describes the motion of the system *relative to the equilibrium position*. In the next subsection, we summarize the mathematical possibilities which arise when solving this differential equation.

We have concentrated on systems with a single model spring and a single model damper, but it is easy to extend the results to situations where more than one model spring or damper is present, acting as before along an x-axis. All that needs to be done is to add an appropriate force term to the right-hand side of Newton's second law for each component present. For example, if there are two model springs, with stiffnesses k_1 and k_2, then for motion relative to the equilibrium position we again obtain Equation (2.4), with $k = k_1 + k_2$. In other words, the combined effect of the two model springs is equivalent to that of a single model spring with stiffness $k_1 + k_2$. A similar result holds for model dampers: the combined effect of two model dampers, with damping constants r_1 and r_2, is equivalent to that of a single model damper with damping constant $r_1 + r_2$.

2.3 Weak, critical and strong damping

A mechanical system whose equation of motion is of the form (2.3) or (2.4) is called a **damped linear harmonic oscillator**, or **damped harmonic oscillator** for short. In the absence of damping, the equation reduces to that of a simple harmonic oscillator, whose motion you studied in *Unit 7*.

In this subsection we shall summarize the types of behaviour which can occur for a damped harmonic oscillator. We concentrate on the equation of motion

During this subsection, you may like to refer to Procedure 1.1 in *Unit 3*.

$$m\ddot{x} + r\dot{x} + kx = 0, \tag{2.4}$$

for which the motion of the particle is described relative to its equilibrium position. The auxiliary equation for Equation (2.4) is

$$m\lambda^2 + r\lambda + k = 0,$$

whose roots are

$$\lambda_1 = \frac{-r + \sqrt{r^2 - 4mk}}{2m} \quad \text{and} \quad \lambda_2 = \frac{-r - \sqrt{r^2 - 4mk}}{2m}. \tag{2.5}$$

The form of solution falls into one of three types, depending on whether the expression $r^2 - 4mk$ is positive, negative or zero. These three cases correspond respectively to strong, weak and critical damping.

Before examining each case in turn, we introduce the **damping ratio**

$$\alpha = \sqrt{\frac{r^2}{4mk}} = \frac{r}{2\sqrt{mk}}, \tag{2.6}$$

which makes more transparent some of the mathematical descriptions. For example, since $r^2 - 4mk = 4mk(\alpha^2 - 1)$, the conditions for strong, weak and critical damping can be expressed in terms of the damping ratio as $\alpha > 1$, $\alpha < 1$ and $\alpha = 1$, respectively. Whereas the damping *constant* r provides an absolute value for the damping force per unit speed exerted on the particle, the damping *ratio* gives a measure of how important damping is *relative* to the mass m and spring stiffness k of the system. Note that α is a dimensionless quantity, since the dimensions of r are the same as those of $\sqrt{mk}$.

Exercise 2.6

Increasing the damping constant r (while keeping the mass m and stiffness k fixed) will increase the damping ratio α. What other changes in parameters will increase α?

Exercise 2.7

For the spring–damper system shown on the video in Section 1, the mass was $m = 0.711\,\text{kg}$ and the spring stiffness was $k = 23\,\text{N}\,\text{m}^{-1}$. The damping constants r (in $\text{N}\,\text{s}\,\text{m}^{-1}$) for tubes A–D were, respectively, 0.15, 0.92, 1.33, 8.42. Find the corresponding damping ratios, and verify that tubes A–C provide weak damping while tube D provides strong damping.

We now look in turn at each of the three cases of damping identified above, but as a preliminary there is a reminder of the situation with no damping that you saw in *Unit 7*.

No damping

If there is no damping, then we have $r = 0$ and $\alpha = 0$. From Equation (2.5), the roots of the auxiliary equation are

$$\lambda_1 = \frac{\sqrt{-4mk}}{2m} = i\sqrt{\frac{k}{m}} \quad \text{and} \quad \lambda_2 = -\frac{\sqrt{-4mk}}{2m} = -i\sqrt{\frac{k}{m}}.$$

The motion is simple harmonic, as described by the solution

$$x(t) = A\cos(\omega t + \phi),$$

where A and ϕ are arbitrary constants, and $\omega = \sqrt{k/m}$ is the *natural* (un-damped) *angular frequency*. In practice, we restrict A to be positive, and call it the *amplitude* of the motion. The *period* of the motion is $\tau = 2\pi/\omega$, and ϕ, restricted to the range $-\pi < \phi \leq \pi$, is called the *phase* or *phase angle*. A graph of $x(t)$, with $\phi = 0$, is shown in Figure 2.12.

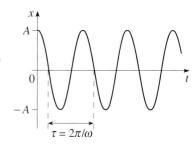

Figure 2.12

We shall refer to the natural angular frequency ω again below.

Weak damping

For weak damping, $r^2 - 4mk < 0$ and $\alpha < 1$. The solution to Equation (2.4) is the product of a decaying exponential and a sinusoidal function, namely

$$x(t) = Ae^{-\rho t}\cos(\nu t + \phi), \tag{2.7}$$

where $\rho = r/(2m)$, $\nu = \sqrt{4mk - r^2}/(2m)$, and A and ϕ are arbitrary constants. (As before, we restrict A to be positive, and the phase ϕ to be within the range $-\pi < \phi \leq \pi$.) A graph of this motion is shown in Figure 2.13.

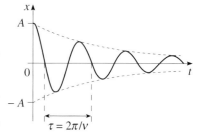

Figure 2.13

For simple harmonic motion, the period is the time to complete one cycle. Here the motion does not repeat itself and so we generalize the definition. The **period** τ of the motion is the time between successive zeros of x where the particle is moving in the same direction. In Equation (2.7) the angular frequency is ν and the period is $\tau = 2\pi/\nu$.

This definition of *period* was used in the special case of Section 1 of *Unit 7*.

To investigate Equation (2.7) further, we write the parameters ρ and ν in terms of the damping ratio $\alpha = r/(2\sqrt{mk})$ and the natural angular frequency $\omega = \sqrt{k/m}$. To do this we first note that

$$\omega\alpha = \sqrt{\frac{k}{m}} \times \frac{r}{2\sqrt{mk}} = \frac{r}{2m} = \rho.$$

The angular frequency ν can also be written in terms of ω and α:

$$\nu = \frac{\sqrt{4mk - r^2}}{2m} = \frac{2\sqrt{mk}\sqrt{1 - r^2/4mk}}{2m} = \sqrt{\frac{k}{m}}\sqrt{1 - \alpha^2} = \omega\sqrt{1 - \alpha^2}.$$

The broken curves in Figure 2.13, corresponding to the two graphs $x = \pm Ae^{-\omega\alpha t}$, indicate how quickly the oscillations decay (larger α gives more rapid decay). The angular frequency $\nu = \omega\sqrt{1 - \alpha^2}$ is less than the natural angular frequency ω; so the period $\tau = 2\pi/\nu$ is greater than the period of undamped oscillations (becoming larger as α increases). If α is close to zero, then the period τ is very close to its undamped value $2\pi/\omega$ (because τ depends on the square of α, namely $\tau = 2\pi/(\omega\sqrt{1 - \alpha^2})$).

The negative exponent $-\omega\alpha t$ ensures that $Ae^{-\omega\alpha t}$ is a decreasing function.

For simple harmonic motion, the amplitude is the constant maximum displacement from the mean position. In this motion the maximum displacement from the mean position is not constant, so we define the **amplitude** to be the positive and continually changing quantity $Ae^{-\omega\alpha t}$. Over one cycle, of period τ, the amplitude of the motion decreases from $Ae^{-\omega\alpha t}$ to $Ae^{-\omega\alpha(t+\tau)}$, which is equivalent to $Ae^{-\omega\alpha t}e^{-\omega\alpha\tau}$, so $Ae^{-\omega\alpha t}$ is multiplied by the factor

$$e^{-\omega\alpha\tau} = \exp\left(-\frac{2\pi\alpha}{\sqrt{1 - \alpha^2}}\right).$$

This effect was apparent in Table 1.2, where the periods for tubes A–C from the video were very close to the undamped value of 1.10 seconds.

This is the amplitude decay factor per cycle, which was used to make predictions for the magnet motion within tubes A–C in Table 1.2.

Exercise 2.8

Suppose that the period of a weakly damped harmonic oscillator is greater by 10% than the corresponding undamped period $2\pi/\omega$. Show that the amplitude of the motion decays by a factor of about 0.056 per cycle.

A conclusion from the result of Exercise 2.8 is that if the period is very different from the undamped value, then few oscillations will be visible on a graph.

Strong damping

Now consider the solution of Equation (2.4) when $r^2 - 4mk > 0$, that is, when $\alpha > 1$. Here the auxiliary equation has real roots, namely

$$\lambda_1 = \frac{-r + \sqrt{r^2 - 4mk}}{2m} \quad \text{and} \quad \lambda_2 = \frac{-r - \sqrt{r^2 - 4mk}}{2m}, \tag{2.5}$$

and the corresponding solution is

$$x(t) = Be^{\lambda_1 t} + Ce^{\lambda_2 t}, \tag{2.8}$$

where B and C are arbitrary constants. In terms of the natural angular frequency ω and the damping ratio α, Equations (2.5) can be written as

$$\lambda_1 = \omega\left(-\alpha + \sqrt{\alpha^2 - 1}\right) \quad \text{and} \quad \lambda_2 = \omega\left(-\alpha - \sqrt{\alpha^2 - 1}\right).$$

Both λ_1 and λ_2 are negative since $\alpha > \sqrt{\alpha^2 - 1}$. Hence solution (2.8) is a sum of two *decaying* exponentials. Solutions of this type predict a return to the equilibrium position without oscillation (see Figure 2.14), although the graph of x against t may cross the t-axis once.

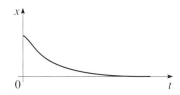

Figure 2.14

Exercise 2.9

As α increases from 1, what happens to the values of λ_1 and λ_2? Which of the exponential terms in Equation (2.8) will be the dominant term for very strongly damped systems?

Critical damping

Finally, we consider the solution of Equation (2.4) when $r^2 - 4mk = 0$, that is, when $\alpha = 1$. Here we have equal roots to the auxiliary equation, namely

$$\lambda_1 = \lambda_2 = -\frac{r}{2m} = -\omega\alpha = -\omega.$$

From Section 4 of *Unit 3*, the corresponding solution is

$$x(t) = (Bt + C)e^{-\omega t},$$

where B and C are arbitrary constants. Solutions of this form do not represent oscillations, although the graph of x against t may cross the t-axis once. The graph (see Figure 2.15) resembles that for strong damping, but the system returns more quickly to close to the equilibrium position.

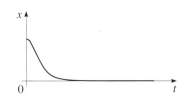

Figure 2.15

In conclusion, note that there is a continuum of behaviour from weak damping, with marked decaying oscillations, through near-critical damping, with a rapid return towards the equilibrium position, to strong damping, with a slower return towards the equilibrium position. Figures 2.12 to 2.15 above show snapshots of the possible behaviour along this continuum — more can be obtained rapidly with the aid of your computer.

3 Forcing the oscillations

All the damped solutions obtained in Section 2 have the property that they tend over time towards the equilibrium position of the particle, with the motion dying away. Sometimes, in addition to the effect of the model spring and damper, we need to model a further force which acts to keep the system moving. For example, the sit-ski may go over bumpy terrain or an adult may push the baby in the baby bouncer. The motion of a model spring–damper system which is subjected to an additional time-dependent force is said to be **forced**.

This was investigated in Section 4 of *Unit 3*.

There are several distinct ways of providing the forcing to a damped particle–spring system. In Subsection 3.1 we look at the case in which a periodic force is applied to the particle itself. This could, for example, model the regular forcing of the baby bouncer motion by pushing the baby. In Subsection 3.2 we turn to alternative possibilities in which the force arises due to the prescribed displacement of some point of the system other than the particle itself. The end of the model spring or damper not attached to the particle would be such a point. For example, the baby bouncer motion could be forced by the action of a motor which moves the top end of the spring up and down. For the sit-ski suspension, it is the base of the model spring–damper which is displaced, due to contact with an uneven surface beneath. In Subsection 3.3 we summarize mathematically how the amended equation of motion may be solved.

3.1 Direct forcing

As a first model, we assume that the forcing is not just periodic, but sinusoidal. In *Unit 21* you will see that any periodic force can be expressed as a sum of sinusoidal terms of different frequencies. It follows from the principle of superposition that if we can find a particular integral of the equation of motion for a 'typical' sinusoidal input then, by taking an appropriate sum of such solutions, we obtain the particular integral for any periodic input. The assumption of sinusoidal forcing is not therefore as restrictive as it might seem initially.

Unit 3, Theorem 1.1

Example 3.1

Consider the baby bouncer which was described in Example 2.2, with spring stiffness $k = 200\,\mathrm{N\,m^{-1}}$ and damping constant $r = 0.2\,\mathrm{N\,s\,m^{-1}}$. The baby plus parts of the apparatus suspended from the spring has mass $10\,\mathrm{kg}$. Suppose that, by alternately pushing downwards and pulling upwards on the baby, an adult exerts a direct sinusoidal force of amplitude 10 newtons and frequency 1 hertz (1 cycle per second).

(a) Modelling the baby as a particle, formulate the equation of motion for the baby.

(b) Find the general solution of the equation of motion, and interpret this to predict what motion the baby will undergo in the long term. Is this affected by the initial conditions?

Solution

(a) The model assumes that the baby does not touch the ground and that the motion is completely vertical. The model spring–damper diagram for the system is shown in Figure 3.1(a), and Figure 3.1(b) is the corresponding force diagram. The origin is taken, as in Example 2.2, to be at the top of the spring, with the x-axis pointing downwards.

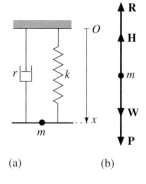

Figure 3.1

There are four forces to consider. Three of these are the same as in Example 2.2, namely the weight $\mathbf{W} = mg\mathbf{i}$, the model spring force $\mathbf{H} = -k(x - l_0)\mathbf{i}$ and the resistance force $\mathbf{R} = -r\dot{x}\mathbf{i}$. In addition, we have the sinusoidal force provided by the adult. With a suitable choice of time origin, this can be represented as $\mathbf{P} = P\cos(\Omega t)\mathbf{i}$, where the amplitude is $P = 10$ newtons and the angular frequency is $\Omega = 2\pi\,\mathrm{rad\,s^{-1}}$ (corresponding to 1 hertz). Newton's second law gives

$$m\ddot{x}\mathbf{i} = \mathbf{W} + \mathbf{H} + \mathbf{R} + \mathbf{P} = mg\mathbf{i} - k(x - l_0)\mathbf{i} - r\dot{x}\mathbf{i} + P\cos(\Omega t)\mathbf{i},$$

which leads, after resolution in the $\mathbf{i}$-direction, to the equation of motion

$$m\ddot{x} + r\dot{x} + kx = mg + kl_0 + P\cos(\Omega t).$$

The first two terms on the right-hand side can again be written as kx_{eq}, where $x_{\mathrm{eq}} = mg/k + l_0$ is the equilibrium position of the baby in the absence of forcing. Substituting the given values for m, k, r, P and Ω in the equation of motion, we obtain

$$10\ddot{x} + 0.2\dot{x} + 200x = 200x_{\mathrm{eq}} + 10\cos(2\pi t). \tag{3.1}$$

If the equilibrium position were chosen as the origin, then there would be no constant term on the right-hand side of the equation of motion.

(b) The complementary function is the same as that found in Example 2.2, which was

$$Ae^{-0.01t}\cos(4.5t + \phi),$$

where A and ϕ are arbitrary constants. The particular integral will be the sum of two terms, the first of which (again as in Example 2.2) is the constant x_{eq}. According to the principle of superposition, we need to add to this a particular integral corresponding to the sinusoidal term on the right-hand side. With a trial function of the form

See Unit 3, Subsection 2.2.

$$x_{\mathrm{p}} = B\cos(2\pi t) + C\sin(2\pi t),$$

we find $B = -5.1337 \times 10^{-2}$ and $C = 3.3120 \times 10^{-4}$, so

$$x_{\mathrm{p}} = -5.1337 \times 10^{-2}\cos(2\pi t) + 3.3120 \times 10^{-4}\sin(2\pi t).$$

This can also be written in the alternative sinusoidal form as

$$x_{\mathrm{p}} = 5.1338 \times 10^{-2}\cos(2\pi t - 3.1351).$$

When the numerical values are rounded to two significant figures, the general solution of the equation of motion becomes

$$x = Ae^{-0.01t}\cos(4.5t + \phi) + x_{\mathrm{eq}} + 5.1 \times 10^{-2}\cos(2\pi t - 3.1),$$

where A and ϕ are arbitrary constants which are determined by the initial conditions. Whatever these conditions are, the magnitude of the complementary function will decay gradually towards zero, as observed in Section 2. The initial conditions therefore have no influence on the long-term behaviour. After a long time, the motion will be given simply by the remainder of the general solution,

$$x = x_{\mathrm{eq}} + 5.1 \times 10^{-2}\cos(2\pi t - 3.1).$$

The predicted motion settles down to steady oscillations about the mean position x_{eq}, with amplitude 5.1×10^{-2} metres (about $5\,\mathrm{cm}$). These oscillations have the same angular frequency 2π as the input sinusoidal force $10\cos(2\pi t)\mathbf{i}$, but the output is out of phase with the input by almost π. This means that when the displacement is at its maximum (at the lowest point for the baby), the $\mathbf{i}$-component of the force exerted by the adult is at its minimum, and vice versa. The baby reaches the highest point as the adult pushes down hardest, reaches the lowest point as the adult pulls up hardest, and passes through the equilibrium position as the adult momentarily exerts no force. ■

This example shows several features typical of such forcing problems. The complementary function dies away with time, regardless of the initial conditions, since, in all cases, the complementary function corresponds to one of the damped but unforced systems seen in Section 2. For this reason, the complementary function is referred to in this context as the **transient** part of the solution, while the remainder (corresponding to the particular integral, which does not die away) is called the **steady-state** solution of the equation of motion. The particular integral does not depend upon the initial conditions, so neither does the steady-state behaviour. Another common feature is that the frequency of the steady-state solution is the same as that of the sinusoidal input force, but the output is out of phase with the input.

> This terminology was introduced in *Unit 3*, Section 4, where the differential equations were investigated.

Exercise 3.1

(a) Without performing any detailed calculations or algebra, say how the solution to Example 3.1 would alter if the amplitude of the forcing oscillations were reduced to 2 newtons, say, by the baby pushing with its feet on the floor rather than being pushed by an adult.

(b) Suppose that a heavier or lighter baby is placed in the baby bouncer. Without going into details, say what aspects of the long-term motion predicted in Example 3.1 will alter, and what will remain the same.

*Exercise 3.2

Bathroom scales are modelled by a model spring–damper system. The spring stiffness is k and the damping constant is r. A girl of mass m is on the scales. By alternately pushing down against and pulling up on an adjacent towel rail, she manages to alter her effective weight on the scales by an amount modelled as an input force $\mathbf{P} = mg\cos(\Omega t)\mathbf{i}$, where the $\mathbf{i}$-direction is upwards. Draw the force diagram for this situation. Taking the origin at the base of the model spring, obtain the equation of motion. What long-term behaviour is predicted by this model?

You have seen that the effect of a directly applied sinusoidal force on a model spring–damper system is modelled by an equation of motion of the form

$$m\ddot{x} + r\dot{x} + kx = kx_{\text{eq}} + P\cos(\Omega t), \tag{3.2}$$

where P and Ω are the amplitude and angular frequency of the applied force, and x_{eq} is the equilibrium position of the particle in the absence of forcing.

Initially, the behaviour of the system depends upon both the particular integral and complementary function of Equation (3.2), with the arbitrary constants in the complementary function being determined by the initial conditions of the situation. However, the complementary function dies away with time (is transient), and the particular solution then takes the form (equal to the particular integral)

$$x = x_{\text{eq}} + B\cos(\Omega t) + C\sin(\Omega t) = x_{\text{eq}} + A\cos(\Omega t + \phi).$$

This represents sinusoidal oscillations about the equilibrium position, which are independent of the initial conditions.

The model predicts that the steady-state output oscillations have the same frequency as the input forcing, but a different phase. The values of the output amplitude A and phase ϕ depend upon the configuration of the system, and on the values of the parameters m, k, r, P and Ω.

3.2 *Forcing by displacement*

We look in this subsection at examples of spring–damper systems in which the forcing is not applied directly to the particle where the mass of the system is concentrated. Suppose, for instance, that the baby bouncer from Example 2.2 is adapted by the addition of a motor at the top, which moves the top of the spring up and down sinusoidally with time. This situation is represented in Figure 3.2.

The precise form of the model spring force exerted upon the particle which represents the baby must differ from that seen before, because now both ends of the spring are in motion. However, Hooke's law continues to apply, so the force on the particle due to the model spring is

$$\mathbf{H} = -k(l - l_0)\widehat{\mathbf{s}},$$

where the spring has stiffness k and natural length l_0, and $\widehat{\mathbf{s}}$ is a unit vector in the direction from the centre of the spring towards the particle. The novel aspect introduced by this new situation is how the spring length l is changing. The following example illustrates how this is used.

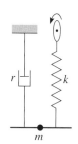

Figure 3.2

Example 3.2

Consider the baby bouncer which was described in Examples 2.2 and 3.1, with spring stiffness $k = 200 \,\mathrm{N\,m^{-1}}$ and damping constant $r = 0.2 \,\mathrm{N\,s\,m^{-1}}$. As before, the baby plus parts of the apparatus suspended from the spring has mass 10 kg. Suppose that a small motor causes the top of the spring to oscillate sinusoidally, with amplitude 0.04 metres and period 1 second. Suppose also that the damping is regarded as due to air resistance alone, so that the top of the model damper remains fixed.

(a) Derive the equation of motion for the particle representing the baby.

(b) Find the general solution of the equation of motion, and interpret this to predict what motion the baby will undergo in the long term.

(c) Say in general terms what would happen if the period of the oscillations at the top of the spring were to be changed to 2 seconds.

Solution

(a) As before, the model assumes that the baby does not touch the ground. The configuration of the apparatus is shown in Figure 3.3(a), with the force diagram in Figure 3.3(b). The origin is chosen to be at the mean position of the top of the spring, and the direction of the x-axis is downwards. The position of the top of the spring is then given by $y\mathbf{i}$, where we take $y = a\cos(\Omega t)$. The particular given oscillations have amplitude $a = 0.04$ metres and angular frequency $\Omega = 2\pi \,\mathrm{rad\,s^{-1}}$.

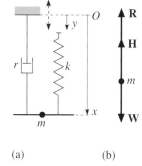

(a)   (b)

Figure 3.3

There are three forces to consider. Two of these are as in the previous analyses of the baby bouncer, namely, the weight $\mathbf{W} = mg\mathbf{i}$ and the resistance force $\mathbf{R} = -r\dot{x}\mathbf{i}$. Since the model spring has length $l = x - y$, the force which it exerts on the particle is

$$\mathbf{H} = -k(l - l_0)\widehat{\mathbf{s}} = -k(x - y - l_0)\mathbf{i}.$$

Newton's second law gives

$$m\ddot{x}\mathbf{i} = \mathbf{W} + \mathbf{H} + \mathbf{R} = mg\mathbf{i} - k(x - y - l_0)\mathbf{i} - r\dot{x}\mathbf{i},$$

which leads to the equation of motion

$$m\ddot{x} + r\dot{x} + kx = mg + kl_0 + ky.$$

On putting $x_{\mathrm{eq}} = mg/k + l_0$ and $y = a\cos(\Omega t)$, this becomes

$$m\ddot{x} + r\dot{x} + kx = kx_{\mathrm{eq}} + ak\cos(\Omega t). \tag{3.3}$$

31

On substituting in the given values for m, k, r, a and Ω, we obtain

$$10\ddot{x} + 0.2\dot{x} + 200x = 200x_{\text{eq}} + 8\cos(2\pi t).$$

(b) The equation of motion is almost identical to that obtained in Example 3.1 (see Equation (3.1)). The only difference is that the amplitude of the sinusoidal term on the right-hand side is 8, rather than 10. Thus the solution here is obtained by taking that in Example 3.1(b), but scaling the particular integral x_{p} for the sinusoidal term by $\frac{8}{10}$. This gives the steady-state solution

A similar approach was adopted to solve Exercise 3.1(a).

$$x = x_{\text{eq}} + 4.1 \times 10^{-2}\cos(2\pi t - 3.1).$$

The baby undergoes oscillations as before, but now of amplitude of about 4 cm.

(c) If the period changes to 2 seconds, then the forcing angular frequency becomes $\Omega = \pi\,\text{rad s}^{-1}$. The corresponding steady-state solution will also have this angular frequency, but its amplitude and phase depend upon Ω as well as on m, k, r and a, so it is not possible to deduce what these are from the previous solution. We would need to use a fresh trial function, of the form $B\cos(\pi t) + C\sin(\pi t)$. ∎

Note that, in contrast to Example 3.1, the equation of motion in Example 3.2 does not involve an additional force. The effect of the motor is modelled entirely by the inclusion of the term y in the expression for the spring force, and the fact that y is a function of time. Although the mechanism is different, Example 3.2(b) demonstrates that the effect of the motor displacing the top of the model spring is the same as that obtainable by direct sinusoidal forcing with a suitable amplitude and the same angular frequency. Leaving aside the particular values of the parameters, the equation of motion for direct forcing with amplitude P is Equation (3.2), while the equation of motion for prescribed displacement oscillations of amplitude a is Equation (3.3). The two match, provided that we put $P = ak$, and the mathematical solution and interpretation are then essentially the same in either case.

The model of the baby bouncer in Example 3.2 assumed that the top of the model spring moved, but that the top of the model damper was fixed. Suppose instead that the chief cause of damping is not air resistance but the internal damping in the spring. Then it is appropriate to model the situation by assuming that the top end of the model damper performs the same motion as the top end of the model spring (see Figure 3.4).

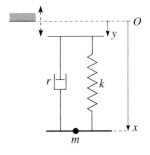

Figure 3.4

This leads to an amended model in which a new expression is required for the damping resistance force. You showed in Exercise 2.1(b) that if the model damper extends from $x\mathbf{i}$ (where the particle is) to $y\mathbf{i}$, then the corresponding resistance force upon the particle is given by

$$\mathbf{R} = -r\dot{l}\,\widehat{\mathbf{s}} = -r(\dot{x} - \dot{y})\mathbf{i}.$$

Exercise 3.3

(a) Modify the model of the baby bouncer with motor, from Example 3.2, to represent the top of the model damper being attached to the top of the model spring and hence experiencing the same forced sinusoidal displacement. How does the equation of motion compare with that for direct forcing?

(b) Describe how you would find the steady-state solution, and hence the type of motion predicted by the model (but do not do the detailed calculations).

Exercise 3.4

The model sit-ski which you considered in Exercise 2.3 has spring natural length 0.2 metres, stiffness $30\,000\,\mathrm{N\,m^{-1}}$ and damping constant $6300\,\mathrm{N\,s\,m^{-1}}$. During testing, the sit-ski carries a skier plus seat of mass 60 kg. To simulate the effect of travelling over uneven ground, the base of the sit-ski is subjected to regular sinusoidal oscillations, with amplitude 0.1 metres and angular frequency $\pi\,\mathrm{rad\,s^{-1}}$ as shown in Figure 3.5. Derive the equation of motion, taking the origin to be at the mean level of the sit-ski base. Hence describe in general terms the long-term motion predicted by the model.

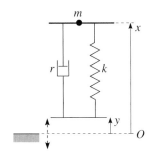

Figure 3.5

You have now seen a case where the model spring alone was subjected to a forcing displacement at the end not attached to the particle, and other cases where the forcing point was located on both the model spring and damper together. A third possibility is where the model damper alone is displaced by a forcing displacement (and you are asked to consider this case at the end of the section). Here again, a very similar equation of motion results, with a sinusoid on the right-hand side which is similar to the corresponding term for direct forcing.

See Exercise 3.6.

Under certain circumstances, the position x of the particle relative to some fixed point may be of less interest than its position z relative to the forcing point. Since $z = x - y$, it is a simple matter to obtain the solution for z from that for x, since the forcing input term y is a known function. Alternatively, we can set up a differential equation directly for z rather than for x.

For example, the equation

$$m\ddot{x} + r\dot{x} + kx = kx_{\mathrm{eq}} + r\dot{y} + ky$$

arose in both Exercises 3.3 and 3.4. On replacing x by $y + z$, this becomes

$$m\ddot{z} + r\dot{z} + kz = kx_{\mathrm{eq}} - m\ddot{y},$$

which with $y = a\cos(\Omega t)$ gives

$$m\ddot{z} + r\dot{z} + kz = kx_{\mathrm{eq}} + ma\Omega^2\cos(\Omega t).$$

This is yet another occurrence of a differential equation of the form (3.2), so similar comments apply as to the method of solution and output behaviour.

Whether the forcing is applied via a direct sinusoidal force or by sinusoidal displacement to one end of the spring and/or damper, and whether the output is measured relative to a fixed point (x) or to the forcing point (z), the solution of the equation of motion is the sum of two parts: the complementary function (transient), which dies away and becomes negligible, and the particular integral, representing a steady-state sinusoidal oscillation about the equilibrium position, with the same frequency as the input forcing.

The process of finding a particular integral which corresponds to a sinusoidal forcing function is time-consuming, as described so far, and we have only gone over this step in full for one example. The computer can be used to undertake this task, but in the next subsection we indicate how it is also possible to calculate the output amplitude and phase more rapidly from suitable formulae.

3.3 The steady-state solution

It is tedious to look from scratch for sinusoidal particular integrals for in-homogeneous differential equations. In this subsection we shall solve this problem once for a large number of possible cases. While this requires a fair amount of algebraic manipulation, the result obtained saves much further work. It is also a starting point for the discussion in Section 4.

We start from the differential equation

$$m\ddot{x} + r\dot{x} + kx = kx_{\text{eq}} + P\cos(\Omega t), \tag{3.2}$$

where m, r, k, x_{eq}, P and Ω are constants. This equation can be regarded as representing all of the equations of motion which arose earlier in this section, provided that all of the constants which appear in it (except possibly x_{eq}) are positive. Where there is forcing applied to a model damper, the sinusoidal term on the right-hand side includes a phase shift and hence appears initially as $P\cos(\Omega t + \psi)$. However, such a phase can readily be 'transformed away' by moving the time origin from $t = 0$ to $t = -\psi/\Omega$. In a similar way, the kx_{eq} term on the right-hand side of Equation (3.2) can be 'transformed away' by choosing a new origin for x at the equilibrium position, $x = x_{\text{eq}}$. This permits us to concentrate on the slightly simpler equation

See Exercises 3.3, 3.4 and 3.6.

$$m\ddot{x} + r\dot{x} + kx = P\cos(\Omega t). \tag{3.4}$$

Once a solution to this has been obtained, we may, if desired, express it in terms of the original x- and t-coordinates, by adding x_{eq} to it and by reversing the phase shift (adding ψ to the phase obtained).

The general solution of Equation (3.4) will be the sum of a complementary function and a particular integral. The complementary function is found as in Subsection 2.3 and, as shown there, dies away in all cases (is transient). We concentrate here on finding general expressions which determine the particular integral of Equation (3.4). These provide a complete description of the steady-state behaviour of any system which Equation (3.4) represents.

The right-hand side of this differential equation is a sinusoid with angular frequency Ω. This means that the particular integral will also be sinusoidal, with the same frequency, so we start with a trial solution

$$x_{\text{p}} = B\cos(\Omega t) + C\sin(\Omega t),$$

where B and C are constants to be found in terms of m, r, k, P and Ω. The first two derivatives of the trial function are

$$\dot{x}_{\text{p}} = -\Omega B\sin(\Omega t) + \Omega C\cos(\Omega t), \quad \ddot{x}_{\text{p}} = -\Omega^2 B\cos(\Omega t) - \Omega^2 C\sin(\Omega t).$$

Substituting into Equation (3.4) gives

$$m\left(-\Omega^2 B\cos(\Omega t) - \Omega^2 C\sin(\Omega t)\right) + r\left(-\Omega B\sin(\Omega t) + \Omega C\cos(\Omega t)\right)$$
$$+ k\left(B\cos(\Omega t) + C\sin(\Omega t)\right) = P\cos(\Omega t).$$

On equating the coefficients of $\cos(\Omega t)$ and of $\sin(\Omega t)$ here, we have

$$-m\Omega^2 B + r\Omega C + kB = P, \quad -m\Omega^2 C - r\Omega B + kC = 0.$$

The second of these equations gives $B = (k - m\Omega^2)C/(r\Omega)$, and by substituting this expression for B into the first equation, we obtain

$$-\frac{m\Omega^2(k - m\Omega^2)C}{r\Omega} + r\Omega C + \frac{k(k - m\Omega^2)C}{r\Omega} = P,$$

that is,

$$\frac{\left((k - m\Omega^2)^2 + r^2\Omega^2\right)C}{r\Omega} = P.$$

We can compare coefficients here because the cosine and sine functions are *linearly independent*: if $a\sin rx + b\cos rx = 0$ for all x, then $a = b = 0$.

The required expressions for B and C are therefore

$$C = \frac{Pr\Omega}{\left(k - m\Omega^2\right)^2 + r^2\Omega^2} \quad \text{and} \quad B = \frac{P(k - m\Omega^2)}{\left(k - m\Omega^2\right)^2 + r^2\Omega^2}. \tag{3.5}$$

The alternative formulation for the sinusoidal particular integral of Equation (3.4) is $x_p = A\cos(\Omega t + \phi)$, where the amplitude A of the motion is given by $A = \sqrt{B^2 + C^2}$, that is,

$$A = \frac{P}{\sqrt{\left(k - m\Omega^2\right)^2 + r^2\Omega^2}}. \tag{3.6}$$

The phase ϕ satisfies the pair of equations

$$A\cos\phi = B, \quad A\sin\phi = -C.$$

Now the expression for C is always positive, so $\sin\phi < 0$ and ϕ lies in the third or fourth quadrant. Since arccos is defined to give values in the first or second quadrant, it follows that the formula $\phi = -\arccos(B/A)$ will apply in all cases, that is,

The fact that ϕ is negative shows that the output lags behind the input.

$$\phi = -\arccos\left(\frac{k - m\Omega^2}{\sqrt{\left(k - m\Omega^2\right)^2 + r^2\Omega^2}}\right). \tag{3.7}$$

For any values of the constants m, r, k, P and Ω, the steady-state solution

$$x = B\cos(\Omega t) + C\sin(\Omega t) = A\cos(\Omega t + \phi)$$

is completely determined by either Equations (3.5) (first form) or Equations (3.6) and (3.7) (second form).

*Exercise 3.5

(a) In Example 3.1 we studied the baby bouncer with direct forcing applied, for which $m = 10\,\text{kg}$, $k = 200\,\text{N m}^{-1}$, $r = 0.2\,\text{N s m}^{-1}$, $P = 10\,\text{N}$ and $\Omega = 2\pi\,\text{rad s}^{-1}$. Use Equations (3.6) and (3.7) to check the values quoted in Example 3.1 for the amplitude and phase of the steady-state solution.

(b) Example 3.2 concerned the baby bouncer with forcing at the top of the model spring alone. The values of m, k and r were as in part (a). Use Equation (3.6), with $P = ak$ and $a = 0.04$ metres, to find whether the forcing period of 2 seconds referred to in Example 3.2(c) would give a greater or lesser steady-state amplitude than the 4 cm which was found for a forcing period of 1 second.

(c) Use Equation (3.6) to estimate the steady-state output amplitude for the sit-ski testing scenario described in Exercise 3.4. Here $m = 60\,\text{kg}$, $k = 30\,000\,\text{N m}^{-1}$, $r = 6300\,\text{N s m}^{-1}$, $a = 0.1\,\text{m}$ and $\Omega = \pi\,\text{rad s}^{-1}$. Take $P = a\sqrt{k^2 + r^2\Omega^2}$ (as explained in the solution to Exercise 3.3(a)).

Suppose that we are looking at a forced displacement of the model spring alone, as in Example 3.2. Then we have $P = ak$ in Equation (3.6), which gives

In other cases P will also depend on the amplitude a of the input, but in a different manner.

$$\frac{A}{a} = \frac{k}{\sqrt{\left(k - m\Omega^2\right)^2 + r^2\Omega^2}}. \tag{3.8}$$

Now A/a is the ratio of the amplitude A of the steady-state output oscillations to the amplitude a of the input forcing displacement. In other words, $M = A/a$ is the amplitude **magnification factor** caused by the forcing process.

It is possible to write the right-hand side of Equation (3.8) in terms of two dimensionless constants:

- the damping ratio, $\alpha = r/(2\sqrt{mk})$, which was introduced in Subsection 2.3;

- the ratio $\beta = \Omega/\omega$ of the forcing angular frequency Ω and the natural angular frequency of the system, $\omega = \sqrt{k/m}$.

Note that M itself, as the ratio of two lengths, is also dimensionless.

After some algebraic manipulation, we find that the magnification factor, $M = A/a$, is given by

$$M = \left(\left(1 - \beta^2 \right)^2 + 4\alpha^2 \beta^2 \right)^{-1/2}. \tag{3.9}$$

From this formula, we can predict the extent to which input oscillations are magnified in amplitude for any values of α and β. Thus we can also examine how M varies with changes to α and β, which corresponds to investigating how the system response depends upon the input forcing frequency and on other parameters of the system. This is done in the next section.

In this section you have seen how to model the behaviour of systems such as damped harmonic oscillators maintained in a state of vibration by some external sinusoidal force or displacement. There are many examples of forced spring–damper systems, in addition to those which have been modelled so far. For instance, a vehicle suspension going over rumble strips, cobbles or a cattle grid; an idling engine causing the body of a stationary bus to vibrate; people walking in step over a bridge. The model predicts that a sinusoidal forcing input produces a sinusoidal output vibration of the same frequency.

End-of-section Exercise

Exercise 3.6

Modify the model of the baby bouncer with motor, from Example 3.2, to represent the top of the model damper alone being made to undergo a sinusoidal motion, with the top of the model spring held fixed (see Figure 3.6). Find the form of the equation of motion, without substituting in numerical values. How does this equation of motion compare with the direct forcing Equation (3.2)?

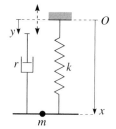

Figure 3.6

4 *Forced vibrations and resonance*

At the end of Section 3 we derived alternative formulae (Equations (3.8) and (3.9)) for the magnification factor by which input oscillations are enlarged in amplitude by a particular type of spring–damper system. As well as providing amplitude output values in specific cases, this enables us to study how the magnification depends on the input parameters, and especially on the forcing angular frequency. It turns out that, for some systems, there is a marked peak in amplitude magnification close to a certain forcing angular frequency. This phenomenon is known as *resonance*, and we take a look at this in Subsection 4.1. The remaining video sequences for this unit are associated with Subsection 4.2. The particle–spring system with magnetic damping from Section 1 is modified by a forcing motor at the top of the spring. The model constructed in Section 3 can be applied to predict what magnification factor would occur for certain input frequencies, and the estimates obtained may be compared with experimental outcomes.

4.1 Resonance

Consider once more a spring–damper system in which the forcing point is attached to the model spring only, while the model damper has one end fixed. As pointed out at the end of Section 3, the magnification factor $M = A/a$, from the input forced displacement amplitude a to the steady-state output amplitude A, is given for such a system by

$$M = \frac{k}{\sqrt{\left(k - m\Omega^2\right)^2 + r^2\Omega^2}} = \left(\left(1 - \beta^2\right)^2 + 4\alpha^2\beta^2\right)^{-1/2}, \tag{4.1}$$

The baby bouncer of Example 3.2 is such a system.

See Equations (3.8) and (3.9).

where $\alpha = r/(2\sqrt{mk})$ and $\beta = \Omega/\omega$. Here the system has mass m, spring stiffness k, damping constant r and natural angular frequency $\omega = \sqrt{k/m}$. The input forcing angular frequency is Ω.

For a given damping ratio α (and hence for given values of the system parameters m, k and r), the magnification factor M is a function of β. From the graph of this function, you can read off the rough magnification factor for the system for any input forcing angular frequency. Several graphs of M against β, for different fixed values of α, are shown in Figure 4.1.

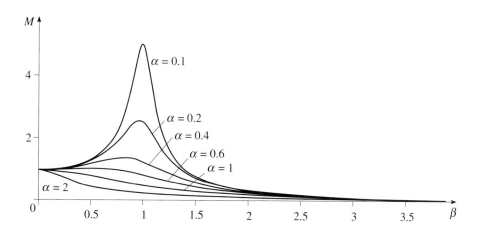

Figure 4.1

The graphs predict that for some (but not all) damping ratios, there is a maximum magnification factor at a certain positive forcing frequency, and this phenomenon is called **resonance**. If the damping is strong ($\alpha > 1$) or critical ($\alpha = 1$), then no resonance occurs, and the magnification factor decreases throughout as β increases. Nor does resonance occur with weak damping, unless the value of α is beneath a particular threshold level. For smaller values of α, however, there is resonance, and its effect becomes more and more significant as α decreases towards zero. Note that for small values of α, resonance occurs in the vicinity of $\beta = 1$, that is, when the forcing angular frequency Ω is close to the natural angular frequency ω of the system.

You will see below that this threshold value is
$$\alpha = 1/\sqrt{2} \simeq 0.7.$$

Now that we have seen from Figure 4.1 that the model predicts the phenomenon of resonance, let us see if we can derive this analytically directly from Equation (4.1). So we consider $M = M(\beta)$ to be a function of β, and we wish to find the maximum magnification as β varies. The easiest way to do this is to recognize $M(\beta)$ as a composite function, i.e. $M(\beta) = f(g(\beta^2))$, where

Another approach is to differentiate $M(\beta)$ directly.

$$f(u) = u^{-1/2} \quad \text{and} \quad g(x) = (1 - x)^2 + 4\alpha^2 x.$$

Now $f(u)$ is a strictly decreasing function for positive u, with no local maxima or minima (as shown in Figure 4.2). So a *minimum* of $g(x)$ corresponds to a *maximum* of $f(g(x))$. So we need to find the minima of $g(x)$.

Note that $g(\beta^2)$ is always positive, since $\alpha > 0$ and $\beta^2 > 0$.

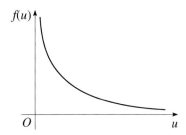

Figure 4.2

Now consider $g(x)$, which is a quadratic with a positive coefficient of x^2 and so has a single local minimum (which is also the global minimum). To find the location of the minimum, we differentiate $g(x)$:

$$g'(x) = 2(1 - x) \times (-1) + 4\alpha^2 = 2x + 4\alpha^2 - 2.$$

So the derivative is zero when $x = 1 - 2\alpha^2$.

Alternatively, the minimum can be found without calculus, by completing the square.

Putting the above results together gives that $f(g(x))$ has a unique global maximum at $x = 1 - 2\alpha^2$. So $M(\beta) = f(g(\beta^2))$ has a single maximum when $\beta^2 = 1 - 2\alpha^2$. Note that if $1 - 2\alpha^2 < 0$, then there are no real values of β satisfying this equation. These results are worth remembering.

Resonance frequency

The frequency at which resonance occurs is given by

$$\beta = \sqrt{1 - 2\alpha^2}. \tag{4.2}$$

Resonance can occur when (and only when) $1 - 2\alpha^2 > 0$.

By substituting in this value, we can show that the maximum magnification factor is given by

$$M = \frac{1}{2\alpha\sqrt{1 - \alpha^2}}.$$

Let us now return to the baby bouncer example.

Exercise 4.1 _____

The baby bouncer from Example 3.2, with a baby plus seat of mass $10\,\mathrm{kg}$, has damping ratio

$$\alpha = \frac{r}{2\sqrt{mk}} = \frac{0.2}{2\sqrt{10 \times 200}} \simeq 0.002,$$

and natural angular frequency

$$\omega = \sqrt{\frac{k}{m}} = \sqrt{\frac{200}{10}} \simeq 4.47\,\mathrm{rad\,s^{-1}}.$$

What amplitude of oscillations for the baby are predicted for a forcing input (at the top of the spring) with amplitude $a = 0.04$ metres and angular frequency ω? Comment on your result.

Resonance is found in many physical systems, and in some is desirable. Thus a radio receiver may be tuned to an input signal of a particular carrier frequency, and inputs of other carrier frequencies have much lower magnification factor at that frequency. However, there are other situations where resonance is most undesirable. In the case of a vehicle suspension, a large magnification factor when the vehicle goes over regular bumps would certainly be uncomfortable, and might also be dangerous and destructive.

4.2   *Forcing in practice*

The remaining video sequences for this unit involve the addition of a motor to the particle–spring system with magnetic damping, which you saw earlier. This motor has the effect of forcing the top of the spring to undergo a sinusoidal displacement, while the tubes which cause the damping remain fixed. An appropriate model for this situation is the same as that developed for the baby bouncer in Example 3.2 (see Figure 3.3). The corresponding equation of motion is as before,

$$m\ddot{x} + r\dot{x} + kx = kx_{\text{eq}} + ak\cos(\Omega t), \tag{3.3}$$

if the origin is taken at the mean position of the top of the spring. However, with the alternative choice of origin at the equilibrium position of the particle (as on the video), this becomes

$$m\ddot{x} + r\dot{x} + kx = ak\cos(\Omega t),$$

which is of the form of Equation (3.4) with $P = ak$. Equations (4.1) give the magnification factor, which is the ratio of the amplitude of the sinusoidal particular integral to the amplitude of the input forcing displacement. The video looks at the forced motion for each of tubes A, C and D, for different sets of initial conditions. The model predicts that the transient part of the solution dies away with time, leaving a sinusoidal steady-state solution. This is illustrated in Figure 4.3 below for each of the tubes, where the input forcing has angular frequency $\Omega = \frac{4}{3}\pi \, \text{rad s}^{-1}$ (equivalent to $\frac{2}{3}$ hertz or to 40 cycles per minute, as on the next part of the video).

As before, the experimental apparatus has particle mass $m = 0.711 \, \text{kg}$ and model spring stiffness $k = 23 \, \text{N m}^{-1}$. The amplitude of the input forcing is $a = 0.03$ metres, hence the value of $P = ak$ is 0.69 newtons. The damping constants, in N s m^{-1} (as found for Table 1.1), are

The quantity P is referred to on the video as P_0.

$$r = 0.15 \text{ (tube A)}, \quad r = 1.33 \text{ (tube C)}, \quad r = 8.42 \text{ (tube D)}.$$

You found the corresponding damping ratios in Exercise 2.7. According to Equations (4.1), the magnification factors for the steady-state output amplitude as compared with the input amplitude will be

$$M = 2.2 \text{ (tube A)}, \quad M = 1.9 \text{ (tube C)}, \quad M = 0.6 \text{ (tube D)}. \tag{4.3}$$

These magnifications are visible on the graphs in Figure 4.3.

The graphs and the values (4.3) for M are predictions of the model, which may be compared with the outcomes of actual experiments. View the video with this in mind.

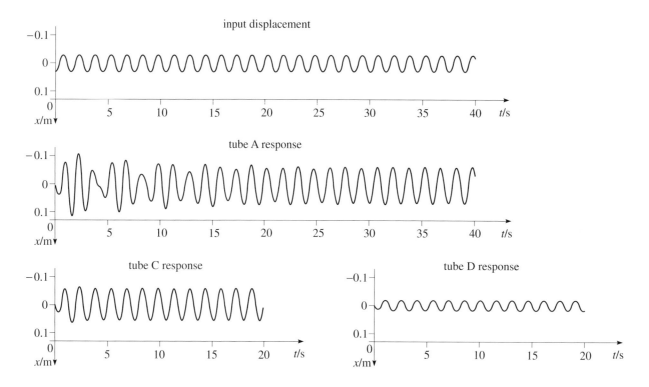

Figure 4.3   Predictions from model for tubes A, C and D, with $\Omega = \frac{4}{3}\pi\,\mathrm{rad\,s^{-1}}$, $x(0) = 0$ and $\dot{x}(0) = 0$

Watch Part 3 of the video for this unit now.

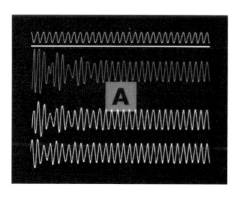

Figure 4.4   Output traces for tube A with $\Omega = \frac{4}{3}\pi\,\mathrm{rad\,s^{-1}}$

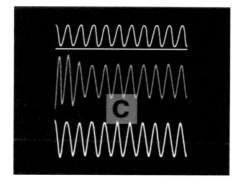

Figure 4.5   Output traces for tube C with $\Omega = \frac{4}{3}\pi\,\mathrm{rad\,s^{-1}}$

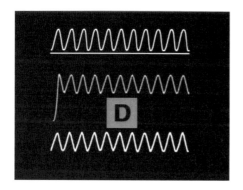

Figure 4.6   Output traces for tube D with $\Omega = \frac{4}{3}\pi\,\mathrm{rad\,s^{-1}}$

The experiments shown on the video confirm the predictions of the model in the following respects.

- There is, for each tube, an apparently sinusoidal steady-state solution, independent of the specific initial conditions (see Figures 4.4–4.6), together with a transient part which dies away.
- The transient part of the motion dies away more rapidly when the damping is stronger.
- The angular frequency of the steady-state solution is identical to that of the input forcing.
- The amplitude magnification factors for this forcing frequency (which can be measured from Figures 4.4–4.6) decline as the amount of damping increases, from tube A through tube C to tube D.
- For tubes A and C the output has larger amplitude than the input, while for tube D there is attenuation (lower output than input amplitude).

The measured values of the magnification factor are, approximately, given by

$$M = 2 \text{ (tube A)}, \quad M = 1.8 \text{ (tube C)}, \quad M = 0.8 \text{ (tube D)}, \qquad (4.4)$$

which may be compared with the predicted values (4.3) of the model.

It is possible to perform these measurements, and to compare the values obtained with the values (4.4) given below.

The value of M for tube C is that quoted on the video. Measurements from Figure 4.5 suggest that $M = 1.6$ may be closer.

The remainder of the video concerns how, for each tube, the steady-state oscillations of the suspended mass alter with changes to the input forcing frequency. The experiment is run with the forcing oscillations at 40, 60 and 80 cycles per minute, for which the angular frequency Ω (in rad s^{-1}) has the respective values $\frac{4}{3}\pi$, 2π and $\frac{8}{3}\pi$. The corresponding predictions of the model for the magnification factors M are given in Table 4.1 below. These values may be obtained from Equations (4.1).

Table 4.1   Magnification factors predicted by the model

Tube	Damping constant, r (N s m^{-1})	Damping ratio, α	Magnification factor, M, for $\Omega = \frac{4}{3}\pi$	$\Omega = 2\pi$	$\Omega = \frac{8}{3}\pi$
A	0.15	0.02	2.2	4.5	0.9
C	1.33	0.16	1.9	2.4	0.8
D	8.42	1.04	0.6	0.4	0.3

Note that the values predicted at the intermediate angular frequency, $\Omega = 2\pi \,\text{rad s}^{-1}$, for tubes A and C are higher than those at the higher or lower frequency. This amounts to a prediction that resonance will occur. Indeed, the model predicts resonance in these cases close to the natural angular frequency of the system, which is

$$\omega = \sqrt{\frac{k}{m}} = \sqrt{\frac{23}{0.711}} \simeq 5.7 \,\text{rad s}^{-1}.$$

This corresponds to forcing at a frequency of about 54 cycles per minute.

Watch Part 4 of the video now.

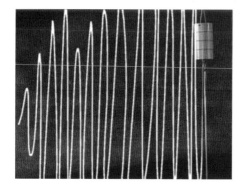

Figure 4.7   Output trace for tube A
with $\Omega = 2\pi \, \mathrm{rad\,s^{-1}}$

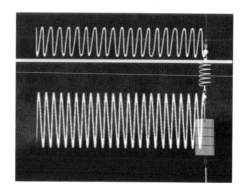

Figure 4.8   Output trace for tube A
with $\Omega = \frac{8}{3}\pi \, \mathrm{rad\,s^{-1}}$

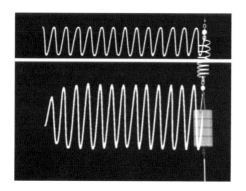

Figure 4.9   Output trace for tube C
with $\Omega = 2\pi \, \mathrm{rad\,s^{-1}}$

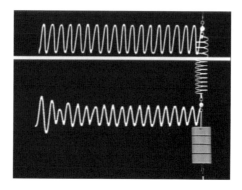

Figure 4.10   Output trace for tube C
with $\Omega = \frac{8}{3}\pi \, \mathrm{rad\,s^{-1}}$

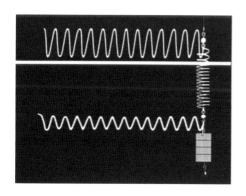

Figure 4.11   Output trace for tube D
with $\Omega = 2\pi \, \mathrm{rad\,s^{-1}}$

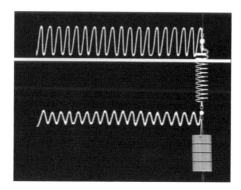

Figure 4.12   Output trace for tube D
with $\Omega = \frac{8}{3}\pi \, \mathrm{rad\,s^{-1}}$

The results for the video experiments with forcing at angular frequency $\Omega = \frac{4}{3}\pi \, \mathrm{rad \, s^{-1}}$ are as shown earlier, in Figures 4.4–4.6, with magnification factors as given in (4.4). The video traces for the other experiments are shown in Figures 4.7–4.12.

From these traces, the approximate magnification factors in Table 4.2 may be derived. (The trace for tube A with $\Omega = 2\pi \, \mathrm{rad \, s^{-1}}$ shows that the motion went off the scale, indicating an amplitude magnification greater than 4.)

It is possible to estimate these experimental magnification factors by taking measurements directly from the video traces.

Table 4.2   Magnification factors obtained from experiment

Tube	Magnification factor, M, for		
	$\Omega = \frac{4}{3}\pi \, \mathrm{rad \, s^{-1}}$	$\Omega = 2\pi \ \mathrm{rad \, s^{-1}}$	$\Omega = \frac{8}{3}\pi \, \mathrm{rad \, s^{-1}}$
A	2	> 4	2
C	1.8	2.3	0.7
D	0.8	0.5	0.5

Comparing these values with those predicted by the model in Table 4.1, the qualitative agreement is quite good. The model predicts correctly that the magnification factors for the weakly damped systems of tubes A and C will be greater than 1 at certain frequencies and that those for the strongly damped motion of tube D will be less than 1 in each case. The predictions of resonance for tubes A and C, and more markedly for A, are borne out by the actual experiments.

Although not shown on the video, the experiments were carried out once more for tubes A and C, at a forcing frequency of 50 cycles per minute (for which $\Omega = \frac{5}{3}\pi \, \mathrm{rad \, s^{-1}}$). The observed magnification factor for tube C was about 2.7, while the behaviour for tube A was again beyond the limits of the apparatus. The corresponding predictions from the model are, respectively, $M = 2.95$ and $M = 6.4$.

The model makes a number of simplifying assumptions: the model spring behaviour is one assumption, linear damping is another, and a pure sinusoidal input forcing displacement is a third. Hence it is not surprising that the numerical predictions are somewhat at odds with the experimental values obtained.

Despite this, there is a significant degree of qualitative agreement between the behaviour of the model and that of the real system. In particular, the phenomenon of resonance was observed as predicted.

5 Damping and forcing on the computer

Each activity in this section refers to work you have done earlier in the unit or is a spin-off from the video. The computer algebra package allows you to investigate the effects of changes to the various parameters of the system under discussion.

Use your computer to complete the following activities.

Activity 5.1

In this activity we show how the four experiments described in Section 1 were analysed.

In the first part of the video a magnet was dropped down each of four tubes in turn and the time to fall one metre was measured. The times recorded were: $0.64\,\text{s}$ (tube A); $2.52\,\text{s}$ (tube B); $3.60\,\text{s}$ (tube C); $22.60\,\text{s}$ (tube D). This experiment was modelled in Example 1.1, which led to Equation (1.1) as the position function. You will see that this leads to the values of the damping constant r for each tube, as quoted in Table 1.1.

Now consider the damped particle–spring system considered in Subsection 1.3. You will see how the equation of motion (Equation (1.3)) derived leads to predictions of the motion as shown in Figure 1.5.

Activity 5.2

The following damped particle–spring systems were considered in Subsection 2.2. Data should be taken as in the example or exercise referred to.

(a) The motion of the baby bouncer in Example 2.2 was obtained for a case in which the mass of the baby is $10\,\text{kg}$. Experiment with different values of the mass, in order to predict whether a lighter or heavier baby will enjoy a better ride (larger amplitude oscillations after a specified time).

(b) The model of the sit-ski in Exercise 2.3 had spring stiffness $30\,000\,\text{N}\,\text{m}^{-1}$. Experiment with different values of the stiffness, and note the predicted effect on the skier.

(c) The model for the motion of a float in a fuel tank in Example 2.3 had damping constant $21\,\text{N}\,\text{s}\,\text{m}^{-1}$. Experiment with different values for the damping constant, in order to design a system in which the float will return close to its equilibrium position as quickly as possible after any disturbance.

(d) In Example 3.1, the baby bouncer was subjected to direct sinusoidal forcing with angular frequency $2\pi\,\text{rad}\,\text{s}^{-1}$. Using the data from Example 3.1, confirm the long-term predictions of the model as quoted there.

Now experiment with different values of the forcing angular frequency, to see whether there are frequencies which produce oscillations for the baby of significantly larger amplitude.

Outcomes

After studying this unit you should be able to:

- understand the meanings of damping, forcing and resonance;
- explain and apply the linear damping model;
- distinguish between weak, critical and strong damping, and be aware of the distinctive features of each case;
- appreciate the role of the damping ratio;
- apply the model spring and model damper force specifications to situations in which either spring or damper, or both, may undergo a forced displacement at the end away from the particle;
- model direct forcing to the particle where appropriate;
- derive an equation of motion, based upon Newton's second law, for models which feature a model spring and model damper, with or without forcing, and formulate appropriately the initial conditions for a particular motion;
- formulate the equation of motion either with the origin at the equilibrium position of the particle or at some other fixed point;
- solve the resulting initial-value problem for a damped but unforced harmonic oscillator;
- find the particular integral for a sinusoidally forced and damped harmonic oscillator;
- interpret the solutions of an equation of motion in terms of the situation from which the model arose;
- understand the terms transient and steady-state, as applied to the solutions of forced and damped harmonic oscillators, and explain the essential features of each of these;
- find via formulae the amplitude and phase of a steady-state solution in terms of the amplitude and angular frequency of the input forcing and other parameters of the system;
- find the magnification factor for the steady-state output amplitude as compared with an input forced displacement amplitude for the model spring;
- identify whether resonance may occur or will not occur in a system, and where it may occur, say what approximate input angular frequency will cause it for small damping ratios.

Solutions to the exercises

Section 1

1.1 The equilibrium extension is
$$\frac{mg}{k} = \frac{0.711 \times 9.81}{23} \simeq 0.30\,\text{m}.$$

1.2 Equation (1.3) is
$$m\ddot{x} + r\dot{x} + kl = mg + kl_0.$$
If the origin for x is chosen at the fixed top end of the spring, then the displacement of the particle from that origin is $x = l$, and the equation of motion takes the inhomogeneous form
$$m\ddot{x} + r\dot{x} + kx = mg + kl_0.$$
This can also be written as
$$m\ddot{x} + r\dot{x} + kx = kx_{\text{eq}},$$
where $x_{\text{eq}} = l_0 + mg/k$ is the equilibrium displacement of the particle. (With this choice of origin, we have $x_{\text{eq}} = l_{\text{eq}}$.)

1.3 (a) Strong damping is needed, as the train should bounce back as little as possible from the buffers.

(b) Critical or strong damping is called for, but not so strong as to make the door close too slowly.

(c) Near-critical damping is appropriate, as the fuel gauge should revert quickly to a true reading and not oscillate much.

(d) Strong damping is needed, as oscillations between the vehicles could be dangerous and should be avoided.

(e) Near-critical damping is required, perhaps slightly on the weak side of critical to allow for the envisaged range of weights. This situation is similar to that of kitchen scales, which is discussed in the previous text.

Section 2

2.1 (a) Suppose first that the x-axis is in the same direction as that of $\hat{\mathbf{s}}$, so that $\hat{\mathbf{s}} = \mathbf{i}$. Then, with one end of the model damper attached to the particle at x and the other end fixed, we have $\dot{x} = \dot{l}$ (regardless of the choice of origin for x). Hence the resistance force is
$$\mathbf{R} = -r\dot{l}\,\hat{\mathbf{s}} = -r\dot{x}\mathbf{i}.$$
If, on the other hand, the x-axis is in the opposite direction to that of $\hat{\mathbf{s}}$, then $\hat{\mathbf{s}} = -\mathbf{i}$, but also $\dot{x} = -\dot{l}$, so the same expression for $\mathbf{R}$ results.

(b) The vector $x\mathbf{i} - y\mathbf{i} = (x - y)\mathbf{i}$ has length l and the same direction as $\hat{\mathbf{s}}$, so $(x - y)\mathbf{i} = l\hat{\mathbf{s}}$. Hence we have
$$\mathbf{R} = -r\dot{l}\,\hat{\mathbf{s}} = -r(\dot{x} - \dot{y})\mathbf{i}.$$
(This approach also provides an alternative way of tackling part (a), where y is constant and so $\dot{y} = 0$.)

2.2 (a)

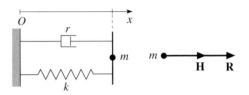

From Equation (2.1), the model spring force is
$$\mathbf{H} = -k(l - l_0)\hat{\mathbf{s}} = -k(x - l_0)\mathbf{i}.$$
From Exercise 2.1(a), the resistance force is
$$\mathbf{R} = -r\dot{l}\,\hat{\mathbf{s}} = -r\dot{x}\mathbf{i}.$$
The equation of motion is therefore
$$m\ddot{x}\mathbf{i} = \mathbf{H} + \mathbf{R} = -k(x - l_0)\mathbf{i} - r\dot{x}\mathbf{i},$$
which after resolution in the $\mathbf{i}$-direction gives
$$m\ddot{x} + r\dot{x} + kx = kl_0.$$
Substituting in $k = 140\,\text{N}\,\text{m}^{-1}$, $r = 180\,\text{N}\,\text{s}\,\text{m}^{-1}$, $m = 40\,\text{kg}$ and $l_0 = 0.5\,\text{m}$, we have
$$40\ddot{x} + 180\dot{x} + 140x = 70,$$
that is,
$$4\ddot{x} + 18\dot{x} + 14x = 7.$$
Since we have
$$r^2 - 4mk = 100(18^2 - 4 \times 4 \times 14) = 10^4,$$
which is positive, the damping is strong.

(b) The train meets the buffers first at $x = l_0 = 0.5$ and at time $t = 0$. It is then moving in the negative x-direction, with speed $1\,\text{m}\,\text{s}^{-1}$. Hence the appropriate initial conditions are
$$x(0) = 0.5, \quad \dot{x}(0) = -1.$$

(c) The solution is given as
$$x = 0.5 - 0.4e^{-t} + 0.4e^{-3.5t}.$$
Maximum compression of the buffers occurs when
$$\dot{x} = 0.4e^{-t} - 1.4e^{-3.5t} = 0,$$
that is, when $e^{-2.5t} = \frac{2}{7}$ or $t = 0.4\ln 3.5 \simeq 0.50\,\text{s}$. The corresponding value of x is $0.33\,\text{m}$, so the maximum compression is $0.50 - 0.33 = 0.17\,\text{m}$.
As explained in Example 2.1, the train leaves the buffers when
$$\ddot{x} = -0.4e^{-t} + 4.9e^{-3.5t} = 0,$$
that is, when $e^{-2.5t} = \frac{4}{49}$ or $t = 0.8\ln 3.5 \simeq 1.00\,\text{s}$. The corresponding value of x is $0.37\,\text{m}$, and the corresponding velocity (with which the train leaves the buffers) is $\dot{x}\mathbf{i}$, where $\dot{x} = 0.10\,\text{m}\,\text{s}^{-1}$.

(d) Since we now have
$$r^2 - 4mk = 100(12^2 - 4 \times 4 \times 14) = -8 \times 10^3,$$
which is negative, the damping is weak. The solution will now be expressible as an exponential times a sinusoid. (However, oscillations will not be visible in the motion of the train, since this is never pulled towards the buffers. What is observable is only part of one oscillation, before the train leaves the buffers.)

With weaker damping, we would expect that:

- the spring will be compressed more than before;
- it will take longer for the spring to reach maximum compression and subsequently for the train to leave the buffers, though this must occur before the spring has returned to its natural length;
- the spring will bounce back further from maximum compression before the train parts company with the buffers;
- the parting speed of the train will be higher.

(All these expectations are borne out by the solution in this case.)

2.3 (a)

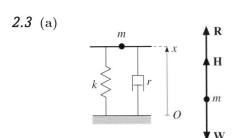

The model spring force is $\mathbf{H} = -k(x - l_0)\mathbf{i}$, the weight is $\mathbf{W} = -mg\mathbf{i}$ and the resistance force is $\mathbf{R} = -r\dot{x}\mathbf{i}$. Newton's second law gives

$$m\ddot{x}\mathbf{i} = \mathbf{H} + \mathbf{W} + \mathbf{R} = -k(x - l_0)\mathbf{i} - mg\mathbf{i} - r\dot{x}\mathbf{i},$$

which leads to the equation of motion

$$m\ddot{x} + r\dot{x} + kx = kx_{\text{eq}},$$

where $x_{\text{eq}} = l_0 - mg/k$. On substituting the values given for parameters, we have

$$60\ddot{x} + 6300\dot{x} + 30\,000x = 5411.4,$$

that is, $\ddot{x} + 105\dot{x} + 500x = 90.19$.

(b) The required initial conditions are

$$x(0) = 0.2, \quad \dot{x}(0) = 0.$$

(c) As given, but with $x_{\text{eq}} = 0.180\,\text{m}$, the particular solution is

$$x = 0.180 + 0.021e^{-5t} - 0.001e^{-100t}.$$

The third term decays very quickly, and so it is the second term in which we are interested. It reduces to 0.001 metres when

$$e^{-5t} = 0.001/0.021 \simeq 0.048,$$

that is, when

$$t = -0.2\ln 0.048 \simeq 0.61\,\text{s}.$$

The model predicts that the sit-ski will take just over half a second for the amplitude to reduce to 0.001 metres and hence for the displacement of the skier to be that close to the equilibrium position.

2.4 (a) Take x as the downward displacement of the bottom of the float from the surface of the liquid, as shown in Figure 2.10. The upthrust from the fluid is $\mathbf{U} = -2mg(x/d)\mathbf{i}$, the weight is $\mathbf{W} = mg\mathbf{i}$ and the damping resistance force is $\mathbf{R} = -r\dot{x}\mathbf{i}$.

Hence, using Newton's second law, we obtain

$$m\ddot{x}\mathbf{i} = \mathbf{W} + \mathbf{U} + \mathbf{R} = mg\mathbf{i} - (2mg/d)x\mathbf{i} - r\dot{x}\mathbf{i},$$

which leads to the equation of motion

$$m\ddot{x} + r\dot{x} + (2mg/d)x = mg.$$

Once the parameter values have been substituted, this becomes

$$0.1\ddot{x} + 11\dot{x} + 98.1x = 0.981,$$

that is, $\ddot{x} + 110\dot{x} + 981x = 9.81$. The initial conditions are $x(0) = 0$ and $\dot{x}(0) = 0$.

(b) The particular solution is given as

$$x = 0.001\,08e^{-100.2t} - 0.0111e^{-9.79t} + 0.01 \text{ (metres)}.$$

The last term represents the equilibrium position. The first involves $e^{-100.2t}$, which dies away very quickly, and the other term is the dominant term in the variable part of the solution, namely $-0.0111e^{-9.79t}$. The magnitude of this will reduce to 0.001 metres when $e^{-9.79t} = 0.090$, that is, when $t = -(\ln 0.090)/9.79 \simeq 0.25\,\text{s}$. Hence the model predicts that the displacement of the float will be within 1 mm of its equilibrium position in about a quarter of a second.

2.5 Critical damping will occur when $r^2 - 4mk$ is zero. The corresponding mass is therefore

$$m = \frac{r^2}{4k} = 125\,\text{kg}.$$

So a person whose mass was exactly 125 kg would produce critical damping when he or she stood on the scales. However, if a person with a slightly larger mass stood on the scales, then $r^2 - 4mk$ would be negative and there would be weak damping (decaying oscillations). If a person with a slightly smaller mass stood on the scales, then $r^2 - 4mk$ would be positive and there would be strong damping.

(This is a correct answer, but in reality you would not be able to detect any noticeable difference in the way the scales behaved for slight variations around critical damping. In the case which is technically weak damping, any oscillations would die down so quickly that they would be imperceptible. In the case of the technically strong damping, the return towards the equilibrium position would be slightly slower than with critical damping, but imperceptibly so.)

2.6 The damping ratio $\alpha = r/(2\sqrt{mk})$ will be increased if either m is decreased (with r and k fixed), or k is decreased (with r and m fixed).

2.7 For tube A, we have the damping ratio

$$\alpha = \frac{r}{2\sqrt{mk}} = \frac{0.15}{2\sqrt{0.711 \times 23}} \simeq 0.02.$$

Similarly, we obtain $\alpha \simeq 0.11$ (tube B), $\alpha \simeq 0.16$ (tube C) and $\alpha \simeq 1.04$ (tube D). The first three values satisfy $\alpha < 1$, so the motion in tubes A–C is weakly damped. For tube D, we see that $\alpha > 1$, confirming strong damping. (However, this is not far from critical damping, for which $\alpha = 1$.)

2.8 If $\tau = 2\pi/\nu = 1.1 \times 2\pi/\omega$, where $\nu = \omega\sqrt{1 - \alpha^2}$, then we have $1.1\sqrt{1 - \alpha^2} = 1$, with solution $\alpha \simeq 0.417$. The amplitude decay factor per cycle is therefore

$$\exp\left(-\frac{2\pi\alpha}{\sqrt{1 - \alpha^2}}\right) \simeq 0.056.$$

2.9 As α increases from 1, the value of $\sqrt{\alpha^2 - 1}$ becomes increasingly close to α, so the magnitude of λ_1 decreases towards zero, while λ_2 tends towards $-2\omega\alpha$, which increases in magnitude with α. Since both λ_1 and λ_2 are negative, it is the exponential with the exponent of smaller magnitude which dominates for large α, that is, the $e^{\lambda_1 t}$ term.

(In fact, for large α, we have $\lambda_1 \simeq -\omega/(2\alpha)$, since $\lambda_1\lambda_2 = \omega^2$.)

Section 3

3.1 (a) The solution would proceed in the same way as in Example 3.1, only this time P would be $2\,\text{N}$ instead of $10\,\text{N}$. Since the differential equation is linear, this change has the effect of scaling the constants B and C by the factor 0.2. Hence the predicted motion about the equilibrium position in the long term would consist of oscillations with the same angular frequency and phase as before, but with one fifth of the amplitude. The baby would then bounce with an amplitude of about $10^{-2}\,\text{m}$, or $1\,\text{cm}$.

(b) If the mass m of the baby is changed, then this will change the complementary function, but the latter still dies away with time. The value of x_{eq} will be changed (becoming smaller if the baby plus seat is lighter than $10\,\text{kg}$, or larger if the baby is heavier). The steady-state behaviour will still consist of sinusoidal oscillations about the (new) equilibrium position, with the same angular frequency, but the values of the constants B and C will be different. The amplitude and phase of the output oscillations may both be different.

3.2

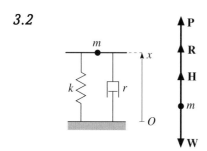

The forces acting are the weight, $\mathbf{W} = -mg\mathbf{i}$, the spring force, $\mathbf{H} = -k(x - l_0)\mathbf{i}$, the damping resistance $\mathbf{R} = -r\dot{x}\mathbf{i}$ and the girl's input force $\mathbf{P} = mg\cos(\Omega t)\mathbf{i}$, so Newton's second law gives

$$m\ddot{x}\mathbf{i} = \mathbf{W} + \mathbf{H} + \mathbf{R} + \mathbf{P}$$
$$= -mg\mathbf{i} - k(x - l_0)\mathbf{i} - r\dot{x}\mathbf{i} + mg\cos(\Omega t)\mathbf{i}.$$

This leads to the equation of motion

$$m\ddot{x} + r\dot{x} + kx = kl_0 - mg + mg\cos(\Omega t)$$
$$= kx_{\text{eq}} + mg\cos(\Omega t),$$

where $x_{\text{eq}} = l_0 - mg/k$. This differential equation is of the same form as that derived for the baby bouncer in Example 3.1. The values of the parameters will differ, but the model predicts the same overall long-term behaviour, namely, oscillations of angular frequency Ω about the equilibrium position, with a steady-state displacement function of the form

$$x = x_{\text{eq}} + A\cos(\Omega t + \phi).$$

The values of A and ϕ here may be calculated (using a sinusoidal trial function in the manner of Example 3.1) from the values for m, k, r and Ω.

3.3 (a) The weight $\mathbf{W} = mg\mathbf{i}$ and model spring force $\mathbf{H} = -k(x - y - l_0)\mathbf{i}$ are as in Example 3.2. The damping resistance force is now $\mathbf{R} = -r(\dot{x} - \dot{y})\mathbf{i}$. This change leads to the amended equation of motion

$$m\ddot{x} + r\dot{x} + kx = mg + kl_0 + r\dot{y} + ky.$$

On putting $x_{\text{eq}} = mg/k + l_0$ and $y = a\cos(\Omega t)$ (so that also $\dot{y} = -a\Omega\sin(\Omega t)$), this becomes

$$m\ddot{x} + r\dot{x} + kx$$
$$= kx_{\text{eq}} + ka\cos(\Omega t) - ra\Omega\sin(\Omega t). \qquad \text{(S.1)}$$

On substituting in the values for m, k, r, a and Ω given in Example 3.2, we obtain

$$10\ddot{x} + 0.2\dot{x} + 200x = 200x_{\text{eq}} + 8\cos(2\pi t)$$
$$- 0.016\pi\sin(2\pi t).$$

Comparing Equation (S.1) with the direct forcing equation (3.2), the form of the sinusoid on the right-hand side is different, in that a sine appears as well as the cosine term. This is to some extent a superficial difference, since we can re-express the sinusoid on the right-hand side of Equation (S.1) using its alternative form, that is,

$$ka\cos(\Omega t) - ra\Omega\sin(\Omega t) = P\cos(\Omega t + \psi).$$

The connection between the two forms is given by

$$P\cos\psi = ka, \quad P\sin\psi = ra\Omega,$$

or by

$$P = a\sqrt{k^2 + r^2\Omega^2}, \quad \psi = \arctan(r\Omega/k).$$

Equation (S.1) then becomes

$$m\ddot{x} + r\dot{x} + kx = kx_{\text{eq}} + P\cos(\Omega t + \psi),$$

and this now differs from the form of the direct forcing equation (3.2) only by a shift of phase.

(b) The steady-state solution will be the constant x_{eq} plus a sinusoid of the form $B\cos(\Omega t) + C\sin(\Omega t)$, which can also be written in the form $A\cos(\Omega t + \phi)$. In order to find the values for B and C (and hence subsequently A and ϕ), substitute the trial particular integral $B\cos(\Omega t) + C\sin(\Omega t)$ into the differential equation and equate coefficients of $\cos(\Omega t)$ and $\sin(\Omega t)$, to obtain simultaneous equations in B and C.

Then $A = \sqrt{B^2 + C^2}$ gives the amplitude of the vibration, and the phase ϕ is the solution of the pair of equations $\cos\phi = B/A$, $\sin\phi = -C/A$. Hence the model again predicts steady-state oscillations, of the same frequency as the input forcing displacement.

(In fact, because the given damping constant r is so small compared with the mass m and stiffness k, the solution for the case here is almost indistinguishable from that obtained in Example 3.2.)

3.4

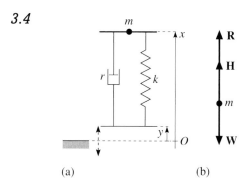

(a)   (b)

The forces acting are the weight, $\mathbf{W} = -mg\mathbf{i}$, the model spring force $\mathbf{H} = -k(l - l_0)\widehat{\mathbf{s}} = -k(x - y - l_0)\mathbf{i}$ and the damping resistance $\mathbf{R} = -r(\dot{x} - \dot{y})\mathbf{i}$, where $y = a\cos(\Omega t)$. This leads to the equation of motion

$$m\ddot{x} + r\dot{x} + kx = kl_0 - mg + r\dot{y} + ky$$
$$= kx_{\mathrm{eq}} + ka\cos(\Omega t) - ra\Omega\sin(\Omega t),$$

where $x_{\mathrm{eq}} = l_0 - mg/k$. With the numerical values inserted (and taking $g = 9.81\,\mathrm{m\,s^{-2}}$), this becomes

$$60\ddot{x} + 6300\dot{x} + 30\,000x = 30\,000x_{\mathrm{eq}} + 3\,000\cos(\pi t)$$
$$- 630\pi\sin(\pi t),$$

or

$$\ddot{x} + 105\dot{x} + 500x = 90.2 + 50\cos(\pi t) - 10.5\pi\sin(\pi t).$$

The form of this equation is the same as that considered in Exercise 3.3, and hence the same approach to finding a particular integral and general conclusions apply. The model predicts steady-state oscillations of the same angular frequency $\pi\,\mathrm{rad\,s^{-1}}$ as the input forcing displacement.

3.5 (a) Equation (3.6) gives $A \simeq 0.051\,338\,\mathrm{m}$ and Equation (3.7) gives $\phi \simeq -3.1351\,\mathrm{rad}$, in agreement with the result quoted in the solution to Example 3.1.

(b) Here we have $P = ak = 8\,\mathrm{N}$. For a period of 2 seconds, the angular frequency is $\Omega = \pi\,\mathrm{rad\,s^{-1}}$. According to Equation (3.6), the corresponding output amplitude in the steady state is $A \simeq 0.079\,\mathrm{m}$. This is about $8\,\mathrm{cm}$, which is twice the amplitude which was found for a forcing period of $1\,\mathrm{s}$.

(c) Here we have

$$P = 0.1\sqrt{30\,000^2 + 6300^2\pi^2} \simeq 3594\,\mathrm{N},$$

which leads to $A \simeq 0.101\,\mathrm{m}$. This output amplitude is almost the same as that of the input forcing.

3.6 The solution is very similar to that for Exercise 3.3. As there, the weight is $\mathbf{W} = mg\mathbf{i}$ and the damping resistance is $\mathbf{R} = -r(\dot{x} - \dot{y})\mathbf{i}$, but now the model spring force is $\mathbf{H} = -k(x - l_0)\mathbf{i}$. The resulting equation of motion is

$$m\ddot{x} + r\dot{x} + kx = mg + kl_0 + r\dot{y}.$$

On putting $x_{\mathrm{eq}} = mg/k + l_0$ and $y = a\cos(\Omega t)$ (so that $\dot{y} = -a\Omega\sin(\Omega t)$), this becomes

$$m\ddot{x} + r\dot{x} + kx = kx_{\mathrm{eq}} - ra\Omega\sin(\Omega t).$$

This is of the same form as Equation (3.2) except for a phase shift, since

$$-ra\Omega\sin(\Omega t) = P\cos(\Omega t + \psi)$$

provided that $P = ra\Omega$ and $\psi = \frac{\pi}{2}$.

Section 4

4.1 We have $\alpha \simeq 0.002$ and $\beta = \Omega/\omega = 1$. According to Equation (4.1), the corresponding magnification factor is

$$M = \left(\left(1 - \beta^2\right)^2 + 4\alpha^2\beta^2\right)^{-1/2} = (2\alpha)^{-1} \simeq 250.$$

The steady-state output oscillations are therefore predicted to have amplitude

$$A = Ma \simeq 250 \times 0.04 = 10\,\mathrm{m}.$$

The system will not in fact be able to sustain an oscillation of this amplitude! For one thing, the natural length of the model spring used to represent a baby bouncer will be nowhere near $10\,\mathrm{m}$. However, the model may be useful to the extent of predicting a potential catastrophe which needs to be avoided.

(Note that the forcing angular frequency of $4.47\,\mathrm{rad\,s^{-1}}$, which is predicted to cause such a breakdown, lies between $\pi\,\mathrm{rad\,s^{-1}}$ and $2\pi\,\mathrm{rad\,s^{-1}}$, for which we found earlier that the predicted output amplitudes were only $8\,\mathrm{cm}$ and $4\,\mathrm{cm}$, respectively. The large magnification factors occur for a fairly narrow range of values of the input forcing frequency.)

UNIT 18   Normal modes

Study guide for Unit 18

This unit continues the mechanics part of the course; in particular, it builds on the earlier units that dealt with oscillations, *Units 7* and *17*. In order to solve the equations of motion derived for the mechanical systems studied, it uses the methods for solving systems of differential equations which were developed in *Unit 11*. Like *Unit 11*, this unit draws heavily on the discussion of eigenvalues and eigenvectors in *Unit 10*.

The five sections in this unit should be studied in numerical order. Section 1 contains the main ideas of the unit and is longer than the other sections. You should therefore allow more time for studying it. Section 5, on the other hand, is shorter than average.

There is a video sequence associated with Section 1.

You will need to use your computer in Section 3 to study the multimedia package that comprises the section.

The ideas in this unit will be made use of in *Unit 19*, which analyses similar mechanical systems but concentrates on the effect of having an external force influencing the system. In addition, some of the ideas in Section 4 will be developed further in *Unit 22*.

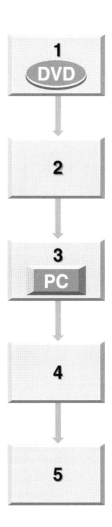

Introduction

In *Unit 7* you studied the simple harmonic motion of oscillating mechanical systems, in particular those involving model springs. A typical example of such a system is shown in Figure 0.1, where an object modelled as a particle is connected by a model spring (of natural length l_0 and stiffness k) to a fixed wall; the particle is constrained to move in a straight line on a frictionless horizontal surface. In *Unit 7* the equation of motion for this system was found to be

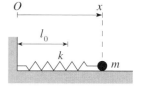

Figure 0.1

$$m\ddot{x} + kx = kl_0.$$

The solution of this differential equation can be written in the form

$$x(t) = l_0 + A\cos(\omega t + \phi),$$

where x is the displacement from the wall, and ω $(= \sqrt{k/m})$, A and ϕ are, respectively, the angular frequency, the amplitude and the phase angle of the oscillations executed by the particle.

Damping and forcing were incorporated in the simple harmonic motion model in *Unit 17* to make it more realistic. This unit extends the basic model in a different way, to take account of another aspect of the motion of oscillating mechanical systems — the fact that usually more than one part of the system is free to move.

Damping and forcing are not considered in this unit.

A simple mechanical system, typical of those considered in this unit, and its schematic representation are shown in Figure 0.2. The diagram shows two particles connected by model springs to one another and to two fixed walls. Each particle is free to move, so the motion of the system is not as straightforward as the simple harmonic motion considered above — unlike simple harmonic motion, it is, in general, not sinusoidal. But there are particular solutions to the equation of motion for such systems that *do* correspond to each part of the system oscillating backwards and forwards sinusoidally with the same frequency. These particular solutions are called *normal modes*. This unit is concerned with finding the normal modes of simple oscillating mechanical systems and showing how *any* motion of such a system can be built up from normal modes.

Figure 0.2

Section 1 provides an overview of the unit and introduces many of the ideas that underpin the unit; notably it contains several important concepts and definitions. Section 2 looks at systems that are confined to one dimension. Section 3 is a computer section that provides the opportunity to simulate the motions of the mechanical systems studied in the unit. Section 4 is a first step at looking at two-dimensional problems; the context for the discussion is a problem concerned with modelling the behaviour of a guitar string. Finally, Section 5 draws together the results from the preceding sections, showing how they can be used to analyse simple two-dimensional problems.

1   *Oscillations and normal modes*

The important concepts of a normal mode and of degrees of freedom are introduced in Subsection 1.1, with the help of a video sequence. Subsection 1.2 goes on to show how normal modes constitute the building blocks for modelling the motion of oscillating mechanical systems. Subsection 1.3 then explores how certain eigenvectors can be used to determine the initial conditions for the normal mode motion of such a system.

1.1   What is a normal mode?

In real mechanical systems, more than one part of the system is usually free to move. For example, in the system shown in Figure 1.1, a railway engine and two trucks are connected by stiff springs. As the engine starts to move along the track, so do the trucks. However, because of the springs, the motion of the trucks is different from that of the engine — the position of each truck oscillates backwards and forwards relative to the position of the engine. The system can be modelled by three particles connected by two model springs. Since the relative positions of the particles representing the trucks and engine can change, we need to specify not one but three coordinates to describe the configuration of the system — one per particle (as shown in Figure 1.1).

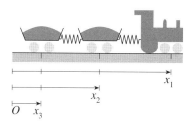

Figure 1.1

> **Definition**
>
> The number of **degrees of freedom** of a system is the smallest number of coordinates needed to describe its configuration (i.e. the positions of the constituent parts of the system) at any instant in time.

The positions of the constituent parts of the system illustrated in Figure 1.1 — that is, the engine and the two trucks (or the particles that model them) — can be specified by giving their displacements from a fixed origin O, as shown in the figure. But there are many other ways of specifying the configuration: for example, we could use a different fixed point for the origin; or we could measure the position of each truck relative to the changing position of the engine, which, in turn, would be determined by reference to a fixed point; and so on. The important thing to note is that, in each case, three pieces of information are required to specify the configuration of the system completely — fewer would leave some element unspecified, more would be superfluous. It is for this reason that we say this system has three degrees of freedom.

In general, any convenient point can be chosen as an origin. Often, for simplicity, an equilibrium position of a system is taken to be the origin.

Exercise 1.1

State the number of degrees of freedom of each of the following mechanical systems. Assume that the railway track is straight and flat, and that the engine and trucks are modelled as particles, and the springs as model springs.

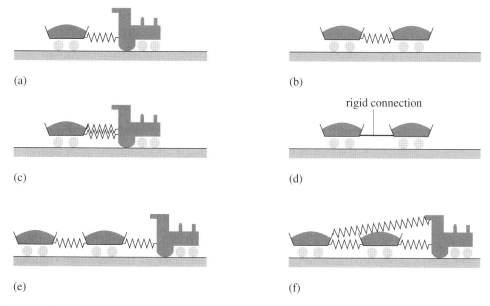

(a)

(b)

(c)

rigid connection

(d)

Note that the rigid connection in (d) effectively ties the trucks together as a single entity that can be modelled as one particle.

(e)

(f)

The concept of degrees of freedom relates to more situations than trains travelling on straight railway tracks. It applies to systems ranging from pendulums to individual molecules. However, determining the number of degrees of freedom of a system is not always as straightforward as in the case of the train considered above — more detailed analysis of the system is often necessary. For example, consider the simple pendulum shown in Figure 1.2. This is a mechanical system that moves in two dimensions, i.e. in a vertical plane, and so we could specify the position of the pendulum bob using a pair of Cartesian coordinates. You might therefore expect that the system would have two degrees of freedom. But the pendulum bob is constrained to move along a circular path in the vertical plane, so only one coordinate, the angle θ, is needed to specify its position. Hence the system has one degree of freedom. Other systems with one degree of freedom include the spring systems that you studied in *Units 7* and *17*. In this unit, however, we concentrate on systems with more than one degree of freedom.

You studied the simple pendulum in *Unit 8*.

Figure 1.2

So, what is the significance of degrees of freedom in relation to normal modes? Degrees of freedom are important in this context as they indicate the number of normal modes that a system has, as you will see in the video for this unit. We begin by looking at some simple mechanical systems with two degrees of freedom and their normal modes.

Watch the video for this unit now.

DVD

From the video it is evident that mechanical systems with two degrees of freedom can behave in simple or complicated ways, depending on the initial positions and velocities of the constituent parts. In the video you observed the motion of the double pendulum pictured in Figure 1.3 below. Two coordinates are needed to specify the configuration of this mechanical system, which therefore has two degrees of freedom. The two coordinates used in the video were the horizontal displacements of the two pendulum bobs: x_1 (for the upper pendulum bob) and x_2 (for the lower pendulum bob). You saw that the system usually moves in a complicated manner, as shown in Figure 1.4. This behaviour is very different from that of the mechanical systems with one degree of freedom studied in *Unit 7*, where the motion is always sinusoidal.

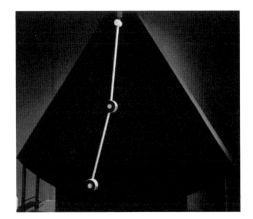

Figure 1.3

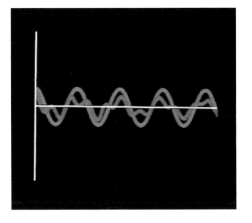

Figure 1.4 Almost all initial conditions result in complicated motion like this.

However, the motion is not always so complicated, and there are situations where both particles move sinusoidally with the same frequency. In the video, two such simple motions were shown, the first of which is illustrated in Figure 1.5. By comparing Figure 1.4 and Figure 1.5(b), you can see that the motion is much more regular in the latter: the particles complete each cycle simultaneously, i.e. the sinusoidal motion is of the same period (and so of the same frequency). Consequently, the motion of the particles in Figure 1.5(b) can be modelled by a pair of equations of the form

$$\begin{cases} x_1(t) = A_1 \cos(\omega t + \phi), \\ x_2(t) = A_2 \cos(\omega t + \phi), \end{cases} \tag{1.1}$$

where $|A_1|$ and $|A_2|$ are the amplitudes of the motions of the particles, ω is the common angular frequency and ϕ is the common phase angle. Such motion is known as a *normal mode* of the system.

Notice that each equation represents simple harmonic motion, as defined in *Unit 7*.

For a normal mode, the coefficients A_1 and A_2 can be positive or negative.

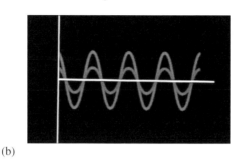

(a)　　　　(b)

The snapshots in (a) include the most extreme points of the motion, when the pendulums are both momentarily at rest.

Figure 1.5   (a) Snapshots, at intervals of one sixth of a cycle, of the motion of a double pendulum system moving in a normal mode.   (b) Traces of the corresponding sinusoidal motions of the pendulum bobs.

Definition

A **normal mode** is a type of motion of a system of particles in which the coordinates of the particles all vary sinusoidally with the same frequency. The angular frequency of the sinusoidal motion is called the **normal mode angular frequency**.

In this context, *normal* means 'standard' and not 'usual'. (In fact, normal modes are unusual in that most modes of motion are not normal modes.)

For each of the systems with *two* degrees of freedom that you saw in the video, you observed *two* normal modes. Generally, the number of distinct normal modes of a system corresponds to the number of degrees of freedom of the system (though we shall not prove this here).

We turn now to another important aspect of motion, which is illustrated in Figure 1.5 above. You may have noticed that when one of the pendulum bobs moves from left to right, so does the other, and similarly when one moves from right to left, so does the other. This type of motion, in which two particles move in the same direction, is said to be **in-phase motion**. As you saw in the video, not all normal mode motion is in-phase: it can also be **phase-opposed motion**, which occurs, as you might expect, when two particles move in opposite directions, as illustrated in Figure 1.6.

This correspondence occurs in *all* cases if we extend the definition of normal modes to include what is known as *rigid body motion*. Such motion is discussed in Subsection 2.2.

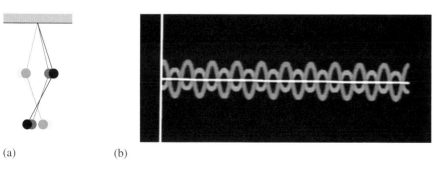

(a)　　　　　　(b)

The snapshots in (a) include the most extreme points of the motion, when the pendulums are both momentarily at rest.

Figure 1.6   (a) Snapshots, at intervals of one sixth of a cycle, of the motion of a double pendulum system moving in a phase-opposed normal mode.   (b) Traces of the corresponding sinusoidal motions of the pendulum bobs.

If you look at Figure 1.5(b) you will see that, for the in-phase motion, the phase angles of the two sinusoids are the same. In contrast, you can see in Figure 1.6(b) that, for the phase-opposed motion, the phase angles of the two sinusoids differ by π. This is true in general: the sinusoids representing normal mode motion have phase angles that either are the same (in which case the motion is in-phase), or differ by π (in which case the motion is phase-opposed). In both cases, though, equations of the form (1.1) can be used to represent the normal mode motion.

This is because $\cos(\omega t + \phi + \pi) = -\cos(\omega t + \phi)$, and the negative sign can be absorbed into the coefficient A_i (which can be negative or positive).

If two particles are moving in a normal mode with their motion aligned with a common axis, there are only three situations that can occur: the particles move in-phase, or they are phase-opposed, or one or both particles are stationary. By extension, in a system with three or more particles, each pair of particles can be considered separately; thus, for any particular pair, the particles can be in-phase, or phase-opposed, or stationary, relative to each other.

Exercise 1.2

For each of the following sets of graphs showing the motion of two (or three) particles, state whether or not the motion represented is normal mode motion. If it is, state whether the motion of each pair of particles is in-phase or phase-opposed.

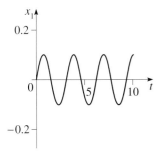 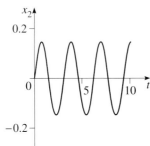

(a)

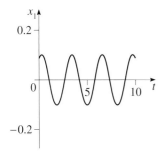 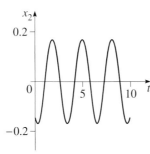 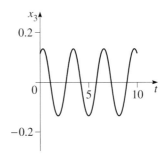

(b)

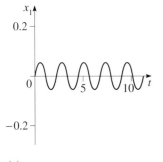 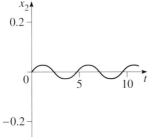

(c)

1.2 Analysing oscillating mechanical systems

In this subsection you will see how to obtain the equations of normal mode motion for an oscillating mechanical system, and how these equations can be combined to model any motion of such a system. We examine two systems which are similar to those you saw in the video. We begin by deriving the equations of motion for one of these systems, using techniques familiar from *Units 5* and *7*.

Example 1.1

Consider two particles of masses m_1 and m_2, joined to each other and to two fixed walls by three identical model springs of stiffness k and natural length l_0, as shown in Figure 1.7. The particles are constrained to move across a frictionless horizontal surface in the straight line joining the points of attachment (i.e. the motion is one-dimensional). To simplify the analysis, the distance between the fixed walls is assumed to be exactly three times the natural length of the springs; hence the equilibrium position of the system is that shown in Figure 1.7(a). Two coordinates are needed to specify the positions of the particles in the system; therefore the system has two degrees of freedom. The simplest option for the coordinates is to measure the displacement of each particle from its equilibrium position. These displacements are labelled x_1 and x_2 in Figure 1.7(b), and are measured from the origins O_1 and O_2, respectively.

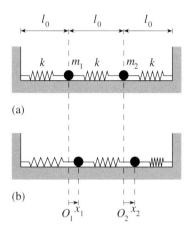

Figure 1.7

What are the equations of motion for this oscillating system?

Solution

To obtain the equations of motion for this system, Newton's second law is applied to each of the particles separately. In order to do this, the first step is to draw two force diagrams — one for each particle.

You have already met the idea (in *Unit 5*, in relation to particles in equilibrium) that, when considering the forces acting on the particles in a system, each particle can be treated separately. This is the first time in the course that this principle has been applied to a system in motion.

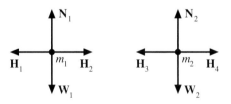

Here the weights of the particles are denoted by $\mathbf{W}_1$ and $\mathbf{W}_2$, the normal reactions of the surface on the particles by $\mathbf{N}_1$ and $\mathbf{N}_2$, and the forces exerted by the springs on the particles by $\mathbf{H}_1$, $\mathbf{H}_2$, $\mathbf{H}_3$ and $\mathbf{H}_4$. Since the motion is horizontal, the two vertical forces on each particle must balance one another ($\mathbf{W}_1 + \mathbf{N}_1 = \mathbf{0}$, $\mathbf{W}_2 + \mathbf{N}_2 = \mathbf{0}$), so the total force (i.e. the resultant force) on the first particle is $\mathbf{F}_1 = \mathbf{H}_1 + \mathbf{H}_2$ and that on the second particle is $\mathbf{F}_2 = \mathbf{H}_3 + \mathbf{H}_4$. Now we apply Newton's second law to the first particle and obtain

You have seen one-particle systems analysed in this way in *Unit 7*.

$$m_1\ddot{\mathbf{r}}_1 = \mathbf{H}_1 + \mathbf{H}_2, \tag{1.2}$$

where $\mathbf{r}_1$ is the position vector of the first particle with respect to its equilibrium position, i.e. $\mathbf{r}_1 = x_1\mathbf{i}$, with $\mathbf{i}$ being a unit vector in the direction of positive x_1 and x_2. Similarly, for the second particle,

$$m_2\ddot{\mathbf{r}}_2 = \mathbf{H}_3 + \mathbf{H}_4. \tag{1.3}$$

The four forces due to the springs can then be modelled using Hooke's law. First, recall from *Unit 7* that, according to Hooke's law, a model spring of natural length l_0 and stiffness k exerts a force on an object attached to one end of the spring, such that the force is given by $\mathbf{H} = -k(l - l_0)\,\widehat{\mathbf{s}}$, where l is the length of the spring and $\widehat{\mathbf{s}}$ is a unit vector directed from the centre of the spring to the point where the object is attached. For the force $\mathbf{H}_1$, which is the force exerted by the left-hand spring on the first particle, we have $l = l_0 + x_1$ and $\widehat{\mathbf{s}} = \mathbf{i}$, so

$$\mathbf{H}_1 = -k((l_0 + x_1) - l_0)\mathbf{i} = -kx_1\mathbf{i}.$$

For the force $\mathbf{H}_2$, we have $l = l_0 + x_2 - x_1$ and $\widehat{\mathbf{s}} = -\mathbf{i}$, so

$$\mathbf{H}_2 = -k((l_0 + x_2 - x_1) - l_0)(-\mathbf{i}) = k(x_2 - x_1)\mathbf{i}.$$

For the force $\mathbf{H}_3$, we can apply Hooke's law again, or we can simply note that all the data are the same as for $\mathbf{H}_2$ (since we are considering the same spring) except that now $\widehat{\mathbf{s}} = \mathbf{i}$, thus

$$\mathbf{H}_3 = -k(x_2 - x_1)\mathbf{i}.$$

For the force $\mathbf{H}_4$, we have $l = l_0 - x_2$ and $\widehat{\mathbf{s}} = -\mathbf{i}$, so

$$\mathbf{H}_4 = -k((l_0 - x_2) - l_0)(-\mathbf{i}) = -kx_2\mathbf{i}.$$

Now that all the forces have been modelled, they can be substituted into Equations (1.2) and (1.3), giving

$$\begin{cases} m_1\ddot{\mathbf{r}}_1 = -kx_1\mathbf{i} + k(x_2 - x_1)\mathbf{i}, \\ m_2\ddot{\mathbf{r}}_2 = -k(x_2 - x_1)\mathbf{i} - kx_2\mathbf{i}. \end{cases} \tag{1.4}$$

But $\mathbf{r}_1 = x_1\mathbf{i}$ and $\mathbf{r}_2 = x_2\mathbf{i}$, therefore $\ddot{\mathbf{r}}_1 = \ddot{x}_1\mathbf{i}$ and $\ddot{\mathbf{r}}_2 = \ddot{x}_2\mathbf{i}$. Substituting for $\ddot{\mathbf{r}}_1$ and $\ddot{\mathbf{r}}_2$ in Equations (1.4), resolving in the $\mathbf{i}$-direction and collecting terms gives

$$\begin{cases} m_1\ddot{x}_1 = -2kx_1 + kx_2, \\ m_2\ddot{x}_2 = kx_1 - 2kx_2. \end{cases} \tag{1.5}$$

These differential equations are the equations of motion for the oscillating mechanical system depicted in Figure 1.7. ∎

> Hooke's law tells us that the forces exerted at either end of a model spring are always equal in magnitude but opposite in direction. We shall frequently make use of this property, which is a consequence of Newton's third law. (Compare this property of model springs with that of model strings discussed in *Unit 5*.)

Equations (1.5) can be written in matrix form as

$$\ddot{\mathbf{x}} = \begin{bmatrix} \ddot{x}_1 \\ \ddot{x}_2 \end{bmatrix} = \begin{bmatrix} -2k/m_1 & k/m_1 \\ k/m_2 & -2k/m_2 \end{bmatrix} \begin{bmatrix} x_1 \\ x_2 \end{bmatrix} = \mathbf{A}\mathbf{x}. \tag{1.6}$$

The equation $\ddot{\mathbf{x}} = \mathbf{A}\mathbf{x}$ is referred to as the (*matrix*) *equation of motion* for the mechanical system, and the matrix $\mathbf{A}$ is called the **dynamic matrix** of the system.

In *Unit 11* you saw that, provided $\mathbf{A}$ has distinct real eigenvalues, the general solution of such an equation can be expressed as a linear combination of exponentials, sinusoids and linear terms. Since Equation (1.6) models the motion of an oscillating mechanical system (without damping or forcing), we would expect only sinusoids in the general solution because sinusoids best represent this type of periodic motion. Thus we would anticipate a general solution of the form

$$\mathbf{x}(t) = \mathbf{v}_1(D_1\cos(\omega_1 t) + D_2\sin(\omega_1 t)) + \mathbf{v}_2(D_3\cos(\omega_2 t) + D_4\sin(\omega_2 t)),$$

comprising four linearly independent terms, where $\mathbf{v}_1$ and $\mathbf{v}_2$ are eigenvectors corresponding to the eigenvalues λ_1 and λ_2 of $\mathbf{A}$, and $\omega_1 = \sqrt{-\lambda_1}$, $\omega_2 = \sqrt{-\lambda_2}$, while D_1, D_2, D_3 and D_4 are arbitrary constants. For present purposes, we shall rewrite this general solution in the form

$$\mathbf{x}(t) = C_1\mathbf{v}_1\cos(\omega_1 t + \phi_1) + C_2\mathbf{v}_2\cos(\omega_2 t + \phi_2), \tag{1.7}$$

where the four arbitrary constants D_1, D_2, D_3 and D_4 have been replaced by the four arbitrary constants C_1, C_2, ϕ_1 and ϕ_2.

> See Procedure 4.1 in *Unit 11*.

> In fact, as you will see in Subsection 2.2, there can also be linear terms in the solution.

> You saw in *Units 7* and *17* that $B\cos(\omega t) + C\sin(\omega t)$ can be rewritten in the form $A\cos(\omega t + \phi)$, where $B = A\cos\phi$ and $C = -A\sin\phi$.

One specific solution of Equation (1.7), obtained by putting $C_1 = 1$ and $C_2 = 0$, is $\mathbf{x}(t) = \mathbf{v}_1 \cos(\omega_1 t + \phi_1)$, which can be written in the form

$$\begin{cases} x_1(t) = v_{11} \cos\left(\omega_1 t + \phi_1\right), \\ x_2(t) = v_{12} \cos\left(\omega_1 t + \phi_1\right). \end{cases} \tag{1.8}$$

The interesting thing about this solution is that it represents a normal mode of the system in Example 1.1. To see this, look back at the general equations for normal mode motion (1.1) and replace A_1, A_2 and ϕ by v_{11}, v_{12} and ϕ_1, respectively.

In general, any normal mode can be written in vector form as $\mathbf{x}(t) = \mathbf{v} \cos(\omega t + \phi)$, where $\mathbf{v}$ is a constant vector, ω is the normal mode angular frequency and ϕ is a constant scalar.

Similarly, putting $C_1 = 0$ and $C_2 = 1$ in Equation (1.7) gives the solution $\mathbf{x}(t) = \mathbf{v}_2 \cos(\omega_2 t + \phi_2)$, which represents a second normal mode of the system. Hence, Equation (1.7) tells us that the general solution of the equation of motion for the mechanical system in Example 1.1 can be expressed as a linear combination of normal modes.

This finding concerning the solution of the equation of motion is generally fulfilled. This is because the motion of an oscillating mechanical system (without damping or forcing) can be modelled by a system of linear second-order differential equations, such as Equation (1.6), whose coefficient matrix, i.e. the dynamic matrix, has real non-positive eigenvalues, all of which usually are negative. If we put aside for the moment the case where some of the eigenvalues are zero, we have a dynamic matrix with negative eigenvalues. From *Unit 11*, Section 4, this means that, provided these eigenvalues are distinct, the general solution can be written as a linear combination of sinusoids of the form $\mathbf{v} \cos(\omega t + \phi)$, i.e. as a linear combination of normal modes. Furthermore, these normal modes will be linearly independent, since they correspond to linearly independent eigenvectors. Therefore we have the following important result.

We do not prove that the eigenvalues must be non-positive here.

The case where some eigenvalues are zero is considered in Subsection 2.2.

Theorem 1.1

The general solution of the equation of motion for an oscillating mechanical system (without damping or forcing) whose dynamic matrix has distinct non-zero eigenvalues can be written as a linear combination of linearly independent normal modes of the system.

In this case the number of linearly independent normal modes of a system is the same as the number of degrees of freedom of the system.

Theorem 1.1 indicates why normal modes are so important: not only are they especially simple oscillations themselves, but every motion can be expressed in terms of them.

Having established that the solution of the equation of motion obtained in Example 1.1 is likely to be expressible as a linear combination of normal modes, we now use the techniques of *Units 10* and *11* to find those normal modes, and hence the general solution of the equation of motion.

Solving equations of the form $\ddot{\mathbf{x}} = \mathbf{A}\mathbf{x}$ is dealt with in Section 4 of *Unit 11*, while finding eigenvalues and eigenvectors is covered in *Unit 10*.

Example 1.2

Suppose that, in the mechanical system in Example 1.1, each particle has mass $0.1\,\text{kg}$ and each spring has stiffness $0.2\,\text{N}\,\text{m}^{-1}$. Determine the general solution of the equation of motion.

Solution

From the given data, we have $k/m_1 = k/m_2 = 0.2/0.1 = 2$, so the dynamic matrix of the system is

$$\mathbf{A} = \begin{bmatrix} -2k/m_1 & k/m_1 \\ k/m_2 & -2k/m_2 \end{bmatrix} = \begin{bmatrix} -4 & 2 \\ 2 & -4 \end{bmatrix}.$$

To find each normal mode, and hence the general solution of the equation of motion for the system, the first step is to determine the eigenvalues and eigenvectors of the dynamic matrix. The eigenvalues can be found by forming the characteristic equation, and solving the resulting quadratic equation

$$\begin{vmatrix} -4 - \lambda & 2 \\ 2 & -4 - \lambda \end{vmatrix} = \lambda^2 + 8\lambda + 12 = (\lambda + 2)(\lambda + 6) = 0.$$

So the eigenvalues are -2 and -6.

$\boxed{\lambda = -2}$ The eigenvector equations are

$$\begin{bmatrix} -4 - (-2) & 2 \\ 2 & -4 - (-2) \end{bmatrix} \begin{bmatrix} v_1 \\ v_2 \end{bmatrix} = \begin{bmatrix} 0 \\ 0 \end{bmatrix},$$

or equivalently

$$\begin{cases} -2v_1 + 2v_2 = 0, \\ 2v_1 - 2v_2 = 0. \end{cases}$$

These equations both reduce to $v_2 = v_1$, so $\begin{bmatrix} 1 & 1 \end{bmatrix}^T$ is an eigenvector.

$\boxed{\lambda = -6}$ The eigenvector equations are

$$\begin{bmatrix} -4 - (-6) & 2 \\ 2 & -4 - (-6) \end{bmatrix} \begin{bmatrix} v_1 \\ v_2 \end{bmatrix} = \begin{bmatrix} 0 \\ 0 \end{bmatrix},$$

or equivalently

$$\begin{cases} 2v_1 + 2v_2 = 0, \\ 2v_1 + 2v_2 = 0. \end{cases}$$

These equations both reduce to $v_2 = -v_1$, so $\begin{bmatrix} 1 & -1 \end{bmatrix}^T$ is an eigenvector.

As you saw above, each eigenvalue/eigenvector pair gives a normal mode of the system of the form $\mathbf{v}\cos(\omega t + \phi)$, where $\mathbf{v}$ is the eigenvector and $\omega = \sqrt{-\lambda}$, with λ the eigenvalue. For $\lambda = -2$ we have the normal mode angular frequency $\omega_1 = \sqrt{2}\,\mathrm{rad\,s^{-1}}$, and for $\lambda = -6$ we have $\omega_2 = \sqrt{6}\,\mathrm{rad\,s^{-1}}$. Therefore, two linearly independent normal modes of the system are

$$\mathbf{x}(t) = \begin{bmatrix} 1 \\ 1 \end{bmatrix} \cos\left(\sqrt{2}t + \phi_1\right) \quad \text{and} \quad \mathbf{x}(t) = \begin{bmatrix} 1 \\ -1 \end{bmatrix} \cos\left(\sqrt{6}t + \phi_2\right).$$

Hence, by Theorem 1.1, the general solution of the equation of motion is

$$\mathbf{x}(t) = \begin{bmatrix} x_1(t) \\ x_2(t) \end{bmatrix} = C_1 \begin{bmatrix} 1 \\ 1 \end{bmatrix} \cos\left(\sqrt{2}t + \phi_1\right) + C_2 \begin{bmatrix} 1 \\ -1 \end{bmatrix} \cos\left(\sqrt{6}t + \phi_2\right),$$

where C_1, C_2, ϕ_1 and ϕ_2 are arbitrary constants. ∎

Exercise 1.3

Determine the general solution of the equation of motion for the mechanical system considered in Example 1.1 if the particles have mass 0.1 kg and 0.2 kg, respectively, and each spring has stiffness $0.2\,\mathrm{N\,m^{-1}}$. Give your calculations to three decimal places.

The method employed in Examples 1.1 and 1.2 can be generalized to any oscillating mechanical system (without damping or forcing), and takes the form of the following general procedure.

Procedure 1.1   Analysing oscillating mechanical systems

To analyse the motion of a given oscillating mechanical system (without damping or forcing) with n degrees of freedom, proceed as follows.

(a) Model the system using particles in conjunction with model springs, model rods, etc. Draw a sketch of the physical situation and annotate it with any relevant information.   ◀Draw picture▶

(b) Choose n coordinates (denoted by, say, $x_1, \ldots, x_n$) and corresponding origins.   ◀Choose coordinates▶

(c) Draw a force diagram for each particle separately.   ◀Draw force diagram(s)▶

(d) Apply Newton's second law to each particle separately, and resolve each force in the directions of appropriate axes to obtain n linear second-order differential equations of motion.   ◀Apply Newton's 2nd law▶

(e) Write the equations in matrix form as $\ddot{\mathbf{x}} = \mathbf{A}\mathbf{x}$, where $\mathbf{A}$ is the $n \times n$ dynamic matrix of the system.   ◀Solve equation(s)▶

(f) Find the eigenvalues $\lambda_1, \ldots, \lambda_n$ and a corresponding set of linearly independent eigenvectors $\mathbf{v}_1, \ldots, \mathbf{v}_n$ of $\mathbf{A}$. (The eigenvectors $\mathbf{v}_1, \ldots, \mathbf{v}_n$ are often referred to as the **normal mode eigenvectors** of the system.)

> If the eigenvalues are not distinct, the procedure can break down. If any of them are zero, the procedure needs to be adapted as described in Subsection 2.2. If any of them are positive or complex, you have made a mistake!

(g) Determine the normal mode angular frequencies $\omega_1, \ldots, \omega_n$ from the formula $\omega_i = \sqrt{-\lambda_i}$.

(h) Write down the general solution of the equations of motion in the form

$$\mathbf{x}(t) = C_1 \mathbf{v}_1 \cos(\omega_1 t + \phi_1) + \cdots + C_n \mathbf{v}_n \cos(\omega_n t + \phi_n), \quad (1.9)$$

where $C_1, \ldots, C_n$ and $\phi_1, \ldots, \phi_n$ are arbitrary constants.

(i) Interpret the solution in terms of the original problem.   ◀Interpret solution▶

Notes on Procedure 1.1

- As mentioned earlier, the eigenvalues of the dynamic matrix of an oscillating mechanical system (without damping and forcing) are always real and non-positive. However, if the eigenvalues are not distinct or if any of them are zero, Procedure 1.1 will break down as Theorem 1.1 does not apply in such circumstances.

- If we know $x_i(0)$ and $\dot{x}_i(0)$ for each i, then a particular solution of the equations of motion may be obtained. But, to obtain such a solution can involve solving a system of $2n$ equations — even for a mechanical system with just two degrees of freedom, this could mean solving a system of four equations.

  As you will see later, if the mechanical system starts from rest, each ϕ_i can be taken to be zero, and a system of only n equations then needs to be solved.

- When we do not have particular values for the C_i and ϕ_i, it is still possible to obtain some information about the behaviour of the system. For example, knowledge of the normal mode angular frequencies ω_i enables us to determine the frequencies f_i and periods τ_i of the normal modes from the formulae $f_i = \omega_i/(2\pi)$ and $\tau_i = 2\pi/\omega_i$.

  See *Unit 7.*

We now apply Procedure 1.1 to the kind of double pendulum that you saw in the video.

Example 1.3

Consider the motion of a double pendulum where the lower pendulum is attached to the bob of the upper pendulum and where both pendulums are constrained to move in the same vertical plane (see Figure 1.8). The stems of the pendulums have lengths l_1 and l_2, and may be modelled as light model rods. The pendulum bobs have masses m_1 and m_2, and may be modelled as particles. The angles made by the stems of the pendulums to the vertical are denoted by θ_1 and θ_2 (measured anticlockwise from the vertical). The oscillations of both pendulums are sufficiently small for the approximations $\sin\theta_i = \theta_i$ and $\cos\theta_i = 1$ $(i = 1, 2)$ to be applicable at all times during the motion of the system.

◀Draw picture▶

(a) Derive linear equations of motion for the double pendulum.

(b) Suppose that $l_1 = l_2$ and $m_1 = m_2$. What is the general solution of the equations of motion?

(c) If each pendulum has length $50\,\mathrm{cm}$, estimate the periods of the two normal modes.

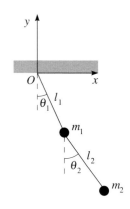

Figure 1.8

Solution

(a) The system has two degrees of freedom — one associated with each pendulum. A suitable choice of coordinates would be the angles θ_1 and θ_2, which are marked on Figure 1.8, as these completely specify the configuration of the system at any given time. However, in order to use Newton's second law to generate equations of motion, we also need a set of Cartesian coordinate axes, which we shall take to have origin O at the point of attachment of the upper pendulum, with the x-axis pointing horizontally to the right and the y-axis vertically upwards, as in Figure 1.8.

◀Choose coordinates▶

The force diagrams for the system are shown below, with $\mathbf{W}_1$ and $\mathbf{W}_2$ denoting the weights of the particles, and $\mathbf{T}_1$, $\mathbf{T}_2$ and $\mathbf{T}_3$ denoting tension forces exerted on the particles by the model rods.

◀Draw force diagram(s)▶

We model the forces on the particles due to the model rods as tension forces in the same way that we model forces on a particle due to model strings.

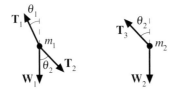

Applying Newton's second law to the two particles separately, we obtain

◀Apply Newton's 2nd law▶

$$m_1\ddot{\mathbf{r}}_1 = \mathbf{W}_1 + \mathbf{T}_1 + \mathbf{T}_2, \quad m_2\ddot{\mathbf{r}}_2 = \mathbf{W}_2 + \mathbf{T}_3,$$

where $\mathbf{r}_1 = x_1\mathbf{i} + y_1\mathbf{j}$ and $\mathbf{r}_2 = x_2\mathbf{i} + y_2\mathbf{j}$ are the position vectors of the two pendulum bobs relative to O. Resolving in the $\mathbf{i}$- and $\mathbf{j}$-directions gives

$$\begin{cases} m_1\ddot{x}_1 = -|\mathbf{T}_1|\sin\theta_1 + |\mathbf{T}_2|\sin\theta_2, \\ m_1\ddot{y}_1 = -m_1 g + |\mathbf{T}_1|\cos\theta_1 - |\mathbf{T}_2|\cos\theta_2, \end{cases} \begin{cases} m_2\ddot{x}_2 = -|\mathbf{T}_3|\sin\theta_2, \\ m_2\ddot{y}_2 = -m_2 g + |\mathbf{T}_3|\cos\theta_2. \end{cases}$$

From Figure 1.9 we can deduce the following relationships between the linear coordinates and the angular coordinates:

$$x_1 = l_1\sin\theta_1, \quad x_2 = l_1\sin\theta_1 + l_2\sin\theta_2,$$
$$y_1 = -l_1\cos\theta_1, \quad y_2 = -l_1\cos\theta_1 - l_2\cos\theta_2.$$

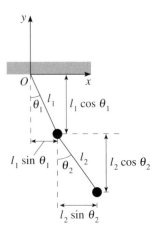

Figure 1.9

Now, since the oscillations of the pendulums are small, we can use the small-angle approximations specified in the question, i.e. $\sin\theta_i \simeq \theta_i$ and $\cos\theta_i \simeq 1$ $(i = 1, 2)$, in the two previous sets of equations, to obtain

$$\begin{cases} m_1\ddot{x}_1 \simeq -|\mathbf{T}_1|\theta_1 + |\mathbf{T}_2|\theta_2, \\ m_1\ddot{y}_1 \simeq -m_1 g + |\mathbf{T}_1| - |\mathbf{T}_2|, \end{cases} \quad \begin{cases} m_2\ddot{x}_2 \simeq -|\mathbf{T}_3|\theta_2, \\ m_2\ddot{y}_2 \simeq -m_2 g + |\mathbf{T}_3|, \end{cases} \quad (1.10)$$

and

$$x_1 \simeq l_1\theta_1, \quad x_2 \simeq l_1\theta_1 + l_2\theta_2,$$
$$y_1 \simeq -l_1, \quad y_2 \simeq -l_1 - l_2.$$

These small-angle approximations will ensure that the resulting differential equations are linear.

From $x_1 \simeq l_1\theta_1$, an approximation for the horizontal acceleration can be derived by differentiation as $\ddot{x}_1 \simeq l_1\ddot{\theta}_1$. Similarly, differentiating $x_2 \simeq l_1\theta_1 + l_2\theta_2$ gives $\ddot{x}_2 \simeq l_1\ddot{\theta}_1 + l_2\ddot{\theta}_2$. As the expressions above for y_1 and y_2 are constants, it follows that $\ddot{y}_1 \simeq 0$ and $\ddot{y}_2 \simeq 0$. (The physical interpretation of this is that for small oscillations the pendulum bobs do not move vertically.) These approximations for the horizontal and vertical accelerations can then be substituted into Equation (1.10) to give

Differentiation of these approximations is valid provided that θ_1 and θ_2 not only are small, but also do not vary too rapidly.

$$\begin{cases} m_1 l_1 \ddot{\theta}_1 \simeq -|\mathbf{T}_1|\theta_1 + |\mathbf{T}_2|\theta_2, \\ 0 \simeq -m_1 g + |\mathbf{T}_1| - |\mathbf{T}_2|, \end{cases} \quad \begin{cases} m_2(l_1\ddot{\theta}_1 + l_2\ddot{\theta}_2) \simeq -|\mathbf{T}_3|\theta_2, \\ 0 \simeq -m_2 g + |\mathbf{T}_3|. \end{cases} \quad (1.11)$$

From the last equation in (1.11) we obtain $|\mathbf{T}_3| \simeq m_2 g$. By Newton's third law we have $|\mathbf{T}_2| = |\mathbf{T}_3|$, therefore $|\mathbf{T}_2| \simeq m_2 g$. This can be substituted into the third equation in (1.11) to yield $|\mathbf{T}_1| \simeq (m_1 + m_2)g$. If we then substitute for $|\mathbf{T}_1|$, $|\mathbf{T}_2|$ and $|\mathbf{T}_3|$ in the first two equations in (1.11), we have

Newton's third law tells us that the forces exerted at either end of a model rod must be equal in magnitude but opposite in direction. Recall the case of a model string in *Unit 5*.

$$\begin{cases} m_1 l_1 \ddot{\theta}_1 \simeq -(m_1 + m_2)g\theta_1 + m_2 g\theta_2, \\ m_2(l_1\ddot{\theta}_1 + l_2\ddot{\theta}_2) \simeq -m_2 g\theta_2. \end{cases}$$

To put these equations into a standard form, i.e. with only one second derivative on the left-hand side of each, first divide by the masses to get

$$\begin{cases} l_1\ddot{\theta}_1 \simeq -\left(1 + \dfrac{m_2}{m_1}\right)g\theta_1 + \dfrac{m_2}{m_1}g\theta_2, \\ l_1\ddot{\theta}_1 + l_2\ddot{\theta}_2 \simeq -g\theta_2. \end{cases} \quad (1.12)$$

Next subtract the first equation from the second to eliminate the $l_1\ddot{\theta}_1$ term from the left-hand side, giving

$$l_2\ddot{\theta}_2 \simeq -g\theta_2 - \left(-\left(1 + \frac{m_2}{m_1}\right)g\theta_1 + \frac{m_2}{m_1}g\theta_2\right)$$

$$= \left(1 + \frac{m_2}{m_1}\right)g\theta_1 - \left(1 + \frac{m_2}{m_1}\right)g\theta_2. \quad (1.13)$$

Now divide the first equation in (1.12) by l_1, and Equation (1.13) by l_2, to obtain equations with one second derivative on the left-hand side of each. Thus we arrive at the following linear second-order differential equations of motion for the double pendulum when it is undergoing small oscillations:

Since this is a *model* of the motion, there is no need to retain the $\simeq$ signs.

$$\begin{cases} \ddot{\theta}_1 = -\left(1 + \dfrac{m_2}{m_1}\right)\dfrac{g}{l_1}\theta_1 + \dfrac{m_2}{m_1}\dfrac{g}{l_1}\theta_2, \\ \ddot{\theta}_2 = \left(1 + \dfrac{m_2}{m_1}\right)\dfrac{g}{l_2}\theta_1 - \left(1 + \dfrac{m_2}{m_1}\right)\dfrac{g}{l_2}\theta_2. \end{cases}$$

(b) In the case where $l_1 = l_2 \ (= l)$ and $m_1 = m_2$, the equations of motion become

◀Solve equation(s)▶

$$\begin{cases} \ddot{\theta}_1 = -\dfrac{2g}{l}\theta_1 + \dfrac{g}{l}\theta_2, \\ \ddot{\theta}_2 = \dfrac{2g}{l}\theta_1 - \dfrac{2g}{l}\theta_2. \end{cases}$$

To solve these, we write them in matrix form as

$$\begin{bmatrix} \ddot{\theta}_1 \\ \ddot{\theta}_2 \end{bmatrix} = \frac{g}{l}\begin{bmatrix} -2 & 1 \\ 2 & -2 \end{bmatrix}\begin{bmatrix} \theta_1 \\ \theta_2 \end{bmatrix}.$$

Following Procedure 4.1 in *Unit 11*, we now need to find the eigenvalues and eigenvectors of the dynamic matrix $\mathbf{A} = \dfrac{g}{l}\begin{bmatrix} -2 & 1 \\ 2 & -2 \end{bmatrix}$. However, this is equivalent to finding the eigenvalues and eigenvectors of $\mathbf{B} = \begin{bmatrix} -2 & 1 \\ 2 & -2 \end{bmatrix}$, provided that we remember to scale these eigenvalues by the factor g/l later. The characteristic equation of $\mathbf{B}$ is

Recall from *Unit 10* that if λ is an eigenvalue of $\mathbf{B}$ with eigenvector $\mathbf{v}$, then $p\lambda$ is an eigenvalue of $p\mathbf{B}$ with the same eigenvector $\mathbf{v}$.

$$\begin{vmatrix} -2-\lambda & 1 \\ 2 & -2-\lambda \end{vmatrix} = \lambda^2 + 4\lambda + 2 = 0.$$

Therefore the eigenvalues of $\mathbf{B}$ are $\lambda = -2 \pm \sqrt{2}$.

$\boxed{\lambda = -2 + \sqrt{2}}$ The eigenvector equations are

$$\begin{bmatrix} -2-(-2+\sqrt{2}) & 1 \\ 2 & -2-(-2+\sqrt{2}) \end{bmatrix}\begin{bmatrix} v_1 \\ v_2 \end{bmatrix} = \begin{bmatrix} 0 \\ 0 \end{bmatrix},$$

or equivalently

$$\begin{cases} -\sqrt{2}v_1 + v_2 = 0, \\ 2v_1 - \sqrt{2}v_2 = 0. \end{cases}$$

Both these equations simplify to $v_2 = \sqrt{2}v_1$, so $\begin{bmatrix} 1 & \sqrt{2} \end{bmatrix}^T$ is an eigenvector.

$\boxed{\lambda = -2 - \sqrt{2}}$ The eigenvector equations are

$$\begin{bmatrix} -2-(-2-\sqrt{2}) & 1 \\ 2 & -2-(-2-\sqrt{2}) \end{bmatrix}\begin{bmatrix} v_1 \\ v_2 \end{bmatrix} = \begin{bmatrix} 0 \\ 0 \end{bmatrix},$$

or equivalently

$$\begin{cases} \sqrt{2}v_1 + v_2 = 0, \\ 2v_1 + \sqrt{2}v_2 = 0. \end{cases}$$

Both these equations simplify to $v_2 = -\sqrt{2}v_1$, so $\begin{bmatrix} 1 & -\sqrt{2} \end{bmatrix}^T$ is an eigenvector.

After we have scaled by g/l, we obtain the eigenvalues of the dynamic matrix as $\lambda_1 = -g(2-\sqrt{2})/l$ and $\lambda_2 = -g(2+\sqrt{2})/l$. Since $\omega_i = \sqrt{-\lambda_i}$, the normal mode angular frequencies are

Note that $2 > \sqrt{2}$, so both eigenvalues are negative.

$$\omega_1 = \sqrt{\frac{g(2-\sqrt{2})}{l}}, \quad \omega_2 = \sqrt{\frac{g(2+\sqrt{2})}{l}}.$$

From Equation (1.9), the general solution of the equations of motion can then be written as

$$\begin{bmatrix} \theta_1(t) \\ \theta_2(t) \end{bmatrix} = C_1\begin{bmatrix} 1 \\ \sqrt{2} \end{bmatrix}\cos(\omega_1 t + \phi_1) + C_2\begin{bmatrix} 1 \\ -\sqrt{2} \end{bmatrix}\cos(\omega_2 t + \phi_2).$$

(c) The information that each pendulum has length 50 cm enables us to   ◄Interpret solution►
calculate the normal mode angular frequencies as

$$\omega_1 = \sqrt{\frac{g(2-\sqrt{2})}{0.5}} \simeq 3.390\,\text{rad s}^{-1}, \quad \omega_2 = \sqrt{\frac{g(2+\sqrt{2})}{0.5}} \simeq 8.185\,\text{rad s}^{-1}.$$

The periods of oscillation of the two normal modes of the double pendulum are

$$\tau_1 = \frac{2\pi}{\omega_1} \simeq 1.853\,\text{s}, \quad \tau_2 = \frac{2\pi}{\omega_2} \simeq 0.768\,\text{s}.$$

So this model predicts that the periods of oscillation of the normal modes are approximately 0.8 s and 1.9 s. ∎

Notice how, in this example, we used small-angle approximations to produce a system of *linear* differential equations; otherwise the equations would have been non-linear.

You met similar techniques for linearizing systems of non-linear differential equations in *Unit 13*.

Exercise 1.4

Figure 1.10 shows a mechanical system in which a particle of mass m is free to move along a smooth straight horizontal bar. The particle is subject to the forces exerted by two identical model springs of stiffness k and natural length l_0, and to the force exerted by a pendulum of length l suspended from the particle. The bar is twice the natural length of each spring, so the system is in equilibrium when the springs are at their natural lengths, i.e. not extended or compressed. The pendulum stem may be modelled as a light model rod and its bob as a particle of mass m. Assume that the oscillations of the pendulum are small, and hence that small-angle approximations (as in Example 1.3) are valid. The displacement x_1 of the sliding particle is measured from its equilibrium position O and the displacement of the pendulum is given by the angle θ (measured anticlockwise from the vertical), as shown in the figure.

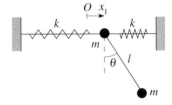

Figure 1.10

(a) Derive linear equations of motion for the system in terms of x_1 and θ.

(b) If $k = 1\,\text{N m}^{-1}$, $m = 1\,\text{kg}$ and $l = 1$ metre, find the normal mode angular frequencies to two decimal places.

1.3 *Interpretation of normal mode eigenvectors*

In the video the normal mode oscillations of several mechanical systems were demonstrated. But how did we know the initial conditions required to make a system oscillate in a normal mode? This question is answered in this subsection, by using the normal mode eigenvectors. Before we do this, we derive a result that is useful in describing systems where all the particles start from rest. We shall illustrate the argument in relation to a system with two degrees of freedom, though the argument can be generalized to a system with any number of degrees of freedom.

For a system with two degrees of freedom, the general solution of the equation of motion for the system (Equation (1.9)) becomes

$$\mathbf{x}(t) = C_1\mathbf{v}_1\cos(\omega_1 t + \phi_1) + C_2\mathbf{v}_2\cos(\omega_2 t + \phi_2).$$

Differentiating this gives

$$\dot{\mathbf{x}}(t) = -\omega_1 C_1\mathbf{v}_1\sin(\omega_1 t + \phi_1) - \omega_2 C_2\mathbf{v}_2\sin(\omega_2 t + \phi_2).$$

Initially, at $t = 0$,

$$\dot{\mathbf{x}}(0) = -\omega_1 C_1 \mathbf{v}_1 \sin \phi_1 - \omega_2 C_2 \mathbf{v}_2 \sin \phi_2.$$

Applying the condition that all the particles start from rest, i.e. $\dot{\mathbf{x}}(0) = \mathbf{0}$, gives

$$\mathbf{0} = -\omega_1 C_1 \mathbf{v}_1 \sin \phi_1 - \omega_2 C_2 \mathbf{v}_2 \sin \phi_2. \tag{1.14}$$

Notice that this initial condition is satisfied if $\phi_1 = \phi_2 = 0$. We shall now show that we may assume that $\phi_1 = \phi_2 = 0$.

Since the two normal mode eigenvectors are linearly independent, the only way that a linear combination of them can be zero is if all the coefficients are zero, i.e. if

$$\omega_1 C_1 \sin \phi_1 = 0 \quad \text{and} \quad \omega_2 C_2 \sin \phi_2 = 0.$$

Looking again at the situation we have just been considering, where the normal mode angular frequencies are non-zero, we have

$$C_1 \sin \phi_1 = 0 \quad \text{and} \quad C_2 \sin \phi_2 = 0.$$

You will see mechanical systems with zero normal mode angular frequencies later.

From the first equation, either $C_1 = 0$ or $\sin \phi_1 = 0$. If $C_1 = 0$ then the normal mode does not contribute to the motion $\mathbf{x}(t)$ and the value of ϕ_1 is irrelevant, so we can choose $\phi_1 = 0$. If $\sin \phi_1 = 0$ then either $\phi_1 = 0$ or $\phi_1 = \pi$. If $\phi_1 = \pi$ then the term $C_1 \mathbf{v}_1 \cos(\omega t + \pi)$ becomes $-C_1 \mathbf{v}_1 \cos(\omega t)$, and we can include the minus sign in the normal mode eigenvector $\mathbf{v}_1$ and choose $\phi_1 = 0$. So the first equation implies that either $\phi_1 = 0$ or we have a free choice and may take $\phi_1 = 0$. Similarly, we may take $\phi_2 = 0$. This is an important result, worth remembering.

Recall that for normal modes we take $-\pi < \phi \le \pi$.

Systems starting from rest

If one of the initial conditions of a mechanical system is that all the particles start from rest, then we may assume that all the phase angles are zero.

Now we use this result to find a suitable initial condition for normal mode motion when all the particles start from rest. As before, consider a system with two degrees of freedom to illustrate the argument. If the system starts from rest, then, by the above result, all the phase angles are zero. So the general motion of the two-degrees-of-freedom system can be written as

$$\mathbf{x}(t) = C_1 \mathbf{v}_1 \cos(\omega_1 t) + C_2 \mathbf{v}_2 \cos(\omega_2 t). \tag{1.15}$$

Initially, at $t = 0$, this becomes

$$\mathbf{x}(0) = C_1 \mathbf{v}_1 + C_2 \mathbf{v}_2 \tag{1.16}$$

Suppose that the system is initially at a position corresponding to the first normal mode eigenvector, i.e. at a position $\mathbf{x}(0) = k\mathbf{v}_1$ for some constant $k \ne 0$. Then substituting for $\mathbf{x}(0)$ in Equation (1.16), we obtain

$$k\mathbf{v}_1 = C_1 \mathbf{v}_1 + C_2 \mathbf{v}_2. \tag{1.17}$$

Remember, from *Unit 10*, that if $\mathbf{v}$ is an eigenvector, then so is $k\mathbf{v}$ for any non-zero constant k.

Since the eigenvectors $\mathbf{v}_1$ and $\mathbf{v}_2$ are linearly independent, we can equate their respective coefficients on either side of Equation (1.17), thereby finding that $C_1 = k \ne 0$ and $C_2 = 0$. Substituting into Equation (1.15) gives

$$\mathbf{x}(t) = k\mathbf{v}_1 \cos(\omega_1 t). \tag{1.18}$$

Therefore, if we start the system from rest at a position $\mathbf{x}(0) = k\mathbf{v}_1$, it will move with the normal mode motion given by Equation (1.18). Similarly, starting the system from rest at $\mathbf{x}(0) = k\mathbf{v}_2$ results in the normal mode motion given by $x(t) = k\mathbf{v}_2\cos(\omega_2 t)$. Generalizing this argument to any number of degrees of freedom gives the following result.

> **Normal modes of systems starting from rest**
>
> If all the particles within a mechanical system start from rest at positions given by the elements of a normal mode eigenvector, then the system will oscillate in the corresponding normal mode.

The following example illustrates how this result can be used.

Example 1.4

In Example 1.2 the following general solution was derived for the positions of two particles, each of mass 0.1 kg, joined to one another and to two fixed walls by three identical model springs of stiffness $0.2\,\mathrm{N\,m^{-1}}$ (see Figure 1.7):

$$\mathbf{x}(t) = C_1 \begin{bmatrix} 1 \\ 1 \end{bmatrix} \cos(\sqrt{2}t + \phi_1) + C_2 \begin{bmatrix} 1 \\ -1 \end{bmatrix} \cos(\sqrt{6}t + \phi_2).$$

What initial conditions give rise to normal mode motion in this system when both particles start from rest?

Solution

For the normal mode with angular frequency $\sqrt{2}$ a normal mode eigenvector is $[1\ \ 1]^T$. The positions of the particles are measured from their respective equilibrium positions. So one initial condition for normal mode motion is that each particle starts from rest at a distance 1 cm to the right of its equilibrium position. However, any constant multiple of $[1\ \ 1]^T$ is also an eigenvector, so we can say rather more: a normal mode results if both particles start from rest after being given the *same* displacement. Therefore suitable initial conditions include not only starting both particles from rest 1 cm to the right of their equilibrium positions, but also starting both particles 1 cm to the left, or 10 cm to the right (provided the natural length of the spring is greater than 10 cm), and so on.

For the second normal mode, a normal mode eigenvector is $[1\ \ -1]^T$. Hence another initial condition for normal mode motion is that the first particle starts from rest at a distance 1 cm to the right of its equilibrium position, and the second particle starts from rest 1 cm to the left of its equilibrium position. Again, however, we can say more: a normal mode motion results whenever the particles start from rest after being displaced from equilibrium by equal distances in opposite directions. ∎

*Exercise 1.5

For the double pendulum analysed in Example 1.3, what initial conditions give rise to normal mode motion when both pendulum bobs start from rest?

Another feature of the motion can be read from the normal mode eigenvectors. The signs of the components of the eigenvectors indicate whether the normal mode motion is in-phase or phase-opposed.

For example, consider the double pendulum in the video and Example 1.3. The normal mode eigenvector corresponding to the smallest normal mode frequency is $[1\ \ \sqrt{2}]^T$. The components of this normal mode eigenvector have the same sign. In the video you saw that the normal mode motion was

Note that $[-1\ \ -\sqrt{2}]^T$ is also a normal mode eigenvector for this motion, and its components are not positive but they have the same sign.

in-phase. This is true in general: when two components of a normal mode eigenvector have the same sign, then the corresponding motion is in-phase.

The other normal mode eigenvector of the double pendulum was calculated to be $[1 \quad -\sqrt{2}]^T$ in Example 1.3. Here the two components have opposite signs and, as you saw in the video, the normal mode motion is phase-opposed. Again, this is generally true and we summarize this as follows.

Theorem 1.2

For a normal mode motion, the relative motion of a pair of particles with non-zero coordinates is determined by the components of the corresponding normal mode eigenvector. The motion is:

- in-phase if the components have the same sign;
- phase-opposed if the components have opposite signs.

Example 1.5

Consider the oscillating mechanical system with three degrees of freedom shown in Figure 1.11. Three particles are constrained to move in a straight line between two fixed walls. The particles are attached to one another and to the walls by four identical model springs that are aligned with the direction of movement of the particles. The positions of the particles are measured from their equilibrium positions, as shown in the figure.

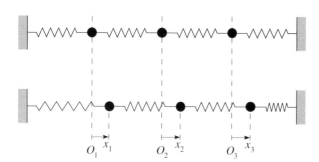

Figure 1.11

A normal mode eigenvector of the lowest angular frequency normal mode is given as $[1 \quad \sqrt{2} \quad 1]^T$. Draw sketches of the mechanical system at the following times while it is oscillating according to this normal mode:

(a) when all the particles are instantaneously at rest at the same time;

(b) one sixth of a cycle after the time in part (a);

(c) one quarter of a cycle after the time in part (a);

(d) half a cycle after the time in part (a).

Is the motion in-phase or phase-opposed?

Solution

As a starting point for the system, consider a time instant when all three particles are instantaneously at rest at the same time. An equation of motion for the given normal mode is $\mathbf{x}(t) = k\mathbf{v}\cos(\omega t)$, where k is a constant and $\mathbf{v} = \begin{bmatrix} 1 & \sqrt{2} & 1 \end{bmatrix}^T$.

As you saw in the boxed result on page 66, for a system starting from rest we can take $\phi = 0$.

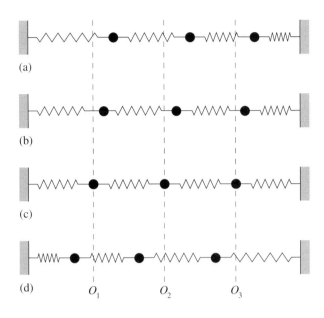

Figure 1.12

(a) In this instance the positions of the particles relative to their equilibrium positions are given by $k\mathbf{v}$, and are sketched in Figure 1.12(a). Thus, if particle 1 is at, say, $x_1 = 2$, then particle 2 will be at $x_2 = 2\sqrt{2}$ and particle 3 at $x_3 = 2$, as determined by $k\mathbf{v} = 2\mathbf{v} = \begin{bmatrix} 2 & 2\sqrt{2} & 2 \end{bmatrix}^T$.

(b) After a sixth of a cycle (i.e. when $\omega t = \frac{2\pi}{6} = \frac{\pi}{3}$), the equation of motion yields $\mathbf{x}(t) = k\mathbf{v}\cos(\omega t) = k\mathbf{v}\cos\frac{\pi}{3} = \frac{1}{2}k\mathbf{v}$, so each particle is half as far from its equilibrium position as it was in part (a), as sketched in Figure 1.12(b).

(c) After a quarter of a cycle (i.e. when $\omega t = \frac{2\pi}{4} = \frac{\pi}{2}$), $\mathbf{x}(t) = k\mathbf{v}\cos\frac{\pi}{2} = \mathbf{0}$, so each particle is at its equilibrium position, as shown in Figure 1.12(c).

(d) After half a cycle (i.e. when $\omega t = \frac{2\pi}{2} = \pi$), $\mathbf{x}(t) = k\mathbf{v}\cos\pi = -k\mathbf{v}$, so each particle is the same distance from its equilibrium position as it was in part (a), but in the opposite direction, as sketched in Figure 1.12(d).

Note that although the particles are at their equilibrium positions, the system is not in equilibrium since the velocities are non-zero. (In fact, the speeds are at a maximum.)

Since all the coordinates of the given normal mode eigenvector have the same sign, all three particles move in-phase with one another, as the sketches in Figure 1.12 illustrate. ∎

Exercise 1.6

Repeat Example 1.5 for the normal modes with the following normal mode eigenvectors.

(i) $\begin{bmatrix} 1 & 0 & -1 \end{bmatrix}^T$ (ii) $\begin{bmatrix} 1 & -\sqrt{2} & 1 \end{bmatrix}^T$

This section concludes by asking you to apply the methods described in this section to another mechanical system.

End-of-section Exercise

Exercise 1.7

Consider the mechanical system with two degrees of freedom, shown in Figure 1.13, in which two identical particles of mass m are attached to one another and to a fixed wall by two identical model springs of stiffness k and natural length l_0. The particles are constrained to move across a frictionless horizontal surface in a straight line along the line of the springs. Let x_1 and x_2 be the displacements of the two particles along this line, measured from the equilibrium positions of the particles as shown in the figure.

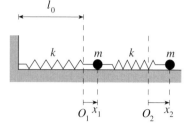

(a) What are the equations of motion for this system?

(b) If $k/m = 2\,\mathrm{N\,kg^{-1}\,m^{-1}}$, determine the normal mode eigenvectors and the angular frequencies. Hence write down the general solution of the matrix equation of motion.

Figure 1.13

(c) Write down an equation from which the constants could be determined in the general solution obtained in part (b), given the initial condition that both particles start from rest with displacements d_1 and d_2, respectively.

2   One-dimensional systems

In this section we look at mechanical systems where particles are restricted to move along a line (such systems have the number of degrees of freedom equal to the number of particles).

Later we investigate systems without this restriction.

A quicker method for deriving the equation of motion is developed in this section that has the advantage that the equation of motion can be derived without first needing to calculate the equilibrium positions of particles.

Subsection 2.1 considers systems that have one or two springs fixed at one end. The equations of motion derived are similar to those derived in Section 1 and are not investigated further. Subsection 2.2 considers free systems that have no components fixed. Here the solution to the equations of motion is different, and so we investigate this.

2.1   Displacement from equilibrium

In this subsection you will see how to obtain the homogeneous equation of motion for a mechanical system (i.e. the equation obtained by taking the origin at the equilibrium position), without first having to find an equilibrium position of the system.

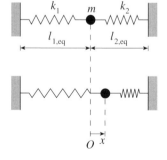

Consider the system made up of a particle of mass m attached to two walls by two model springs of stiffnesses k_1 and k_2, as shown in Figure 2.1, with the particle constrained to move in one dimension along the line of the springs (friction may be neglected). Because the springs have different stiffnesses, the equilibrium position of the system is not obvious. We denote the forces exerted by the springs when the system is in equilibrium by $\mathbf{H}_{1,\mathrm{eq}}$ and $\mathbf{H}_{2,\mathrm{eq}}$, and the corresponding forces when the system is displaced a distance x from the equilibrium position by $\mathbf{H}_1$ and $\mathbf{H}_2$. At equilibrium,

Figure 2.1

$$\mathbf{H}_{1,\mathrm{eq}} + \mathbf{H}_{2,\mathrm{eq}} = \mathbf{0}. \tag{2.1}$$

Applying Hooke's law, we obtain

$$\mathbf{H}_1 = -k_1((l_{1,\text{eq}} + x) - l_{1,0})\mathbf{i}, \qquad \mathbf{H}_{1,\text{eq}} = -k_1(l_{1,\text{eq}} - l_{1,0})\mathbf{i},$$
$$\mathbf{H}_2 = -k_2((l_{2,\text{eq}} - x) - l_{2,0})(-\mathbf{i}), \quad \mathbf{H}_{2,\text{eq}} = -k_2(l_{2,\text{eq}} - l_{2,0})(-\mathbf{i}),$$

where $l_{1,\text{eq}}$ and $l_{2,\text{eq}}$ are the equilibrium lengths of the springs, $l_{1,0}$ and $l_{2,0}$ are the natural lengths of the springs, and $\mathbf{i}$ is a unit vector in the positive x-direction marked on Figure 2.1. From these equations, the changes in the forces exerted by the springs when the particle is displaced a distance x from the equilibrium position are given by

$$\begin{cases} \Delta\mathbf{H}_1 = \mathbf{H}_1 - \mathbf{H}_{1,\text{eq}} = -k_1 x\mathbf{i}, \\ \Delta\mathbf{H}_2 = \mathbf{H}_2 - \mathbf{H}_{2,\text{eq}} = -k_2 x\mathbf{i}. \end{cases} \qquad (2.2)$$

The symbol Δ is an upper-case delta. It is quite commonly used to denote a change in a quantity (just as a lower-case delta, δ, denotes a small change in a quantity).

Then

$$\Delta\mathbf{H}_1 + \Delta\mathbf{H}_2 = (\mathbf{H}_1 + \mathbf{H}_2) - (\mathbf{H}_{1,\text{eq}} + \mathbf{H}_{2,\text{eq}}) = -(k_1 + k_2)x\mathbf{i},$$

and, on substituting from Equation (2.1), we obtain

$$\Delta\mathbf{H}_1 + \Delta\mathbf{H}_2 = \mathbf{H}_1 + \mathbf{H}_2 = -(k_1 + k_2)x\mathbf{i}.$$

So the total force $\mathbf{H}_1 + \mathbf{H}_2$ on the particle when it is displaced a distance x from the equilibrium position is the same as the sum of the changes in the forces, $\Delta\mathbf{H}_1 + \Delta\mathbf{H}_2$. Furthermore, if we apply Newton's second law to the particle when it is displaced a distance x from equilibrium, we find that

$$m\ddot{\mathbf{r}} = \mathbf{H}_1 + \mathbf{H}_2 = \Delta\mathbf{H}_1 + \Delta\mathbf{H}_2 = -(k_1 + k_2)x\mathbf{i},$$

where the position vector $\mathbf{r} = x\mathbf{i}$. Resolving in the $\mathbf{i}$-direction and rearranging gives the equation of motion as

$$m\ddot{x} + (k_1 + k_2)x = 0. \qquad (2.3)$$

Thus we have found the equation of motion without knowing the equilibrium position of the particle, knowing only the changes in the forces acting as given by Equations (2.2).

This method of obtaining an equation of motion can be generalized to any number of forces acting on any particle that has been disturbed from an equilibrium position. If forces $\mathbf{F}_i$ $(i = 1, \dots, n)$ act on a particle disturbed from an equilibrium position, and if $\mathbf{F}_{i,\text{eq}}$ $(i = 1, \dots, n)$ denote the corresponding forces when the particle is in equilibrium while $\Delta\mathbf{F}_i$ $(i = 1, \dots, n)$ denote the changes in the forces from equilibrium, then

$$\sum_{i=1}^{n}\Delta\mathbf{F}_i = \sum_{i=1}^{n}(\mathbf{F}_i - \mathbf{F}_{i,\text{eq}}) = \sum_{i=1}^{n}\mathbf{F}_i - \sum_{i=1}^{n}\mathbf{F}_{i,\text{eq}} = \sum_{i=1}^{n}\mathbf{F}_i,$$

since $\sum_{i=1}^{n}\mathbf{F}_{i,\text{eq}} = \mathbf{0}$. So the total force $\sum_{i=1}^{n}\mathbf{F}_i$ acting on the particle is the same as the total change in the forces $\sum_{i=1}^{n}\Delta\mathbf{F}_i$, which leads to the following useful result based on Newton's second law.

$\sum_{i=1}^{n}\mathbf{F}_{i,\text{eq}} = \mathbf{0}$ is the equilibrium condition for particles, from *Unit 5*.

Particle displaced from equilibrium

If a particle of mass m, displaced from an equilibrium position, is acted on by forces $\mathbf{F}_i$ $(i = 1, \dots, n)$, then its acceleration $\ddot{\mathbf{r}}$ is given by

$$m\ddot{\mathbf{r}} = \sum_{i=1}^{n}\Delta\mathbf{F}_i, \qquad (2.4)$$

Applying Equation (2.4) is equivalent to applying Newton's second law.

where $\mathbf{r}$ is the displacement of the particle from its equilibrium position, and $\Delta\mathbf{F}_i = \mathbf{F}_i - \mathbf{F}_{i,\text{eq}}$ $(i = 1, \dots, n)$, where $\mathbf{F}_{i,\text{eq}}$ is the force corresponding to $\mathbf{F}_i$ when the particle is at its equilibrium position.

Equation (2.4) can provide a useful shortcut in the derivation of the equation of motion for a mechanical system involving a displacement from equilibrium, if the changes in the forces acting can be calculated easily. For a spring displaced along its length, you have seen that the changes in the forces can be calculated easily using Equation (2.2). The general result that applies to any coordinate system for a change of length Δl is

$$\Delta\mathbf{H} = -k\Delta l\,\widehat{\mathbf{s}}, \qquad (2.5)$$

See Sections 4 and 5 for formulae that apply in other cases.

where k is the stiffness of the spring, $\Delta l = l - l_{\mathrm{eq}}$ is the change in the spring's length from its equilibrium value, and $\widehat{\mathbf{s}}$ is a constant unit vector directed from the centre of the spring to the particle.

Another force for which this shortcut is useful is the force $\mathbf{W}$ due to gravity, i.e. the weight of an object, since this force is constant for a given object near the Earth's surface, so $\Delta\mathbf{W} = \mathbf{0}$. Thus the weights of the components of a mechanical system have no effect on the system's equation of motion when the components are displaced from their equilibrium positions. If a normal reaction force $\mathbf{N}$ balances the weight of a particle (such as when objects are placed on a smooth horizontal table), then $\mathbf{N}$ is constant and so $\Delta\mathbf{N} = \mathbf{0}$.

You saw in Unit 7 that the period of oscillations of a mechanical system is the same whether the system is oriented horizontally or vertically.

These results have useful consequences for one- or two-dimensional mechanical systems that can be modelled using only model springs and particles. It means that in deriving the equation of motion for such systems, provided displacements are measured from the equilibrium positions, we can ignore all weights and normal reactions, irrespective of the orientation of the system — in effect, whatever its orientation, the system behaves as if it is in a horizontal plane. We shall adopt the policy of ignoring weights and normal reactions for such systems for the remainder of this unit.

The result also applies to systems involving model rods, as you will see in Unit 19.

Let us now see how these ideas can be applied, by looking at an example similar to the one considered in Example 1.1.

Example 2.1

Consider the mechanical system shown in Figure 2.2. This system consists of two particles of masses m_1 and m_2, which are constrained to move in a straight line across a frictionless horizontal surface while attached by model springs of stiffnesses k_1, k_2 and k_3 to each other and to two fixed walls. Derive the equation of motion for each of the particles.

Unlike the situation in Example 1.1, the springs have different stiffnesses and we do not know the equilibrium positions of the components of the system; hence we need to adopt a different approach from that used in Example 1.1.

Solution

The first step is to draw a force diagram for each particle. We use the usual notation for the spring forces and, as discussed above, we ignore the weights and normal reactions.

$$\xleftarrow{\hspace{1cm}}\overset{m_1}{\bullet}\xrightarrow{\hspace{1cm}} \qquad \xleftarrow{\hspace{1cm}}\overset{m_2}{\bullet}\xrightarrow{\hspace{1cm}}$$
$$\mathbf{H}_1 \qquad\qquad \mathbf{H}_2 \qquad \mathbf{H}_3 \qquad\qquad \mathbf{H}_4$$

Applying Equation (2.4) to each particle gives

$$\begin{cases} m_1\ddot{\mathbf{r}}_1 = \Delta\mathbf{H}_1 + \Delta\mathbf{H}_2, \\ m_2\ddot{\mathbf{r}}_2 = \Delta\mathbf{H}_3 + \Delta\mathbf{H}_4, \end{cases} \qquad (2.6)$$

where $\mathbf{r}_1 = x_1\mathbf{i}$ and $\mathbf{r}_2 = x_2\mathbf{i}$ are the position vectors of the two particles with respect to their (unknown) equilibrium positions, and $\mathbf{i}$ is a unit vector

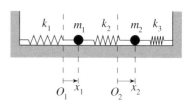

Figure 2.2

in the direction of positive x_1 and x_2. Now we use Equation (2.5) to obtain

$$\Delta\mathbf{H}_1 = -k_1 x_1 \mathbf{i},$$
$$\Delta\mathbf{H}_2 = -k_2(x_2 - x_1)(-\mathbf{i}) = k_2(x_2 - x_1)\mathbf{i},$$
$$\Delta\mathbf{H}_3 = -k_2(x_2 - x_1)\mathbf{i},$$
$$\Delta\mathbf{H}_4 = -k_3(-x_2)(-\mathbf{i}) = -k_3 x_2 \mathbf{i}.$$

Substituting these expressions into Equations (2.6) gives

$$\begin{cases} m_1\ddot{\mathbf{r}}_1 = -k_1 x_1 \mathbf{i} + k_2(x_2 - x_1)\mathbf{i}, \\ m_2\ddot{\mathbf{r}}_2 = -k_2(x_2 - x_1)\mathbf{i} - k_3 x_2 \mathbf{i}. \end{cases}$$

Resolving in the **i**-direction then gives

$$\begin{cases} m_1\ddot{x}_1 = -(k_1 + k_2)x_1 + k_2 x_2, \\ m_2\ddot{x}_2 = k_2 x_1 - (k_2 + k_3)x_2. \end{cases} \tag{2.7}$$

These are the equations of motion for the system illustrated in Figure 2.2. ∎

**Exercise 2.1*

Use Equation (2.4) to derive the equations of motion for the system in Exercise 1.7 (see Figure 1.13).

2.2 Free motion

The one-dimensional mechanical systems studied so far in this unit have all been constrained by being attached to fixed walls. This subsection looks at one-dimensional mechanical systems without fixed points, where free motion (in one dimension) is possible. You will see that the absence of fixed points manifests itself in the dynamic matrix having a zero eigenvalue, and you will see how this affects the normal modes of the system. We begin with an example.

Example 2.2

This example is concerned with the motions of a hydrogen molecule, in particular the vibrations within the molecule. This molecule consists of two atoms of equal mass joined by a bond. We model this as two particles of equal mass m, joined by a model spring of stiffness k. The system is considered to be one-dimensional, so only those vibrations which are along the straight line joining the two atoms are considered.

(a) Derive the equation of motion for this system.

(b) Determine the general solution of this equation of motion for the system in terms of m and k.

(c) Interpret this general solution.

(d) Experimentally, the frequency of vibration for a hydrogen molecule is 1.3×10^{14} Hz. If the mass of a hydrogen atom is 1.67×10^{-27} kg, estimate the stiffness of the bond between the two hydrogen atoms in the molecule.

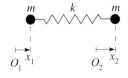

Figure 2.3

Solution

(a) A sketch of the model of the hydrogen molecule is shown in Figure 2.3.   ◄Draw picture►

Choose axes aligned with the spring that joins the two particles, with   ◄Choose coordinates►
two separate origins at the equilibrium positions of the two particles
(i.e. separated by a distance equal to the natural length of the model
spring), as in Figure 2.3. Using the usual notation, we can draw the   ◄Draw force diagram(s)►
following two force diagrams (one for each particle).

Applying Newton's second law (in the form of Equation (2.4)) to each   ◄Apply Newton's 2nd law►
particle, we obtain

$$\begin{cases} m\ddot{\mathbf{r}}_1 = \Delta\mathbf{H}_1, \\ m\ddot{\mathbf{r}}_2 = \Delta\mathbf{H}_2, \end{cases} \qquad (2.8)$$

where $\mathbf{r}_1 = x_1\mathbf{i}$ and $\mathbf{r}_2 = x_2\mathbf{i}$, and $\mathbf{i}$ is a unit vector in the direction of
positive x_1 and x_2. Then, from Equation (2.5),

$$\Delta\mathbf{H}_1 = -k(x_2 - x_1)(-\mathbf{i}) = k(x_2 - x_1)\mathbf{i},$$
$$\Delta\mathbf{H}_2 = -k(x_2 - x_1)\mathbf{i}.$$

Substituting these expressions into Equations (2.8) gives

$$\begin{cases} m\ddot{\mathbf{r}}_1 = \ \ k(x_2 - x_1)\mathbf{i}, \\ m\ddot{\mathbf{r}}_2 = -k(x_2 - x_1)\mathbf{i}. \end{cases}$$

Resolving in the $\mathbf{i}$-direction and using matrix notation, we obtain the
equation of motion that represents the vibrations of a hydrogen molecule:

$$\begin{bmatrix} \ddot{x}_1 \\ \ddot{x}_2 \end{bmatrix} = \begin{bmatrix} -k/m & k/m \\ k/m & -k/m \end{bmatrix} \begin{bmatrix} x_1 \\ x_2 \end{bmatrix}.$$

(b) To find the eigenvalues and eigenvectors of the dynamic matrix, it is   ◄Solve equation(s)►
convenient to take out the common factor k/m and work with the matrix
$\begin{bmatrix} -1 & 1 \\ 1 & -1 \end{bmatrix}$. The eigenvalues are found by solving

$$\begin{vmatrix} -1 - \lambda & 1 \\ 1 & -1 - \lambda \end{vmatrix} = \lambda^2 + 2\lambda = 0.$$

So the eigenvalues are $\lambda = 0$ and $\lambda = -2$. We now proceed to find the
eigenvectors.

$\boxed{\lambda = 0}$ The eigenvector equations are

$$\begin{bmatrix} -1 - 0 & 1 \\ 1 & -1 - 0 \end{bmatrix} \begin{bmatrix} v_1 \\ v_2 \end{bmatrix} = \begin{bmatrix} 0 \\ 0 \end{bmatrix},$$

or equivalently

$$\begin{cases} -v_1 + v_2 = 0, \\ v_1 - v_2 = 0. \end{cases}$$

Both these equations reduce to $v_2 = v_1$, so $[1 \quad 1]^T$ is an eigenvector.

$\boxed{\lambda = -2}$ The eigenvector equations are

$$\begin{bmatrix} -1-(-2) & 1 \\ 1 & -1-(-2) \end{bmatrix} \begin{bmatrix} v_1 \\ v_2 \end{bmatrix} = \begin{bmatrix} 0 \\ 0 \end{bmatrix},$$

or equivalently

$$\begin{cases} v_1 + v_2 = 0, \\ v_1 + v_2 = 0. \end{cases}$$

Both these equations reduce to $v_2 = -v_1$, so $\begin{bmatrix} 1 & -1 \end{bmatrix}^T$ is an eigenvector.

To obtain the eigenvalues of the dynamic matrix, we have to multiply the above eigenvalues by the factor k/m. Hence the dynamic matrix has eigenvalues 0 and $-2k/m$.

In previous examples all the eigenvalues have been negative, so all the terms in the general solution of the equation of motion have been sinusoidal. But this time we have one zero eigenvalue and one negative eigenvalue. You may recall that a zero eigenvalue gives rise to a linear term in the general solution of the equation of motion, so in this case the general solution has the form

See Procedure 4.1 of Unit 11.

$$\begin{bmatrix} x_1(t) \\ x_2(t) \end{bmatrix} = \begin{bmatrix} 1 \\ 1 \end{bmatrix} (A + Bt) + C \begin{bmatrix} 1 \\ -1 \end{bmatrix} \cos(\omega t + \phi),$$

where A, B, C and ϕ are constants, and $\omega = \sqrt{2k/m}$. Therefore there is just one normal mode, with normal mode angular frequency ω, which is given by the sinusoidal term, and one other 'mode', which is given by the linear term.

(c) As just noted, the sinusoidal term in the general solution represents a normal mode. Since a corresponding normal mode eigenvector is $\begin{bmatrix} 1 & -1 \end{bmatrix}^T$, the system will vibrate in this normal mode if it starts from rest with the first particle a distance d from its origin and the second particle a distance $-d$ from its origin, for any non-zero value of d. The angular frequency of the vibrations will be $\omega = \sqrt{2k/m}$.

◀Interpret solution▶

The linear term in the general solution represents a solution of the form $\mathbf{x}(t) = \mathbf{v}(A + Bt)$, where $\mathbf{v} = \begin{bmatrix} 1 & 1 \end{bmatrix}^T$; this corresponds to the linear motion of the system. Now $\dot{\mathbf{x}}(t) = \mathbf{v}B$, so if the system starts from rest, i.e. $\dot{\mathbf{x}}(0) = \mathbf{v}B = 0$, it follows that $B = 0$, giving $\mathbf{x}(t) = \mathbf{v}A = \begin{bmatrix} A & A \end{bmatrix}^T$. Thus if the particles start from rest and equidistant from their equilibrium positions, then they will remain static for all t. Alternatively, putting $\mathbf{x}(0) = \mathbf{0}$, we obtain $\mathbf{x}(0) = \mathbf{v}A = \mathbf{0}$, so $A = 0$, hence $\mathbf{x}(t) = \mathbf{v}Bt$ and $\dot{\mathbf{x}}(t) = \mathbf{v}B = \begin{bmatrix} B & B \end{bmatrix}^T$. The system will move in this mode if the particles start at their equilibrium positions with the same velocity, in which case they will continue to move indefinitely at the same velocity. In both these 'linear modes' the particles remain separated by a distance equal to the natural length of the spring (consequently there are no forces exerted by the spring, and therefore no vibrations).

More specifically in terms of the hydrogen molecule, the normal mode given by the sinusoidal term relates to the vibrations of the atoms within the molecule, while the 'mode' given by the linear term relates to the translational motion of the molecule.

(d) From the given frequency of vibration we can calculate the normal mode angular frequency as

$$\omega = 2\pi f = 2\pi \times 1.3 \times 10^{14} \simeq 8.2 \times 10^{14}\,\mathrm{rad\,s^{-1}}.$$

But $\omega = \sqrt{2k/m}$, so

$$k = \tfrac{1}{2}m\omega^2 = \tfrac{1}{2} \times 1.67 \times 10^{-27} \times \left(8.2 \times 10^{14}\right)^2 \simeq 557\,\mathrm{N\,m^{-1}}.$$

Hence the stiffness of the bond in the hydrogen molecule is about $560\,\mathrm{N\,m^{-1}}$. ■

Hanging a 1 kg object on a spring of this stiffness would extend it by only 2 cm. This suggests that the atoms in a hydrogen molecule are very tightly bonded.

In part (c) of Example 2.2 you saw how a zero eigenvalue leads to a linear term in the general solution of the equation of motion, and how this term can be interpreted as representing linear motion, with the constituent parts of the system staying a fixed distance apart, and with each constituent part either moving with the same velocity or remaining at rest. This type of motion, where all the constituent parts move as one, is given a special name.

Definition

Rigid body motion is the motion that occurs when all the particles of a system move with the distances between them remaining invariant, i.e. the particles move as if part of a rigid body.

Rigid bodies were introduced in *Unit 5*. You may recall that the rigid body model assumes that, whatever forces act on the body, the body does not change shape or vibrate.

If a mechanical system is not constrained by being attached to a fixed object (e.g. the ground or a wall) but is free to move, it is capable of executing rigid body motion. For such a system, one or more of the eigenvalues of the dynamic matrix will be zero. For one-dimensional systems, there is at most one type of rigid body motion (translation along the axis), so there is at most one zero eigenvalue for any dynamic matrix. For two-dimensional systems, there are three possible distinct (i.e. linearly independent) rigid body motions (translation along either axis, plus a rotation), so the situation is more complicated, with up to three zero eigenvalues.

The free motion of two-dimensional systems is discussed in *Unit 19*.

Although a zero eigenvalue does not lead to a normal mode as defined in Section 1, the resulting mode has similar properties and is often loosely referred to as a normal mode, as in the following two exercises. In this unit, if you are asked to determine or analyse normal modes, you should always include these 'linear modes' in your answer.

Sometimes a 'linear mode' is referred to as a 'trivial normal mode'.

Exercise 2.2

Consider a railway engine connected to two trucks, as shown in Figure 2.4. The trucks and the engine are modelled as particles of equal mass m, and the couplings are modelled as model springs of equal stiffness k. Assume that the train travels along a horizontal straight frictionless track and that the engine provides no motive force. The positions of the components of the system are measured from the equilibrium positions shown in the figure.

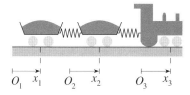

(a) Derive the equation of motion for this system.

Figure 2.4

(b) Use the following information to obtain the general solution of the equation of motion:

$$\begin{bmatrix} -1 & 1 & 0 \\ 1 & -2 & 1 \\ 0 & 1 & -1 \end{bmatrix} \begin{bmatrix} 1 \\ 1 \\ 1 \end{bmatrix} = \begin{bmatrix} 0 \\ 0 \\ 0 \end{bmatrix}, \qquad \begin{bmatrix} -1 & 1 & 0 \\ 1 & -2 & 1 \\ 0 & 1 & -1 \end{bmatrix} \begin{bmatrix} 1 \\ 0 \\ -1 \end{bmatrix} = \begin{bmatrix} -1 \\ 0 \\ 1 \end{bmatrix},$$

$$\begin{bmatrix} -1 & 1 & 0 \\ 1 & -2 & 1 \\ 0 & 1 & -1 \end{bmatrix} \begin{bmatrix} 1 \\ -2 \\ 1 \end{bmatrix} = \begin{bmatrix} -3 \\ 6 \\ -3 \end{bmatrix}.$$

(c) For each normal mode, state the initial conditions that gives rise to it.

End-of-section Exercise

Exercise 2.3

This exercise considers a mechanical system that is not one-dimensional, but belongs here because it is a simple system that exhibits free motion. Since the system is not one-dimensional, the method introduced in this section does not apply and you will need to use the more general approach of Section 1 (see Exercise 1.4).

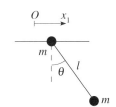

Figure 2.5

Figure 2.5 shows a particle of mass m that slides freely along a smooth straight horizontal bar and has a pendulum suspended from it. Model the pendulum stem as a light model rod of length l, and the bob as a particle of mass m. Assume that the oscillations of the pendulum are small. Measure the displacement x_1 of the sliding particle from a fixed point on the bar and the displacement of the pendulum by the angle θ (measured anticlockwise from the vertical), as shown in the figure.

(a) Derive linear equations of motion for the system, in terms of x_1 and θ.

(b) Find the normal mode angular frequencies and eigenvectors, and hence write down the general solution of the matrix equation of motion.

(c) How does the period of this pendulum compare with the period of a simple pendulum of the same length (with equation of motion $\ddot{\theta} = -(g/l)\theta$)?

(d) For each of the normal modes, draw a sketch of the motion.

3 Visualizing normal modes

In the previous two sections the normal modes of several systems have been calculated. But what does normal mode motion look like? Is it easy to decide when a particular motion is a normal mode of the system? These questions are addressed in the multimedia package for this unit.

Now work through the multimedia package for this unit.

In the multimedia package, several new concepts were introduced. One system considered was a particle moving in a plane in such a way that the projections of its motion onto each axis defined by a normal mode eigenvector were given by a different sinusoid; in this case, the trajectories of the particle are called **Lissajous' figures**. The point was made that such motion can be very complicated (and not necessarily periodic), even though it is composed of two sinusoidal motions at right angles.

The mulitmedia package gave an overview of the problem of modelling a guitar string, which is the subject of the next section. This introduced various new ideas and terms. First, the idea of constructing a **lumped parameter model** was presented. Secondly, a number of terms useful for describing the vibrations of the guitar string were defined: vibrations aligned with the string are called **longitudinal vibrations**, and vibrations at right angles to the string are called **transverse vibrations**. The term **fundamental** is used to describe the normal mode of a system that has the lowest non-zero normal mode angular frequency, and the frequency of this mode is called the **fundamental frequency**. Finally, the term **harmonics** was used as a collective term for the normal modes of a system that are not rigid body motions.

Such a model is defined in Section 4.

4 Modelling a guitar string

In this section a series of models that approximate to the behaviour of a guitar string are analysed. Modelling a guitar string was introduced in the multimedia package you studied in Section 3, but the discussion in this section is self-contained. The models previewed in the multimedia package are derived here.

4.1 The modelling strategy

You might think that we could model a guitar string as a model spring, but this model would not be able to predict the vibrations of the string because, by definition, a model spring has no mass and so, in effect, there would be nothing to vibrate! To model the vibrations of a guitar string, the string has to be represented as having both mass and elasticity. The simplest such model is shown in Figure 4.1(a). In this diagram, all the mass of the string is 'lumped' together as a single particle in the middle of the string, and the elasticity is divided into two identical model springs. Figure 4.1(b) shows a revised model, where the string is represented as two particles of equal mass joined by three identical model springs. Since the revised model in Figure 4.1(b) is, in some sense, closer to the real situation where the mass is continuously distributed along the string, we should expect this to be a better model. Similarly, by increasing the number of particles and springs, we should expect to produce better and better models.

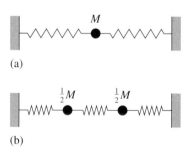

Figure 4.1

In the models of a guitar string described above, the properties of a real object are lumped together into discrete components (e.g. particles and model springs). This type of model is given a special name.

Definition

A model of a real-world system in which properties of the system are lumped together into discrete components (e.g. particles and model springs) is called a **lumped parameter model**.

To make the discussion less abstract, we shall consider a particular string on the guitar: the E string, which has a fundamental frequency of 323 Hz. We shall take an example of an E string that has a stiffness of $4000\,\mathrm{N\,m^{-1}}$, a mass of 0.25 g and a natural length of 0.633 metres. When this string is tuned to the note E, its length is 0.65 metres. We shall model the E string by means of lumped parameter models: the purpose of the modelling is to construct a model of the E string that successfully predicts the fundamental frequency of the string as 323 Hz.

A different sort of model of the E string, as an elastic heavy continuous string, is discussed in *Unit 22*.

Before we begin the modelling, we introduce a quantity that will prove useful.

Definition

The **equilibrium tension in a model spring**, T_{eq}, is defined by the formula

$$T_{\mathrm{eq}} = k(l_{\mathrm{eq}} - l_0), \tag{4.1}$$

where k is the stiffness, l_0 is the natural length and l_{eq} is the equilibrium length of the spring.

The equilibrium tension in a model spring is a scalar quantity which is equal to plus or minus the magnitude of the force exerted by the spring, with the sign depending on whether the spring is extended or compressed when in equilibrium. For the E string modelled as a single model spring, we have

$$T_{\mathrm{eq}} = 4000(0.65 - 0.633) = 68\,\mathrm{N},$$

so the equilibrium tension in the E string is 68 N.

In modelling the E string by means of lumped parameter models, we shall need to ensure that the equilibrium tension in each model spring is the same as the equilibrium tension in the E string modelled as a single spring. This means that although l_{eq}, l_0 and k will change as we introduce more springs, T_{eq} will remain the same, at 68 N. Hence, as we use more springs, the stiffness of these springs increases by the same factor by which their natural length and equilibrium length decrease.

It was noted above that a single-spring model is inadequate when considering the *vibrations* of a guitar string, but we can use a single-spring model for a guitar string that remains *in equilibrium*.

To keep the modelling simple, in any given model we shall use identical model springs.

A basic model of the E string is derived in Subsection 4.2, and this is revised in Subsection 4.3. Subsection 4.4 investigates briefly how further revisions might improve the model.

4.2   A first model

We start by developing the basic model of the guitar string that lumps all the mass at the centre of the string.

Example 4.1

Suppose the E string is modelled with all its mass (0.25 g) lumped together as a particle at the centre of the string, with the particle connected by model springs to endpoints 0.65 metres apart, as shown in Figure 4.2. The equilibrium length of each of the two springs is half the equilibrium length of the E string, so $l_{eq} = 0.65/2 = 0.325$ metres, but the equilibrium tension in each spring is the same as the equilibrium tension in the E string (68 N, as calculated above).

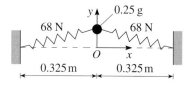

Figure 4.2

In order to simplify the analysis, the following assumptions are made.

- The oscillations are in a horizontal plane. This means that we have a *two-dimensional* mechanical system modelled solely by springs and particles. Consequently (by the argument in Subsection 2.1), if we measure displacements from the equilibrium position of the particle, the force of gravity can be ignored in deriving the equation of motion.
- The particle is displaced in a direction perpendicular to the equilibrium alignment of the springs (i.e. along the y-axis marked on Figure 4.2); therefore the vibrations are transverse. This assumption means that the system behaves as if it has one degree of freedom.
- The oscillations are small, i.e. the displacement y is small compared with the length of the string.

Calculate the fundamental frequency of vibration.

Solution

A diagram of the model of the system is given in Figure 4.2.

◄Draw picture►

Choose the axes that are shown in Figure 4.2, with the origin at the equilibrium position of the particle (i.e. the point half-way between the endpoints).

◄Choose coordinates►

The only two forces affecting the particle's motion are those due to the two springs (as gravity can be ignored), so the force diagram (using the usual notation) is as follows.

◄Draw force diagram(s)►

$$m$$

$$\mathbf{H}_1 \qquad \mathbf{H}_2$$

Newton's second law applied to the particle gives

◄Apply Newton's 2nd law►

$$m\ddot{\mathbf{r}} = \mathbf{H}_1 + \mathbf{H}_2, \tag{4.2}$$

where $\mathbf{r} = y\mathbf{j}$, and $\mathbf{j}$ is a unit vector in the positive y-direction.

Now the forces acting on the particle have to be modelled. The displacement of the particle is not aligned with the springs, therefore the changes in the forces acting cannot be modelled using Equation (2.5). Instead we use the full form of Hooke's law, $\mathbf{H} = -k(l - l_0)\,\widehat{\mathbf{s}}$. First, consider $\mathbf{H}_1$. From Figure 4.3 you can see that a unit vector from the centre of the spring to the particle is $\widehat{\mathbf{s}} = (l_{\mathrm{eq}}\mathbf{i} + y\mathbf{j})/l$, where $l = \sqrt{l_{\mathrm{eq}}^2 + y^2}$. Thus, by Hooke's law,

You will see below that an alternative strategy is to make use of Equation (2.4).

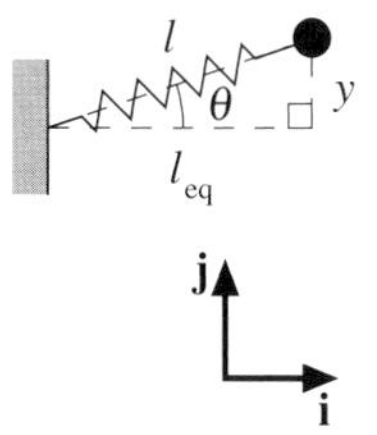

$$\mathbf{H}_1 = -k(l - l_0)\left(\frac{l_{\mathrm{eq}}\mathbf{i} + y\mathbf{j}}{l}\right).$$

Under the assumption that the oscillations are small compared with the length of the string, we can use the approximation $l \simeq l_{\mathrm{eq}}$ to simplify this equation to

$$\mathbf{H}_1 \simeq -k\left(l_{\mathrm{eq}} - l_0\right)\left(\mathbf{i} + \frac{y}{l_{\mathrm{eq}}}\mathbf{j}\right).$$

Figure 4.3

We can then simplify further by using the equation for the equilibrium tension in a model spring, $T_{\mathrm{eq}} = k\left(l_{\mathrm{eq}} - l_0\right)$, to obtain

$$\mathbf{H}_1 \simeq -T_{\mathrm{eq}}\left(\mathbf{i} + \frac{y}{l_{\mathrm{eq}}}\mathbf{j}\right). \tag{4.3}$$

Similarly, for $\mathbf{H}_2$ we have $\widehat{\mathbf{s}} = (-l_{\mathrm{eq}}\mathbf{i} + y\mathbf{j})/l$, hence

$$\mathbf{H}_2 \simeq -T_{\mathrm{eq}}\left(-\mathbf{i} + \frac{y}{l_{\mathrm{eq}}}\mathbf{j}\right).$$

Substituting into Equation (4.2), we obtain the model

$$m\ddot{\mathbf{r}} = -T_{\mathrm{eq}}\left(\mathbf{i} + \frac{y}{l_{\mathrm{eq}}}\mathbf{j}\right) - T_{\mathrm{eq}}\left(-\mathbf{i} + \frac{y}{l_{\mathrm{eq}}}\mathbf{j}\right) = -T_{\mathrm{eq}}\left(\frac{2y}{l_{\mathrm{eq}}}\mathbf{j}\right).$$

As this is a *model* of the motion, we revert to $=$ rather than $\simeq$ signs.

Resolving in the $\mathbf{j}$-direction and rearranging gives

$$\ddot{y} = -\frac{2T_{\mathrm{eq}}}{ml_{\mathrm{eq}}}y.$$

Writing this in the form $\ddot{y} + \omega^2 y = 0$, where $\omega^2 = 2T_{\mathrm{eq}}/(ml_{\mathrm{eq}})$, we can see that this is the equation for simple harmonic motion (as in *Unit 7*). We can therefore write its general solution as

◄Solve equation(s)►

$$y(t) = A\cos(\omega t + \phi),$$

where the angular frequency ω is given by

$$\omega = \sqrt{\frac{2T_{\mathrm{eq}}}{ml_{\mathrm{eq}}}}. \tag{4.4}$$

Substituting from the data in the question, we find that the angular frequency for this vibration is

◄Interpret solution►

$$\omega = \sqrt{\frac{2 \times 68}{(0.25 \times 10^{-3}) \times 0.325}} \simeq 1294\,\mathrm{rad\,s}^{-1}.$$

The fundamental frequency of the guitar string is then obtained by converting the above angular frequency to a frequency:

$$f = \frac{\omega}{2\pi} = \frac{1294}{2\pi} \simeq 206\,\mathrm{s}^{-1}.$$

So the fundamental frequency of vibration predicted by this first model of the guitar's E string is approximately 206 Hz. ∎

The frequency predicted in Example 4.1 is not close to 323 Hz, the experimentally determined fundamental frequency of the E string. This suggests that the model needs modifying. Accordingly, modifications are made in the next exercise and, in a different way, in the next subsection.

*Exercise 4.1

In the multimedia package, it was argued that the model of a guitar string used in Example 4.1 is not the best one-degree-of-freedom model. A better model, based on the argument that the ends of the string are not moving, involves distributing the total mass, M say, between a particle of mass $\frac{1}{2}M$ in the middle of the string and particles of mass $\frac{1}{4}M$ at either end, with two model springs in between, as shown in Figure 4.4. Only the particle of mass $\frac{1}{2}M$ in the middle vibrates. Use Equation (4.4) to find the fundamental frequency of vibration predicted by this model. Comment on your answer.

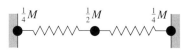

Figure 4.4

In Example 4.1 the particle was displaced by a small amount, $y\mathbf{j}$, and the force exerted by the left-hand spring on the particle was given by Equation (4.3) as

$$\mathbf{H}_1 \simeq -T_{\text{eq}}\left(\mathbf{i} + \frac{y}{l_{\text{eq}}}\mathbf{j}\right) = -T_{\text{eq}}\mathbf{i} - \frac{T_{\text{eq}}}{l_{\text{eq}}}y\mathbf{j}.$$

Now $-T_{\text{eq}}\mathbf{i}$ is simply the force exerted by the spring when the system is in equilibrium, so the approximate change in the force from its equilibrium value is

$$\Delta\mathbf{H}_1 \simeq -\frac{T_{\text{eq}}}{l_{\text{eq}}}y\,\mathbf{j}.$$

This expression for the approximate change in the force due to a spring holds for any model spring when a small displacement $y\mathbf{j}$ is made at one end and at right angles to the equilibrium alignment of the spring. Hence we have the useful approximation

$$\Delta\mathbf{H} \simeq -\frac{T_{\text{eq}}}{l_{\text{eq}}}y\,\mathbf{j}. \tag{4.5}$$

We shall make frequent use of this approximation in the next subsection.

We could have used this approximation and the corresponding one for $\Delta\mathbf{H}_2$, in conjunction with Equation (2.4), to obtain the equation of motion in Example 4.1.

4.3   Revised models

In the previous subsection we looked at two lumped parameter models of the E string of the guitar, both of which behaved as if they had one degree of freedom. In this subsection we shall try to improve the accuracy of our models by considering lumped parameter models of the E string that behave as if they have two or more degrees of freedom.

Example 4.2

The next model of the E string has two identical particles and three identical model springs, as in Figure 4.5. The mass of the string is evenly distributed between the two particles (i.e. 0.125 g each), and the equilibrium length of each spring is $l_{\text{eq}} = 0.65/3 \simeq 0.217$ metres. The equilibrium tension in the springs, T_{eq}, remains the same (68 N) as in previous models. The three assumptions made in Example 4.1 are used again here.

Calculate the fundamental frequency of vibration.

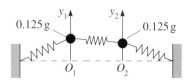

Figure 4.5

Solution

The model of the system is depicted in Figure 4.5.   ◄Draw picture►

Choose the axes that are shown in Figure 4.5, with the origins at the equilibrium positions of the particles.   ◄Choose coordinates►

The force diagrams for the two particles (using the usual notation) are as follows.   ◄Draw force diagram(s)►

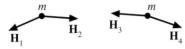

$\mathbf{H}_2$ and $\mathbf{H}_3$ are drawn opposite in direction, which they must be because they are forces exerted by the same model spring.

Applying Equation (2.4) to the two particles in turn, we obtain   ◄Apply Newton's 2nd law►

$$\begin{cases} m\ddot{\mathbf{r}}_1 = \Delta\mathbf{H}_1 + \Delta\mathbf{H}_2, \\ m\ddot{\mathbf{r}}_2 = \Delta\mathbf{H}_3 + \Delta\mathbf{H}_4, \end{cases} \tag{4.6}$$

where $\mathbf{r}_1 = y_1\mathbf{j}$ and $\mathbf{r}_2 = y_2\mathbf{j}$ are the displacements of the first and second particles, respectively, and $\mathbf{j}$ is a unit vector in the positive y-direction.

Now the forces have to be modelled. From approximation (4.5) we have

$$\Delta\mathbf{H}_1 = -\frac{T_{\text{eq}}}{l_{\text{eq}}}y_1\mathbf{j}, \quad \Delta\mathbf{H}_4 = -\frac{T_{\text{eq}}}{l_{\text{eq}}}y_2\mathbf{j}.$$

Since we are modelling here, we write = rather than ≃ when using (4.5).

The computations of the other forces are complicated by the fact that both ends of the central spring are displaced. For the force $\mathbf{H}_2$, the spring is displaced at the left-hand end by $y_1 - y_2$ relative to the right-hand end, so from approximation (4.5) we have

$$\Delta\mathbf{H}_2 = -\frac{T_{\text{eq}}}{l_{\text{eq}}}(y_1 - y_2)\mathbf{j}.$$

If $y_1 > y_2$, the relative displacement is $(y_1 - y_2)\mathbf{j}$. If $y_2 > y_1$, the relative displacement is $(y_2 - y_1)(-\mathbf{j}) = (y_1 - y_2)\mathbf{j}$.

Similarly, we obtain

$$\Delta\mathbf{H}_3 = -\frac{T_{\text{eq}}}{l_{\text{eq}}}(y_2 - y_1)\mathbf{j} = \frac{T_{\text{eq}}}{l_{\text{eq}}}(y_1 - y_2)\mathbf{j}.$$

Substitution into Equations (4.6) gives

This expression for $\Delta\mathbf{H}_3$ can also be obtained by using the fact that $\mathbf{H}_3 = -\mathbf{H}_2$ (since they are forces exerted by the same model spring), and hence $\Delta\mathbf{H}_3 = -\Delta\mathbf{H}_2$.

$$\begin{cases} m\ddot{\mathbf{r}}_1 = -\dfrac{T_{\text{eq}}}{l_{\text{eq}}}y_1\mathbf{j} - \dfrac{T_{\text{eq}}}{l_{\text{eq}}}(y_1 - y_2)\mathbf{j}, \\ m\ddot{\mathbf{r}}_2 = \dfrac{T_{\text{eq}}}{l_{\text{eq}}}(y_1 - y_2)\mathbf{j} - \dfrac{T_{\text{eq}}}{l_{\text{eq}}}y_2\mathbf{j}. \end{cases}$$

Resolving in the $\mathbf{j}$-direction and rearranging, we obtain

$$\begin{cases} \ddot{y}_1 = -2\dfrac{T_{\text{eq}}}{ml_{\text{eq}}}y_1 + \dfrac{T_{\text{eq}}}{ml_{\text{eq}}}y_2, \\ \ddot{y}_2 = \dfrac{T_{\text{eq}}}{ml_{\text{eq}}}y_1 - 2\dfrac{T_{\text{eq}}}{ml_{\text{eq}}}y_2, \end{cases}$$

which can be written in matrix form as

$$\begin{bmatrix} \ddot{y}_1 \\ \ddot{y}_2 \end{bmatrix} = \frac{T_{\text{eq}}}{ml_{\text{eq}}}\begin{bmatrix} -2 & 1 \\ 1 & -2 \end{bmatrix}\begin{bmatrix} y_1 \\ y_2 \end{bmatrix}.$$

To solve this, the eigenvalues of the matrix $\begin{bmatrix} -2 & 1 \\ 1 & -2 \end{bmatrix}$ have to be found by solving   ◄Solve equation(s)►

$$\begin{vmatrix} -2 - \lambda & 1 \\ 1 & -2 - \lambda \end{vmatrix} = \lambda^2 + 4\lambda + 3 = (\lambda + 1)(\lambda + 3) = 0,$$

to give $\lambda = -1$ and $\lambda = -3$. So the eigenvalues of the dynamic matrix are $-T_{\text{eq}}/(ml_{\text{eq}})$ and $-3T_{\text{eq}}/(ml_{\text{eq}})$.

Hence the normal mode angular frequencies are

$$\omega_1 = \sqrt{\frac{T_{\text{eq}}}{ml_{\text{eq}}}} \quad \text{and} \quad \omega_2 = \sqrt{\frac{3T_{\text{eq}}}{ml_{\text{eq}}}}.$$

The objective of this analysis is to calculate the fundamental frequency of vibration. This corresponds to the smaller normal mode angular frequency, and so is given by ◄Interpret solution►

$$f = \frac{\omega_1}{2\pi} = \frac{1}{2\pi}\sqrt{\frac{68}{(0.125 \times 10^{-3}) \times 0.217}} \simeq 252\,\text{s}^{-1}.$$

Therefore the fundamental frequency is approximately 252 Hz.   ∎

The frequency 252 Hz obtained in Example 4.2 is still a long way below the 323 Hz experimental value, but it is much better than the 206 Hz predicted by the model with one degree of freedom in Example 4.1. Further revisions of the model are considered in Exercises 4.2 and 4.3.

*Exercise 4.2

Using the ideas in the multimedia package and Exercise 4.1, the model in Example 4.2 may be improved by taking the two moving particles each to have mass $\frac{1}{3}M$, while the remaining $\frac{1}{3}M$ is modelled by particles placed at either end of the string ($\frac{1}{6}M$ at each end). Only the two particles of mass $\frac{1}{3}M$ vibrate. Find the fundamental frequency of vibration predicted by this model. Comment on your answer.

*Exercise 4.3

Now consider the next refinement in developing lumped parameter models of the E string of the guitar, i.e. the model shown in Figure 4.6, which behaves as if it has three degrees of freedom. In this model, the mass is distributed evenly between three identical particles, with four identical model springs linking the particles to one another and to the endpoints. All the particles vibrate. This model is a refinement of those in Examples 4.1 and 4.2, and so uses the same simplifying assumptions and data.

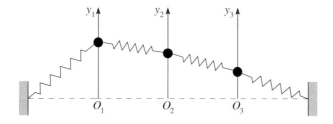

Figure 4.6

(a) Use the axes shown in Figure 4.6 and the methods of Example 4.2 to derive the matrix form of the equation of motion for the system.

(b) The eigenvalues of the matrix

$$\begin{bmatrix} -2 & 1 & 0 \\ 1 & -2 & 1 \\ 0 & 1 & -2 \end{bmatrix}$$

are -0.586, -2 and -3.414. Using this information, calculate the fundamental frequency of vibration predicted by this model. Comment on your answer.

4.4 Approaching the limit

So far in this section we have considered various lumped parameter models of a guitar string. This subsection links together the results of the previous two subsections and investigates the behaviour of the models as the number of degrees of freedom increases. However, we shall look only at models where *all* the mass of the string is assumed to vibrate; we shall not consider the models of Exercises 4.1 and 4.2 where some of the mass does not vibrate.

In Example 4.1, a one-particle model was studied and the fundamental frequency was calculated to be approximately 206 Hz. In Example 4.2, a two-particle model was studied and the fundamental frequency was calculated to be approximately 252 Hz. Exercise 4.3 calculated the fundamental frequency for a three-particle model as approximately 273 Hz. What happens as the number of particles increases beyond three? Does the predicted fundamental frequency become closer and closer to the experimental value of 323 Hz as the number of particles is increased?

To answer these questions, we look at the equations of motion that were derived for the various models and see if a pattern emerges.

In Example 4.1, the equation of motion was

$$\ddot{y} = -\frac{2T_{eq}}{ml_{eq}}y.$$

In order to make the comparisons easier we shall change the notation slightly. The y here is the y-coordinate of the first particle, so we shall call it y_1. The m is the total mass of the guitar string, and we shall call this M. The l_{eq} is the equilibrium length of each spring, and is the distance between the endpoints, L, divided by 2. Therefore the equation of motion can be written as

$$\ddot{y}_1 = \frac{T_{eq}}{M(L/2)} \times (-2) \times y_1. \tag{4.7}$$

In Example 4.2, the equation of motion is

$$\begin{bmatrix} \ddot{y}_1 \\ \ddot{y}_2 \end{bmatrix} = \frac{T_{eq}}{ml_{eq}} \begin{bmatrix} -2 & 1 \\ 1 & -2 \end{bmatrix} \begin{bmatrix} y_1 \\ y_2 \end{bmatrix}.$$

Writing this in terms of the same parameters as Equation (4.7) gives

$$\begin{bmatrix} \ddot{y}_1 \\ \ddot{y}_2 \end{bmatrix} = \frac{T_{eq}}{(M/2)(L/3)} \begin{bmatrix} -2 & 1 \\ 1 & -2 \end{bmatrix} \begin{bmatrix} y_1 \\ y_2 \end{bmatrix}. \tag{4.8}$$

The equation of motion from Exercise 4.3 can be written in terms of M and L as

$$\begin{bmatrix} \ddot{y}_1 \\ \ddot{y}_2 \\ \ddot{y}_3 \end{bmatrix} = \frac{T_{eq}}{(M/3)(L/4)} \begin{bmatrix} -2 & 1 & 0 \\ 1 & -2 & 1 \\ 0 & 1 & -2 \end{bmatrix} \begin{bmatrix} y_1 \\ y_2 \\ y_3 \end{bmatrix}. \tag{4.9}$$

By examining the pattern emerging from Equations (4.7), (4.8) and (4.9), you should be able to predict that the equation of motion for the corresponding four-particle model is

$$\begin{bmatrix} \ddot{y}_1 \\ \ddot{y}_2 \\ \ddot{y}_3 \\ \ddot{y}_4 \end{bmatrix} = \frac{T_{eq}}{(M/4)(L/5)} \begin{bmatrix} -2 & 1 & 0 & 0 \\ 1 & -2 & 1 & 0 \\ 0 & 1 & -2 & 1 \\ 0 & 0 & 1 & -2 \end{bmatrix} \begin{bmatrix} y_1 \\ y_2 \\ y_3 \\ y_4 \end{bmatrix}.$$

This pattern enables a computer program to be written to compute the fundamental frequency f of the corresponding n-particle model, for any positive integer value of n, and then to plot the results on a graph. Such a graph is shown in Figure 4.7. It can be seen that the predicted fundamental frequency approaches the experimental value of 323 Hz. The convergence to this value is rapid at first, but slows down as n increases: a model with ten degrees of freedom predicts 307 Hz, a model with twenty degrees of freedom predicts 318 Hz, and a model with fifty degrees of freedom predicts 320 Hz.

Up to now in this section we have looked at the vibrations of the E string of a guitar under the assumption that the string is displaced only in a direction perpendicular to its equilibrium alignment, i.e. that there is only transverse vibration. But, in practice, there is some *longitudinal vibration* too, i.e. some vibration along the length of the string. The following end-of-section exercises examine this longitudinal vibration.

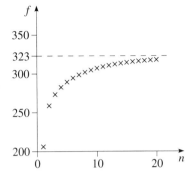

Figure 4.7

End-of-section Exercises

Exercise 4.4

If you look back at the start of Subsection 2.1, you should recognize that the system shown in Figure 2.1 is similar to the one-particle lumped parameter model of the E string considered in Example 4.1. However, in the former case it was assumed that the particle was constrained to move in one dimension along the line of the springs, i.e. we modelled longitudinal vibrations, whereas in Example 4.1 we modelled transverse vibrations. Now, by using the ideas of Subsection 2.1, we can model the longitudinal vibrations in the lumped parameter models of the E string. Example 2.1 did this for what was, in effect, a two-particle lumped parameter model. In this exercise you are asked to extend the ideas of Subsection 2.1 to model the longitudinal vibrations of the three-particle lumped parameter model of the E string, as illustrated in Figure 4.8. (You considered the transverse vibrations in Exercise 4.3.)

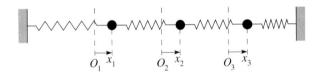

Figure 4.8

(a) Derive the matrix form of the equation of motion for the longitudinal vibrations of this three-particle model.

(b) Verify that $[1 \quad \sqrt{2} \quad 1]^T$, $[1 \quad 0 \quad -1]^T$ and $[1 \quad -\sqrt{2} \quad 1]^T$ are eigenvectors of the dynamic matrix for this model, and hence deduce the eigenvalues of the dynamic matrix.

You met these eigenvectors in Example 1.5 and Exercise 1.6.

(c) Determine the normal mode angular frequencies of the longitudinal vibrations of this model, given that the mass of each particle is $\frac{1}{3}(0.25 \times 10^{-3})$ kg, and that each model spring has natural length and equilibrium length equal to a quarter of the corresponding lengths of the E string (so that, for a fixed equilibrium tension of 68 N, each model spring has stiffness $4 \times 4000 = 16\,000\,\mathrm{N\,m^{-1}}$).

From Equation (4.1), $T_{\mathrm{eq}} = k(l_{\mathrm{eq}} - l_0)$, so for a *constant* T_{eq}, dividing l_{eq} and l_0 by 4 means multiplying k by 4.

Exercise 4.5

The aim of this question is to calculate the fundamental frequency of longitudinal vibration of the E string of a guitar by using a similar argument to the one in Subsection 4.4. Successively more sophisticated models of the longitudinal vibrations of the E string are given by Equation (2.3) (with $k_1 = k_2 = k$ and $x_1 = x$), Equations (2.7) (with $k_1 = k_2 = k_3 = k$ and $m_1 = m_2 = m$) and Equations (S.11) from Solution 4.4, as follows:

$$m\ddot{x}_1 = -2kx_1, \tag{4.10}$$

$$\begin{cases} m\ddot{x}_1 = -2kx_1 + kx_2, \\ m\ddot{x}_2 = kx_1 - 2kx_2, \end{cases} \tag{4.11}$$

$$\begin{cases} m\ddot{x}_1 = -2kx_1 + kx_2, \\ m\ddot{x}_2 = kx_1 - 2kx_2 + kx_3, \\ m\ddot{x}_3 = kx_2 - 2kx_3. \end{cases} \tag{4.12}$$

Suppose that the n-degrees-of-freedom model of the longitudinal vibrations represents the guitar string (mass M, equilibrium length L, natural length L_0 and stiffness K) by $n+1$ identical model springs connecting n particles of equal mass.

(a) Write Equation (4.10) in terms of properties of the guitar string, i.e. T_{eq}, M, L and L_0.

  (*Hint:* Use Equation (4.1) to eliminate the stiffness k from the equation, bearing in mind that the equilibrium tension in each spring is the same as the equilibrium tension in the guitar string.)

(b) Repeat part (a) for Equations (4.11) and (4.12), giving your answers in matrix form.

(c) Use your answers to parts (a) and (b) to deduce the equation of motion for the corresponding four-degrees-of-freedom model of the longitudinal vibrations of the guitar string.

(d) By comparing your answers with the results in Subsection 4.4, show that the ratio of the fundamental frequency for the longitudinal vibrations to the fundamental frequency for the transverse vibrations of the guitar string is $\sqrt{L/(L - L_0)}$. If the fundamental frequency of the transverse vibrations is $323\,\text{Hz}$, calculate the fundamental frequency of the longitudinal vibrations of the guitar string.

5 Two-dimensional systems

This section draws together the results from Sections 2 and 4, and shows that the concept of normal modes can be useful in a variety of different problems. In Section 2 we considered the longitudinal motion of springs. In Section 4 we looked at the transverse motion of springs. In this section the motion considered is not confined to either one of these directions.

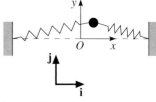

Figure 5.1

Consider the situation depicted in Figure 5.1, in which a particle is displaced from its equilibrium position O by a small amount $x\mathbf{i} + y\mathbf{j}$.

In the case when $y = 0$, the displacement is longitudinal, and by Equation (2.5) the change in the spring force for either spring is

$$\Delta\mathbf{H} = -kx\mathbf{i} \quad \text{when } y = 0. \tag{5.1}$$

In the case when $x = 0$, the displacement is transverse, and by Equation (4.5) the change in the spring force for either spring is

$$\Delta\mathbf{H} = -\frac{T_{\text{eq}}}{l_{\text{eq}}}y\mathbf{j} \quad \text{when } x = 0. \tag{5.2}$$

For the left-hand spring we use Equation (2.5) with $\widehat{\mathbf{s}} = \mathbf{i}$ and change of length x. For the right-hand spring, $\widehat{\mathbf{s}} = -\mathbf{i}$ and the change of length is $-x$.

So it is reasonable to assume that, for a small displacement $x\mathbf{i} + y\mathbf{j}$, the overall change in the spring force is given approximately by the sum of the changes expressed above, i.e. as

$$\Delta\mathbf{H} = -kx\mathbf{i} - \frac{T_{\text{eq}}}{l_{\text{eq}}}y\mathbf{j}, \tag{5.3}$$

where k is the stiffness of the spring, T_{eq} is its equilibrium tension and l_{eq} is its equilibrium length.

Here we assume that Equation (4.5) is an equality rather than an approximation. This assumption is reasonable if the displacement is small.

A better model would have an xy term. But for *small* x and y, xy is very small and can be ignored, resulting in a linear model, which is needed in order to apply the linear methods of this unit.

A sense of how this result can be used is provided by the following example, which concerns a one-particle model of a guitar string.

Example 5.1

Consider the one-particle model of the E string of a guitar discussed in Example 4.1, but now relax the assumption about the direction of displacement of the particle and instead allow the particle to be displaced in any direction in the plane. Relaxation of this assumption means that the system behaves with two degrees of freedom. Show that if the change in the force exerted by a displaced spring can be modelled by Equation (5.3), then the transverse and longitudinal motions of the E string are independent of each other.

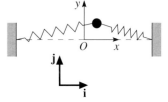

Figure 5.2

Solution

A diagram of the model of the system is given in Figure 5.2.

◄Draw picture►

Choose the axes as shown in Figure 5.2, with the origin at the equilibrium position of the particle.

◄Choose coordinates►

The only two forces affecting the particle's motion are those due to the two springs, so the force diagram (with the usual notation) is as follows.

◄Draw force diagram(s)►

Applying Equation (2.4) gives

◄Apply Newton's 2nd law►

$$m\ddot{\mathbf{r}} = \Delta\mathbf{H}_1 + \Delta\mathbf{H}_2. \tag{5.4}$$

If the particle is displaced by a small amount $x\mathbf{i} + y\mathbf{j}$, then, from Equation (5.3), we have

$$\Delta \mathbf{H}_1 = \Delta \mathbf{H}_2 = -kx\mathbf{i} - \frac{T_{eq}}{l_{eq}} y\mathbf{j},$$

where k, T_{eq} and l_{eq} are as in Example 4.1. Substituting for $\Delta \mathbf{H}_1$ and $\Delta \mathbf{H}_2$ in Equation (5.4) we obtain

$$m\ddot{\mathbf{r}} = -2kx\mathbf{i} - \frac{2T_{eq}}{l_{eq}} y\mathbf{j}.$$

Resolving in the $\mathbf{i}$- and $\mathbf{j}$-directions gives

$$\begin{cases} m\ddot{x} = -2kx, \\ m\ddot{y} = -\dfrac{2T_{eq}}{l_{eq}} y. \end{cases}$$

These two equations are *uncoupled*: one equation contains only x and its derivatives, and the other equation contains only y and its derivatives. So the equations can be solved independently, and the transverse motion (in the y-direction) and the longitudinal motion (in the x-direction) are independent of each other. ∎

The independence of the transverse and longitudinal motions justifies the approach of Section 4.

Exercise 5.1

A spinning shaft is held in place in a horizontal plane by means of four identical springs placed at equal angles around it, as shown in Figure 5.3. If the shaft is modelled as a particle of mass m and the springs are modelled as identical model springs of stiffness k, equilibrium length l_{eq} and equilibrium tension T_{eq}, then, provided that the vibrations of the shaft are small compared with the length of the springs, Equation (5.3) leads to the following equation of motion for the system:

$$\begin{bmatrix} \ddot{x} \\ \ddot{y} \end{bmatrix} = \frac{2(k + T_{eq}/l_{eq})}{m} \begin{bmatrix} -1 & 0 \\ 0 & -1 \end{bmatrix} \begin{bmatrix} x \\ y \end{bmatrix}.$$

(a) Find the normal mode eigenvectors for the system.

(b) Is $[2 \quad 1]^T$ a normal mode eigenvector? If so, find another linearly independent normal mode eigenvector.

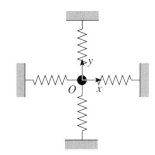

Figure 5.3

The physical interpretation of Exercise 5.1 is that the shaft of the system can oscillate in simple harmonic motion (i.e. in a normal mode) along any direction in the plane. This is shown for one direction in Figure 5.4.

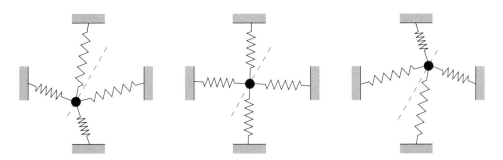

Figure 5.4   A sequence showing the shaft of the system illustrated in Figure 5.3 when it is oscillating in simple harmonic motion at an oblique angle.

Mechanical systems that have two or more equal normal mode angular frequencies, like the system in Figure 5.3, are called **degenerate systems**.

Mechanical systems with a high degree of symmetry are usually degenerate. This is the main feature of normal modes that is not discussed fully in this unit, but fortunately it is not a problem with systems with small numbers of degrees of freedom, such as the ones studied in this unit.

To analyse the normal mode vibrations of a complicated system such as the buckminster-fullerene molecule (which is a spherical molecule with sixty carbon atoms, as shown in Figure 5.5) is, in principle, no more difficult than analysing the mechanical systems studied in this unit — no new ideas are needed. The calculations are, however, much more formidable (the buckminster-fullerene molecule has $3 \times 60 = 180$ degrees of freedom), and for this reason many shortcuts have been devised. Also, to obtain an accurate prediction of the normal mode angular frequencies, we need models that are more accurate than the particle–spring models of this unit. The most accurate models of molecules, for example, are based on quantum mechanics, not Newtonian mechanics, but these are beyond the scope of this course.

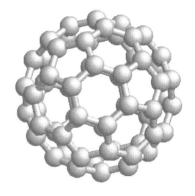

Figure 5.5

Outcomes

After studying this unit you should be able to:

- understand the terms degree of freedom, normal mode, normal mode angular frequency, in-phase motion, phase-opposed motion, rigid body motion and degenerate system, all in the context of an oscillating mechanical system;
- derive the equation of motion for simple one- and two-dimensional oscillating mechanical systems (without damping or forcing);
- solve the equation of motion for simple one- and two-dimensional oscillating mechanical systems by finding the eigenvalues and corresponding normal mode eigenvectors of the dynamic matrix;
- interpret the normal mode eigenvectors of a simple oscillating mechanical system, in terms of the initial conditions required for the system to oscillate in a normal mode;
- model a simple oscillating mechanical system by taking the equilibrium positions of the particles of the system as the origins of coordinates, and using formulae involving the changes in forces;
- understand how to model a simple oscillating mechanical system as a lumped parameter model.

Solutions to the exercises

Section 1

1.1 (a) This system has two degrees of freedom.

(b) This system has two degrees of freedom.

(c) This system has two degrees of freedom. (The additional spring does not alter the number of coordinates needed.)

(d) This system has one degree of freedom.

(e) This system has three degrees of freedom.

(f) This system has three degrees of freedom. (The additional spring does not alter the number of coordinates needed.)

1.2 (a) These graphs represent normal mode motion, since both x_1 and x_2 vary sinusoidally with the same frequency (just over three cycles completed in 10 seconds) and phase angle. The two particles are in-phase.

(b) These three graphs represent normal mode motion, since the three coordinates vary sinusoidally with the same frequency (again, just over three cycles completed in 10 seconds) and phase angle. The particles represented by the coordinates:

    x_1 and x_2 are phase-opposed;

    x_1 and x_3 are in-phase;

    x_2 and x_3 are phase-opposed.

(c) These graphs do not represent normal mode motion. (The period of the second graph is more than twice that of the first.)

1.3 From the given data, $k/m_1 = 2$ and $k/m_2 = 1$. So the dynamic matrix of the system is

$$\begin{bmatrix} -4 & 2 \\ 1 & -2 \end{bmatrix}.$$

The eigenvalues are found by solving the quadratic equation

$$\begin{vmatrix} -4 - \lambda & 2 \\ 1 & -2 - \lambda \end{vmatrix} = \lambda^2 + 6\lambda + 6 = 0,$$

which gives $\lambda_1 = -3 + \sqrt{3} = -1.268$ and $\lambda_2 = -3 - \sqrt{3} = -4.732$.

$\boxed{\lambda_1 = -3 + \sqrt{3}}$ The eigenvector equations are

$$\begin{cases} (-1 - \sqrt{3})v_1 + 2v_2 = 0, \\ v_1 + (1 - \sqrt{3})v_2 = 0. \end{cases}$$

Putting $v_1 = 1$ gives $v_2 = 1.366$, so $[1 \quad 1.366]^T$ is an eigenvector.

$\boxed{\lambda_2 = -3 - \sqrt{3}}$ The eigenvector equations are

$$\begin{cases} (-1 + \sqrt{3})v_1 + 2v_2 = 0, \\ v_1 + (1 + \sqrt{3})v_2 = 0. \end{cases}$$

Putting $v_1 = 1$ gives $v_2 = -0.366$, so $[1 \quad -0.366]^T$ is an eigenvector.

The normal mode angular frequencies are $\omega_1 = \sqrt{-\lambda_1} = 1.126$ and $\omega_2 = \sqrt{-\lambda_2} = 2.175$. So the general solution of the equation of motion for the specified mechanical system can be written as

$$\mathbf{x} = C_1 \begin{bmatrix} 1 \\ 1.366 \end{bmatrix} \cos(1.126t + \phi_1)$$

$$+ C_2 \begin{bmatrix} 1 \\ -0.366 \end{bmatrix} \cos(2.175t + \phi_2).$$

1.4 (a) Using the usual notation, the force diagrams for the particles can be drawn as follows.

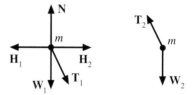

Applying Newton's second law to each particle gives

$$\begin{cases} m\ddot{\mathbf{r}}_1 = \mathbf{H}_1 + \mathbf{H}_2 + \mathbf{T}_1 + \mathbf{W}_1 + \mathbf{N}, \\ m\ddot{\mathbf{r}}_2 = \mathbf{T}_2 + \mathbf{W}_2, \end{cases} \quad \text{(S.1)}$$

where $\mathbf{r}_1 = x_1\mathbf{i} + y_1\mathbf{j}$ and $\mathbf{r}_2 = x_2\mathbf{i} + y_2\mathbf{j}$ are the position vectors, relative to O, of the sliding particle and the pendulum bob, with $\mathbf{i}$ and $\mathbf{j}$ being Cartesian unit vectors in the positive x-direction and vertically upwards, respectively. Now use Hooke's law to model the spring forces. For the force $\mathbf{H}_1$, the length of the spring is $l_0 + x_1$ (since the equilibrium position is at the natural length), so by Hooke's law,

$$\mathbf{H}_1 = -k((l_0 + x_1) - l_0)\mathbf{i} = -kx_1\mathbf{i}.$$

Similarly,

$$\mathbf{H}_2 = -k((l_0 - x_1) - l_0)(-\mathbf{i}) = -kx_1\mathbf{i}.$$

These can be substituted into Equations (S.1), along with $\mathbf{W}_1 = \mathbf{W}_2 = -mg\mathbf{j}$, to yield

$$\begin{cases} m\ddot{\mathbf{r}}_1 = -kx_1\mathbf{i} - kx_1\mathbf{i} + \mathbf{T}_1 - mg\mathbf{j} + \mathbf{N}, \\ m\ddot{\mathbf{r}}_2 = \mathbf{T}_2 - mg\mathbf{j}. \end{cases}$$

Resolving in the $\mathbf{i}$- and $\mathbf{j}$-directions gives

$$\begin{cases} m\ddot{x}_1 = -2kx_1 + |\mathbf{T}_1|\sin\theta, \\ m\ddot{y}_1 = -|\mathbf{T}_1|\cos\theta - mg + |\mathbf{N}|, \\ m\ddot{x}_2 = -|\mathbf{T}_2|\sin\theta, \\ m\ddot{y}_2 = |\mathbf{T}_2|\cos\theta - mg. \end{cases} \quad \text{(S.2)}$$

From Figure 1.10, we can deduce the following relationships between the linear and angular coordinates:

$$x_2 = x_1 + l\sin\theta, \quad y_1 = 0, \quad y_2 = -l\cos\theta.$$

Now we use the small-angle approximations $\sin\theta \simeq \theta$, $\cos\theta \simeq 1$, so $x_2 \simeq x_1 + l\theta$, $y_2 \simeq -l$ (and hence $\ddot{y}_2 \simeq 0$), which on substitution in Equations (S.2) give

$$\begin{cases} m\ddot{x}_1 \simeq -2kx_1 + |\mathbf{T}_1|\theta, \\ 0 \simeq -|\mathbf{T}_1| - mg + |\mathbf{N}|, \\ m\left(\ddot{x}_1 + l\ddot{\theta}\right) \simeq -|\mathbf{T}_2|\theta, \\ 0 \simeq |\mathbf{T}_2| - mg. \end{cases} \quad \text{(S.3)}$$

From the last of these approximations we have $|\mathbf{T}_2| \simeq mg$ and, since the forces exerted at either end of a model rod are equal in magnitude, $|\mathbf{T}_1| = |\mathbf{T}_2| \simeq mg$.

So the first and third of Equations (S.3) become

$$\begin{cases} m\ddot{x}_1 \simeq -2kx_1 + mg\theta, \\ m\left(\ddot{x}_1 + l\ddot{\theta}\right) \simeq -mg\theta. \end{cases} \tag{S.4}$$

(As a check, if $\ddot{x}_1 = 0$ (e.g. the pivot is fixed), then the second of Equations (S.4) gives $\ddot{\theta} \simeq -(g/l)\,\theta$, which is the simple harmonic equation expected for a simple pendulum.)

Subtract the first approximation in Equations (S.4) from the second to obtain another approximation with only one second derivative on the left-hand side:

$$ml\ddot{\theta} \simeq -mg\theta - (-2kx_1 + mg\theta) = 2kx_1 - 2mg\theta.$$

Hence the linear equations of motion for the system shown in Figure 1.10 are

$$\begin{cases} \ddot{x}_1 = -\dfrac{2k}{m}x_1 + g\theta, \\ \ddot{\theta} = \dfrac{2k}{lm}x_1 - \dfrac{2g}{l}\theta. \end{cases}$$

(b) Writing the equations in matrix form gives

$$\begin{bmatrix} \ddot{x}_1 \\ \ddot{\theta} \end{bmatrix} = \begin{bmatrix} -2k/m & g \\ 2k/(lm) & -2g/l \end{bmatrix} \begin{bmatrix} x_1 \\ \theta \end{bmatrix}.$$

From the given data, $k/m = 1/1 = 1\,\mathrm{N\,kg^{-1}\,m^{-1}}$ and $l = 1$ metre, so the dynamic matrix becomes

$$\begin{bmatrix} -2 & g \\ 2 & -2g \end{bmatrix}.$$

The eigenvalues of this matrix are found by solving

$$\begin{vmatrix} -2-\lambda & g \\ 2 & -2g-\lambda \end{vmatrix} = \lambda^2 + 2(1+g)\lambda + 2g = 0,$$

to give

$$\lambda = \frac{-2(1+g) \pm \sqrt{4(1+g)^2 - 8g}}{2}$$

$$= -1 - g \pm \sqrt{1+g^2}.$$

Substituting $g = 9.81$ into this gives the two eigenvalues as -0.95 and -20.67 (to two decimal places). As $\omega = \sqrt{-\lambda}$, these eigenvalues correspond to the two normal mode angular frequencies $0.97\,\mathrm{rad\,s^{-1}}$ and $4.55\,\mathrm{rad\,s^{-1}}$ (to two decimal places).

1.5 The normal mode eigenvectors derived in Example 1.3 were $[1 \quad \sqrt{2}]^T$ and $[1 \quad -\sqrt{2}]^T$. The coordinates chosen to describe the system are the angles θ_1 and θ_2 (see Figure 1.8), so the eigenvectors refer to these angles. The model is based on *small* angular displacements, so an initial condition where $\theta_1 = 1$ and $\theta_2 = \sqrt{2} \simeq 1.4$ (in radians) is not acceptable. Since both the pendulum bobs start from rest, we obtain the following possible initial conditions for normal mode motion by scaling the eigenvectors:

normal mode 1: $\theta_1 = 0.1,\quad \theta_2 = 0.14$ (to 2 d.p.);
normal mode 2: $\theta_1 = 0.1,\quad \theta_2 = -0.14$ (to 2 d.p.).

For mode 1, any initial condition in which the ratio of the initial θ_2 displacement to the initial θ_1 displacement is $\sqrt{2}$ is acceptable, provided both θ_1 and θ_2 are small. Similarly, for mode 2, any initial condition where the ratio is $-\sqrt{2}$ is acceptable, again provided θ_1 and θ_2 are small.

1.6 (i)

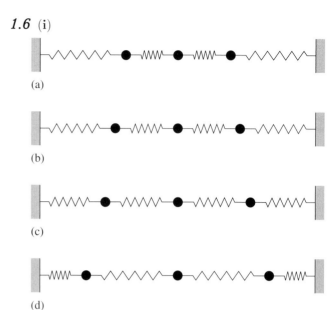

(a)

(b)

(c)

(d)

The central particle is stationary, while the other two particles are phase-opposed.

(ii)

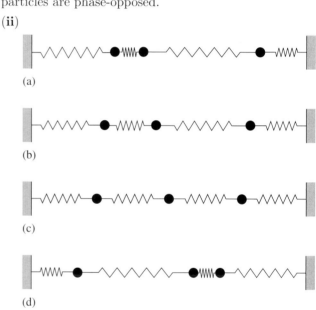

(a)

(b)

(c)

(d)

The particle on the left and the central particle are phase-opposed, as are the particle on the right and the central particle. The particles on the left and right are in-phase.

1.7 (a) The force diagrams for the particles are as follows, where the symbols have their usual meanings.

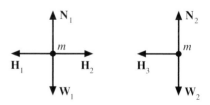

Since the motion is horizontal, $\mathbf{W}_1 + \mathbf{N}_1 = \mathbf{0}$ and $\mathbf{W}_2 + \mathbf{N}_2 = \mathbf{0}$; so the total forces on the particles are $\mathbf{F}_1 = \mathbf{H}_1 + \mathbf{H}_2$ and $\mathbf{F}_2 = \mathbf{H}_3$.

On subtracting the first of these from the second, we obtain

$$ml\ddot\theta \simeq -mg\theta - mg\theta = -2mg\theta.$$

Hence the linear equations of motion for the system are

$$\begin{cases} \ddot{x}_1 = g\theta, \\ \ddot\theta = -\dfrac{2g}{l}\theta. \end{cases}$$

(These equations could also have been obtained by putting $k = 0$ into the result of Exercise 1.4(a).)

(b) Writing the equations of motion in matrix form gives

$$\begin{bmatrix} \ddot{x}_1 \\ \ddot\theta \end{bmatrix} = \begin{bmatrix} 0 & g \\ 0 & -2g/l \end{bmatrix} \begin{bmatrix} x_1 \\ \theta \end{bmatrix}.$$

The eigenvalues are found by solving

$$\begin{vmatrix} 0 - \lambda & g \\ 0 & -2g/l - \lambda \end{vmatrix} = \lambda(\lambda + 2g/l) = 0.$$

So the eigenvalues are $\lambda = 0$ and $\lambda = -2g/l$.

$\boxed{\lambda = 0}$ The eigenvector equations are

$$\begin{bmatrix} 0 - 0 & g \\ 0 & -2g/l - 0 \end{bmatrix} \begin{bmatrix} v_1 \\ v_2 \end{bmatrix} = \begin{bmatrix} 0 \\ 0 \end{bmatrix},$$

or equivalently

$$\begin{cases} gv_2 = 0, \\ 2gv_2/l = 0. \end{cases}$$

Therefore $v_2 = 0$ (there is no restriction on v_1), so $[1 \ \ 0]^T$ is an eigenvector.

$\boxed{\lambda = -2g/l}$ The eigenvector equations are

$$\begin{bmatrix} 0 - (-2g/l) & g \\ 0 & -2g/l - (-2g/l) \end{bmatrix} \begin{bmatrix} v_1 \\ v_2 \end{bmatrix} = \begin{bmatrix} 0 \\ 0 \end{bmatrix},$$

or equivalently

$$\begin{cases} (2g/l)v_1 + gv_2 = 0, \\ 0 = 0. \end{cases}$$

The first equation gives the condition $v_2 = -2v_1/l$, so $[1 \ \ -2/l]^T$ is an eigenvector. The normal mode angular frequencies are calculated from the eigenvalues as $\omega_1 = 0$ and $\omega_2 = \sqrt{2g/l}$.

With these eigenvectors and normal mode angular frequencies, the general solution of the matrix equation of motion is

$$\begin{bmatrix} x_1(t) \\ \theta(t) \end{bmatrix} = \begin{bmatrix} 1 \\ 0 \end{bmatrix}(A + Bt) + C\begin{bmatrix} 1 \\ -\dfrac{2}{l} \end{bmatrix}\cos\left(\sqrt{\dfrac{2g}{l}}\,t + \phi\right).$$

(c) The angular frequency of a simple pendulum is $\sqrt{g/l}$, so the angular frequency of this pendulum, which is $\sqrt{2g/l}$, is larger by a factor of $\sqrt{2}$. Therefore the period of this pendulum is smaller by a factor of $\sqrt{2}$ than that of the simple pendulum.

(d) For the rigid body motion of the system, the whole system is translated along the horizontal bar (with $\theta = 0$), as follows.

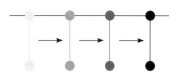

For the non-zero angular frequency, the motion of both particles is oscillatory with the same frequency. The displacement ratio is negative, so the motion is phase-opposed, as shown by the following diagram.

Section 4

4.1 The question suggests using Equation (4.4), which is applicable because the model of the guitar string is the same as that in Example 4.1: only the parameter m is different. Instead of the mass of the whole spring, $0.25\,$g, we substitute half the mass of the spring, $0.125\,$g, because only the central particle (of mass $\tfrac{1}{2}M$) vibrates; the other parameters have the same values as before. Then

$$\omega = \sqrt{\dfrac{2 \times 68}{(0.125 \times 10^{-3}) \times 0.325}} \simeq 1830\,\text{rad\,s}^{-1}.$$

This gives a fundamental frequency of

$$f = \dfrac{\omega}{2\pi} = \dfrac{1830}{2\pi} \simeq 291\,\text{s}^{-1}.$$

So this model predicts a fundamental frequency of approximately $291\,$Hz, which is much closer to the experimental value of $323\,$Hz than the $206\,$Hz predicted in Example 4.1.

4.2 The basic two-particle model applies here because only the two central particles vibrate. This means that the model used in Example 4.2 is relevant, only a parameter (the mass of the particles) has changed. Therefore the analysis is the same as in that example, leading to

$$\omega_1 = \sqrt{\dfrac{68}{((0.25/3) \times 10^{-3}) \times 0.217}} = 1939\,\text{rad\,s}^{-1}.$$

Hence the fundamental frequency is predicted to be

$$f = \dfrac{\omega_1}{2\pi} = \dfrac{1939}{2\pi} \simeq 309\,\text{s}^{-1}.$$

The predicted fundamental frequency of approximately $309\,$Hz is closer to the experimental value of $323\,$Hz than the $252\,$Hz predicted by Example 4.2, and is closer than the $291\,$Hz predicted in Exercise 4.1, so this model is an improvement on the previous ones.

4.3 **(a)** The force diagrams for the three particles (using the usual notation) are as follows.

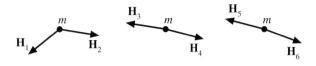

Applying Equation (2.4) to each particle gives
$$
\begin{cases}
m\ddot{\mathbf{r}}_1 = \Delta\mathbf{H}_1 + \Delta\mathbf{H}_2, \\
m\ddot{\mathbf{r}}_2 = \Delta\mathbf{H}_3 + \Delta\mathbf{H}_4, \\
m\ddot{\mathbf{r}}_3 = \Delta\mathbf{H}_5 + \Delta\mathbf{H}_6,
\end{cases}
\tag{S.9}
$$
where $\mathbf{r}_1 = y_1\mathbf{j}$, $\mathbf{r}_2 = y_2\mathbf{j}$ and $\mathbf{r}_3 = y_3\mathbf{j}$ are the displacements of the particles, and $\mathbf{j}$ is a unit vector in the positive y-direction.

Using expression (4.5) to model the forces exerted by the outermost springs, we find
$$
\Delta\mathbf{H}_1 = -\frac{T_{\text{eq}}}{l_{\text{eq}}}y_1\,\mathbf{j}, \quad \Delta\mathbf{H}_6 = -\frac{T_{\text{eq}}}{l_{\text{eq}}}y_3\,\mathbf{j}.
$$
The computations of the other forces are complicated by the fact that both ends of the springs are displaced. For the force $\mathbf{H}_2$, the spring is displaced by $y_1 - y_2$ at the left-hand end relative to the right-hand end, so from Equation (4.5),
$$
\Delta\mathbf{H}_2 = -\frac{T_{\text{eq}}}{l_{\text{eq}}}(y_1 - y_2)\mathbf{j}.
$$
Similarly,
$$
\Delta\mathbf{H}_3 = -\Delta\mathbf{H}_2 = \frac{T_{\text{eq}}}{l_{\text{eq}}}(y_1 - y_2)\mathbf{j},
$$
$$
\Delta\mathbf{H}_4 = -\frac{T_{\text{eq}}}{l_{\text{eq}}}(y_2 - y_3)\mathbf{j},
$$
$$
\Delta\mathbf{H}_5 = -\Delta\mathbf{H}_4 = \frac{T_{\text{eq}}}{l_{\text{eq}}}(y_2 - y_3)\mathbf{j}.
$$
These can be substituted into Equations (S.9) to obtain
$$
\begin{cases}
m\ddot{\mathbf{r}}_1 = -\dfrac{T_{\text{eq}}}{l_{\text{eq}}}y_1\mathbf{j} - \dfrac{T_{\text{eq}}}{l_{\text{eq}}}(y_1 - y_2)\mathbf{j}, \\
m\ddot{\mathbf{r}}_2 = \dfrac{T_{\text{eq}}}{l_{\text{eq}}}(y_1 - y_2)\mathbf{j} - \dfrac{T_{\text{eq}}}{l_{\text{eq}}}(y_2 - y_3)\mathbf{j}, \\
m\ddot{\mathbf{r}}_3 = \dfrac{T_{\text{eq}}}{l_{\text{eq}}}(y_2 - y_3)\mathbf{j} - \dfrac{T_{\text{eq}}}{l_{\text{eq}}}y_3\mathbf{j}.
\end{cases}
$$
Resolving in the $\mathbf{j}$-direction and rearranging gives
$$
\begin{cases}
\ddot{y}_1 = -2\dfrac{T_{\text{eq}}}{ml_{\text{eq}}}y_1 + \dfrac{T_{\text{eq}}}{ml_{\text{eq}}}y_2, \\
\ddot{y}_2 = \dfrac{T_{\text{eq}}}{ml_{\text{eq}}}y_1 - 2\dfrac{T_{\text{eq}}}{ml_{\text{eq}}}y_2 + \dfrac{T_{\text{eq}}}{ml_{\text{eq}}}y_3, \\
\ddot{y}_3 = \dfrac{T_{\text{eq}}}{ml_{\text{eq}}}y_2 - 2\dfrac{T_{\text{eq}}}{ml_{\text{eq}}}y_3,
\end{cases}
$$
which can be written in matrix form as
$$
\begin{bmatrix} \ddot{y}_1 \\ \ddot{y}_2 \\ \ddot{y}_3 \end{bmatrix} = \frac{T_{\text{eq}}}{ml_{\text{eq}}} \begin{bmatrix} -2 & 1 & 0 \\ 1 & -2 & 1 \\ 0 & 1 & -2 \end{bmatrix} \begin{bmatrix} y_1 \\ y_2 \\ y_3 \end{bmatrix}.
$$

(b) The given eigenvalue of smallest magnitude is -0.586, and this corresponds to the fundamental frequency. Therefore the eigenvalue of the dynamic

matrix that has the smallest magnitude is
$$
\lambda_1 = -0.586 \times \frac{T_{\text{eq}}}{ml_{\text{eq}}}.
$$
For this system, $T_{\text{eq}} = 68\,\text{N}$, $m = (0.25 \times 10^{-3})/3\,\text{kg}$ and $l_{\text{eq}} = 0.65/4$ metres, so the corresponding angular frequency is
$$
\omega_1 = \sqrt{\frac{0.586 \times 68}{(0.25 \times 10^{-3}/3) \times (0.65/4)}} \simeq 1715\,\text{rad s}^{-1},
$$
and hence the fundamental frequency is
$$
f_1 = \frac{\omega_1}{2\pi} = \frac{1715}{2\pi} \simeq 273\,\text{s}^{-1}.
$$
So this model has a fundamental frequency of approximately $273\,\text{Hz}$. This is still much smaller than the experimental value of $323\,\text{Hz}$, but it is better than the predictions for the models with one and two degrees of freedom in Examples 4.1 and 4.2; however, it is still not as close to the experimental value as the value found in Exercise 4.2, or even that in Exercise 4.1.

4.4 **(a)** The first step is to draw a force diagram for each particle, using the usual notation.

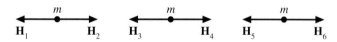

Applying Equation (2.4) to each particle gives
$$
\begin{cases}
m\ddot{\mathbf{r}}_1 = \Delta\mathbf{H}_1 + \Delta\mathbf{H}_2, \\
m\ddot{\mathbf{r}}_2 = \Delta\mathbf{H}_3 + \Delta\mathbf{H}_4, \\
m\ddot{\mathbf{r}}_3 = \Delta\mathbf{H}_5 + \Delta\mathbf{H}_6,
\end{cases}
\tag{S.10}
$$
where $\mathbf{r}_1 = x_1\mathbf{i}$, $\mathbf{r}_2 = x_2\mathbf{i}$ and $\mathbf{r}_3 = x_3\mathbf{i}$ are the position vectors of the particles, and $\mathbf{i}$ is a unit vector in the positive x-direction. Modelling the forces using Equation (2.5), we obtain
$$
\Delta\mathbf{H}_1 = -kx_1\mathbf{i},
$$
$$
\Delta\mathbf{H}_2 = k(x_2 - x_1)\mathbf{i},
$$
$$
\Delta\mathbf{H}_3 = -k(x_2 - x_1)\mathbf{i},
$$
$$
\Delta\mathbf{H}_4 = k(x_3 - x_2)\mathbf{i},
$$
$$
\Delta\mathbf{H}_5 = -k(x_3 - x_2)\mathbf{i},
$$
$$
\Delta\mathbf{H}_6 = -kx_3\mathbf{i}.
$$
Substituting into Equations (S.10) gives
$$
\begin{cases}
m\ddot{\mathbf{r}}_1 = -kx_1\mathbf{i} + k(x_2 - x_1)\mathbf{i}, \\
m\ddot{\mathbf{r}}_2 = -k(x_2 - x_1)\mathbf{i} + k(x_3 - x_2)\mathbf{i}, \\
m\ddot{\mathbf{r}}_3 = -k(x_3 - x_2)\mathbf{i} - kx_3\mathbf{i}.
\end{cases}
$$
Resolving in the $\mathbf{i}$-direction gives the equations of motion for the longitudinal vibrations of the three-particle model as
$$
\begin{cases}
m\ddot{x}_1 = -2kx_1 + kx_2, \\
m\ddot{x}_2 = kx_1 - 2kx_2 + kx_3, \\
m\ddot{x}_3 = kx_2 - 2kx_3,
\end{cases}
\tag{S.11}
$$
which can be written in matrix form as
$$
\begin{bmatrix} \ddot{x}_1 \\ \ddot{x}_2 \\ \ddot{x}_3 \end{bmatrix} = \frac{k}{m} \begin{bmatrix} -2 & 1 & 0 \\ 1 & -2 & 1 \\ 0 & 1 & -2 \end{bmatrix} \begin{bmatrix} x_1 \\ x_2 \\ x_3 \end{bmatrix}.
$$

(b) To verify that the given vectors are eigenvectors, evaluate the products:

$$\begin{bmatrix} -2 & 1 & 0 \\ 1 & -2 & 1 \\ 0 & 1 & -2 \end{bmatrix} \begin{bmatrix} 1 \\ \sqrt{2} \\ 1 \end{bmatrix} = \begin{bmatrix} -2+\sqrt{2} \\ 2-2\sqrt{2} \\ \sqrt{2}-2 \end{bmatrix}$$

$$= (-2+\sqrt{2}) \begin{bmatrix} 1 \\ \sqrt{2} \\ 1 \end{bmatrix};$$

$$\begin{bmatrix} -2 & 1 & 0 \\ 1 & -2 & 1 \\ 0 & 1 & -2 \end{bmatrix} \begin{bmatrix} 1 \\ 0 \\ -1 \end{bmatrix} = \begin{bmatrix} -2 \\ 0 \\ 2 \end{bmatrix} = -2 \begin{bmatrix} 1 \\ 0 \\ -1 \end{bmatrix};$$

$$\begin{bmatrix} -2 & 1 & 0 \\ 1 & -2 & 1 \\ 0 & 1 & -2 \end{bmatrix} \begin{bmatrix} 1 \\ -\sqrt{2} \\ 1 \end{bmatrix} = \begin{bmatrix} -2-\sqrt{2} \\ 2+2\sqrt{2} \\ -\sqrt{2}-2 \end{bmatrix}$$

$$= \left(-2-\sqrt{2}\right) \begin{bmatrix} 1 \\ -\sqrt{2} \\ 1 \end{bmatrix}.$$

It follows that the eigenvalues of the matrix above are $-2+\sqrt{2}$, -2 and $-2-\sqrt{2}$, and the eigenvalues of the dynamic matrix are k/m times these.

(c) Using the given data,

$$\frac{k}{m} = \frac{16\,000}{(0.25 \times 10^{-3})/3} = 192 \times 10^{6}.$$

Hence, from $\omega = \sqrt{-\lambda}$, the normal mode angular frequencies are

$$\omega_1 = \sqrt{192 \times 10^{6} \times (2-\sqrt{2})} \simeq 10\,605 \text{ rad s}^{-1},$$

$$\omega_2 = \sqrt{192 \times 10^{6} \times 2} \simeq 19\,596 \text{ rad s}^{-1},$$

$$\omega_3 = \sqrt{192 \times 10^{6} \times (2+\sqrt{2})} \simeq 25\,603 \text{ rad s}^{-1}.$$

(These angular frequencies are much larger than those for the transverse vibrations, and so the periods of vibration are much shorter.)

4.5 (a) Using the hint, substitute for k from $T_{\text{eq}} = k(l_{\text{eq}} - l_0)$ in Equation (4.10) to obtain

$$\ddot{x}_1 = \frac{-2T_{\text{eq}}}{m(l_{\text{eq}} - l_0)} x_1.$$

Now, in the present case, the equilibrium length of the spring is half the equilibrium length of the guitar string (i.e. $l_{\text{eq}} = L/2$), and the natural length is half the natural length of the guitar string (i.e. $l_0 = L_0/2$), while the mass of the particle is the mass of the guitar string (i.e. $m = M$). This gives the following equation of motion for the longitudinal vibration of the guitar string:

$$\ddot{x}_1 = \frac{2T_{\text{eq}}}{M(L - L_0)}(-2)x_1.$$

(b) As in part (a), use the formula $T_{\text{eq}} = k(l_{\text{eq}} - l_0)$ to eliminate k from the equations. In this case there are three identical springs, so their equilibrium and natural lengths are a third of the equilibrium and natural length of the guitar string, i.e. $l_{\text{eq}} = L/3$ and $l_0 = L_0/3$. Therefore the stiffness of each spring is $k = 3T_{\text{eq}}/(L - L_0)$. The mass of each particle is half the mass of the guitar string, so $m = M/2$, and the equations of motion

become, in matrix form,

$$\begin{bmatrix} \ddot{x}_1 \\ \ddot{x}_2 \end{bmatrix} = \frac{2 \times 3 \times T_{\text{eq}}}{M(L - L_0)} \begin{bmatrix} -2 & 1 \\ 1 & -2 \end{bmatrix} \begin{bmatrix} x_1 \\ x_2 \end{bmatrix}.$$

For the three-degrees-of-freedom model represented by Equations (4.12) we again use $T_{\text{eq}} = k(l_{\text{eq}} - l_0)$, but in this case there are four springs (so $l_{\text{eq}} = L/4$ and $l_0 = L_0/4$) and three particles (so $m = M/3$). Consequently we have

$$\begin{bmatrix} \ddot{x}_1 \\ \ddot{x}_2 \\ \ddot{x}_3 \end{bmatrix} = \frac{3 \times 4 \times T_{\text{eq}}}{M(L - L_0)} \begin{bmatrix} -2 & 1 & 0 \\ 1 & -2 & 1 \\ 0 & 1 & -2 \end{bmatrix} \begin{bmatrix} x_1 \\ x_2 \\ x_3 \end{bmatrix}.$$

(c) For the four-degrees-of-freedom model there are four particles and five springs, which have the effect that the 3 in the above formula becomes a 4 and the 4 becomes a 5. The vectors have four components and the matrix is a 4×4 matrix. So the equation of motion is

$$\begin{bmatrix} \ddot{x}_1 \\ \ddot{x}_2 \\ \ddot{x}_3 \\ \ddot{x}_4 \end{bmatrix} = \frac{4 \times 5 \times T_{\text{eq}}}{M(L - L_0)} \begin{bmatrix} -2 & 1 & 0 & 0 \\ 1 & -2 & 1 & 0 \\ 0 & 1 & -2 & 1 \\ 0 & 0 & 1 & -2 \end{bmatrix} \begin{bmatrix} x_1 \\ x_2 \\ x_3 \\ x_4 \end{bmatrix}.$$

(d) By comparing the above equations of motion with the results derived in Subsection 4.4, it can be seen that the only difference between the transverse and longitudinal vibrational models lies in the constant that multiplies the matrix on the right-hand side of the equation of motion. In fact, the only difference is that the constant in the transverse case includes a factor $1/L$ whereas in the longitudinal case the corresponding factor is $1/(L - L_0)$. Hence the dynamic matrix for the longitudinal model is $(1/(L - L_0))/(1/L) = L/(L - L_0)$ times the dynamic matrix for the transverse model, and the eigenvalues are similarly related.

Denoting f_T, ω_T and λ_T (respectively, f_L, ω_L and λ_L) for the fundamental frequency, the corresponding normal mode angular frequency and the corresponding eigenvalue of the dynamic matrix for the transverse model (respectively, longitudinal model). We have $\lambda_L = \lambda_T L/(L - L_0)$ from the above argument. Hence

$$\omega_L = \sqrt{-\lambda_L} = \sqrt{\frac{-\lambda_T L}{L - L_0}} = \sqrt{\frac{L}{L - L_0}} \sqrt{-\lambda_T}$$

$$= \sqrt{\frac{L}{L - L_0}} \, \omega_T,$$

which yields

$$f_L = \frac{\omega_L}{2\pi} = \sqrt{\frac{L}{L - L_0}} \frac{\omega_T}{2\pi} = \sqrt{\frac{L}{L - L_0}} f_T,$$

i.e. the ratio of f_L to f_T is $\sqrt{L/(L - L_0)}$.

In the case of the E string of the guitar, $L = 0.65$ metres and $L_0 = 0.633$ metres, so the ratio is

$$f_L/f_T = \sqrt{0.65/(0.65 - 0.633)} \simeq 6.2.$$

Therefore, the fundamental frequency of the longitudinal vibration is approximately $6.2 \times 323 \simeq 2000$ Hz.

Section 5

5.1 **(a)** The eigenvalues of the matrix $\begin{bmatrix} -1 & 0 \\ 0 & -1 \end{bmatrix}$ are both -1. Now calculate its eigenvectors.

$\boxed{\lambda = -1}$ The eigenvector equations are

$$\begin{bmatrix} -1-(-1) & 0 \\ 0 & -1-(-1) \end{bmatrix} \begin{bmatrix} v_1 \\ v_2 \end{bmatrix} = \begin{bmatrix} 0 \\ 0 \end{bmatrix},$$

or equivalently

$$\begin{cases} 0 = 0, \\ 0 = 0. \end{cases}$$

These equations are automatically satisfied, so any non-zero vector $[v_1 \quad v_2]^T$ is an eigenvector of the above matrix, and hence any non-zero vector is a normal mode eigenvector of the dynamic matrix.

(b) $[2 \quad 1]^T$ is a normal mode eigenvector since every non-zero vector is a normal mode eigenvector. To find another linearly independent normal mode eigenvector, pick any vector that is not a multiple of $[2 \quad 1]^T$, for example $[1 \quad 0]^T$, $[0 \quad 1]^T$ or $[-1 \quad 2]^T$.

UNIT 19   Systems of particles

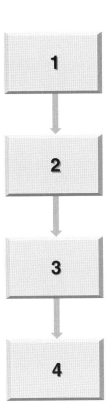

Study guide for Unit 19

This unit builds on ideas from earlier mechanics units in the course: *Units 5, 6, 7, 8, 14* and *18*.

Some of the ideas here are used later in the course, particularly in *Unit 27*.

The recommended study pattern is to study one section per study session, and to study the sections in the order in which they appear.

Introduction

Figure 0.1 shows three positions of a diver performing a forward somersault, and the curves trace out the paths of the diver's head and feet. The motion of the diver is very complicated, which is reflected in the shapes of these curves; but, in spite of this complexity, it is possible to obtain some simple information that adds considerably to our understanding of the dive. Associated with each position of the diver, there is a point known as the diver's *centre of mass*, and this point moves along a simpler path.

Our first objective in this unit is to obtain some useful information on the complicated motion of an object or system, and the concept of centre of mass is crucial to this process. It transpires that, in a number of circumstances, we can justify modelling a complicated system, possibly composed of very many objects, by a single particle of the same mass as the system placed at the centre of mass of the system. This process has the dual benefit of making the behaviour of quite complicated systems much easier to understand and of considerably reducing the work involved when analysing them. It will form a central theme of the unit.

We start, in Section 1, by examining some specific examples of two-particle systems, from which we shall be able to extract some general principles that apply to all two-particle systems and that can be extended to systems involving any number of particles. We move on, in Section 2, to discuss general systems of particles and the important concept of centre of mass. Then, in Section 3, we discuss the behaviour of objects during a collision, and here we introduce the principle of conservation of linear momentum. Section 4 concerns Newton's law of restitution which models the effects of inelasticity in collisions.

You met the idea of centre of mass in *Unit 5*.

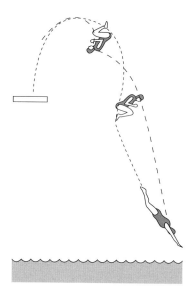

Figure 0.1

1 Two-particle systems

The three mechanical systems illustrated in Figure 1.1 appear to have little in common. However they all illustrate an important principle of mechanics — a principle that we intend to develop in this unit.

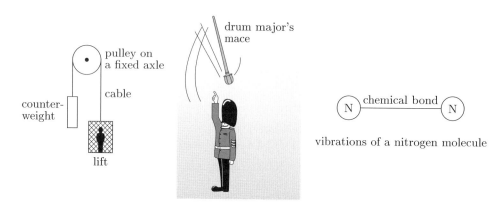

counter-weight

pulley on a fixed axle

cable

lift

drum major's mace

chemical bond

N ——— N

vibrations of a nitrogen molecule

Figure 1.1

In Subsection 1.1 we shall use various techniques from previous units to examine each system in turn. Then, in Subsection 1.2, we shall begin to draw together the ideas common to all three examples. This drawing together will lead to the statement of a general principle for two-particle systems, based on Newton's second law. First, we give a definition.

Definition

A **two-particle system** is a system modelled so that the total mass of the system is divided between two particles.

You have met two-particle systems before. For example, in *Unit 5* you saw how a scarf draped over the edge of a table can be modelled as a two-particle system. In *Unit 18*, many of the particle–spring systems were two-particle systems.

1.1 Examples of two-particle systems

A simple design for a lift

In this example we investigate a (rather impractical) design for a lift, as shown in Figure 1.2(a). The mechanism consists of a lift compartment and a counter-weight, supported by a cable passing over a pulley. We wish to investigate this design with the simplifying assumptions that all frictional forces and air resistance can be ignored.

In order to model this system we shall need to make some more simplifying assumptions. Figure 1.2(b) shows our mathematical model, which consists of two particles of masses m_1 and m_2 connected by a model string passing over a model pulley with its axle fixed at P. We assume that m_2 is greater than m_1, so when the system is released from rest, the lift (i.e. the particle of mass m_2) will begin to move down. We define an x-axis pointing vertically downwards with origin at P, and we denote the vertical displacements of the particles of masses m_1 and m_2 from P by x_1 and x_2, respectively.

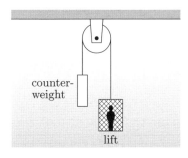

(a)

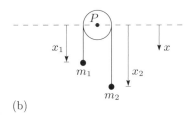

(b)

Figure 1.2

Before investigating the motion of this system we shall look at the system as a whole, in order to derive a result that will be generalized later. The force diagram in Figure 1.3 shows the forces acting on the two particles and on the model pulley.

Now we apply Newton's second law to each particle. The accelerations of the particles of masses m_1 and m_2 are $\ddot{x}_1\mathbf{i}$ and $\ddot{x}_2\mathbf{i}$, and the forces acting on them are $m_1 g\mathbf{i} + \mathbf{T}_2$ and $m_2 g\mathbf{i} + \mathbf{T}_4$, respectively. So Newton's second law gives

$$m_1 g\mathbf{i} + \mathbf{T}_2 = m_1\ddot{x}_1\mathbf{i}, \tag{1.1}$$
$$m_2 g\mathbf{i} + \mathbf{T}_4 = m_2\ddot{x}_2\mathbf{i}. \tag{1.2}$$

We also observe that the axle of the pulley is stationary (i.e. in equilibrium); therefore we have

$$\mathbf{S} + \mathbf{T}_1 + \mathbf{T}_3 = \mathbf{0}. \tag{1.3}$$

On adding Equations (1.1), (1.2) and (1.3), we obtain

$$\mathbf{S} + \mathbf{T}_1 + \mathbf{T}_2 + \mathbf{T}_3 + \mathbf{T}_4 + m_1 g\mathbf{i} + m_2 g\mathbf{i} = m_1\ddot{x}_1\mathbf{i} + m_2\ddot{x}_2\mathbf{i}.$$

The left-hand side of this equation simplifies because we have a model string, which implies that $\mathbf{T}_1 + \mathbf{T}_2 = \mathbf{0}$ and $\mathbf{T}_3 + \mathbf{T}_4 = \mathbf{0}$. So we obtain

$$\mathbf{S} + m_1 g\mathbf{i} + m_2 g\mathbf{i} = m_1\ddot{x}_1\mathbf{i} + m_2\ddot{x}_2\mathbf{i}.$$

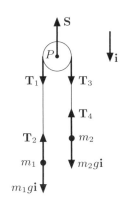

Figure 1.3

The right-hand side of this equation is almost of the mass times acceleration form that we expect from Newton's second law. A little rearrangement puts the equation in this form:

$$\mathbf{S} + m_1 g\mathbf{i} + m_2 g\mathbf{i} = \underbrace{(m_1 + m_2)}_{\text{the total mass}} \frac{m_1\ddot{x}_1 + m_2\ddot{x}_2}{m_1 + m_2}\mathbf{i}. \tag{1.4}$$

The significance of Equation (1.4) will become clear shortly, but for the moment just notice that the right-hand side is the total mass of the system multiplied by an expression that has the dimensions of acceleration.

Exercise 1.1

This exercise completes the analysis of the simple design for a lift described above. Use the notation of Figure 1.3.

(a) Use the facts that the model string is inextensible (i.e. $x_1 + x_2 = $ constant) and that the pulley is a model pulley (so $|\mathbf{T}_1| = |\mathbf{T}_3|$) together with Equations (1.1) and (1.2) to determine the acceleration of the lift, $\ddot{x}_2$.

(b) Use the result of part (a) and Equation (1.2) to determine the magnitude of the tension in the cable.

(c) Use the result of part (b) and Equation (1.3) to determine the magnitude of the reaction force on the pulley, $\mathbf{S}$.

(d) Suppose that the lift and the counter-weight are each of mass $1000\,\text{kg}$, and that a person of mass $65\,\text{kg}$ steps into the lift. Calculate the numerical value of the acceleration of the lift and also the velocity of the lift after it starts from rest and travels $100\,\text{m}$. Comment of the suitability of the lift design.

A drum major's mace

In this example we attempt to model the motion of a drum major's mace. You may have seen a military band with the drum major striding out in front, twirling a long rod with a heavy weight at one end: his mace. Every few strides, he twirls the mace and then hurls it high into the air; it then appears to follow a complicated path until he finally catches it and continues with the twirling. We model the mace as two particles A and B of unequal masses m_1 and m_2, connected by a light model rod of length l, as in Figure 1.4. Our purpose is to try to discover some pattern in the behaviour of the mace (and perhaps provide some useful advice to would-be drum majors).

Figure 1.4

Recall from *Unit 5* that a model rod is a rigid body with length but no breadth or depth. In this case we have a *light* model rod, so it has no mass either.

As you will see later, G is the centre of mass of the system.

We assume that the drum major holds the mace at its 'balance point' G, by which we mean that if we were to balance the model rod on a model pivot at G, then the rod would be in equilibrium. The equilibrium condition for rigid bodies tells us that the sum of the torques on the rod when balanced in this way is zero. This situation and the associated forces are shown in Figure 1.5. Taking the origin for the torques at G, the torque equilibrium equation is

$$(-d_1\mathbf{j}) \times (-m_1 g\mathbf{k}) + (d_2\mathbf{j}) \times (-m_2 g\mathbf{k}) = \mathbf{0}.$$

This simplifies to

$$d_1 m_1 \mathbf{i} - d_2 m_2 \mathbf{i} = \mathbf{0},$$

and resolving in the $\mathbf{i}$-direction gives $d_1 m_1 - d_2 m_2 = 0$, or

$$d_1/d_2 = m_2/m_1. \tag{1.5}$$

You met torques and the equilibrium condition for rigid bodies in *Unit 5*.

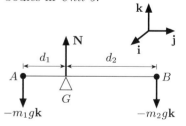

Figure 1.5

From this we see that the ratio d_1/d_2 will be small if m_1 is much larger than m_2. In other words, if the head of the mace is very heavy, then the balance point will be near this end.

We now suppose that the drum major throws the mace into the air, and at the same time he gives it a flick in such a way that the mace turns end-over-end in a vertical plane. If we ignore the effects of air resistance and

Drum majors holds their maces near the end, whereas drum majorettes hold their batons near the centre. Presumably this is because a drum majorette's baton is more centrally balanced.

simplify the notation by writing $\mathbf{g}$ for $-g\mathbf{k}$, then Figure 1.6 shows the forces acting on the mace and its position at time t (in terms of position vectors relative to an origin O, the point at which the mace was released). The rod gives rise to a force $\mathbf{R}_1$ on particle A and a force $\mathbf{R}_2$ on particle B.

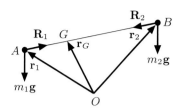

Figure 1.6

It turns out that the position of G is of crucial importance. It will be useful later if we express the position vector of G in terms of the position vectors of A and B. Consider the displacement vectors $\overrightarrow{AG} = \mathbf{r}_G - \mathbf{r}_1$ and $\overrightarrow{GB} = \mathbf{r}_2 - \mathbf{r}_G$ (see Figure 1.6). We know that $|\overrightarrow{AG}| = d_1$ and $|\overrightarrow{GB}| = d_2$, so $|\overrightarrow{AG}|/|\overrightarrow{GB}| = d_1/d_2 = m_2/m_1$, by Equation (1.5). Hence $m_1 \overrightarrow{AG} = m_2 \overrightarrow{GB}$, or equivalently

$$m_1(\mathbf{r}_G - \mathbf{r}_1) = m_2(\mathbf{r}_2 - \mathbf{r}_G),$$

which can be rearranged to give the position vector of G as

$$\mathbf{r}_G = \frac{m_1\mathbf{r}_1 + m_2\mathbf{r}_2}{m_1 + m_2}. \tag{1.6}$$

Differentiating Equation (1.6) twice with respect to time, we obtain the following expression for the acceleration of the point G in terms of the accelerations $\ddot{\mathbf{r}}_1$ and $\ddot{\mathbf{r}}_2$ of the points A and B:

$$\ddot{\mathbf{r}}_G = \frac{m_1\ddot{\mathbf{r}}_1 + m_2\ddot{\mathbf{r}}_2}{m_1 + m_2}. \tag{1.7}$$

The total force on particle A is $\mathbf{R}_1 + m_1\mathbf{g}$ and the total force on particle B is $\mathbf{R}_2 + m_2\mathbf{g}$. So, applying Newton's second law to particles A and B in turn, we obtain

$$\mathbf{R}_1 + m_1\mathbf{g} = m_1\ddot{\mathbf{r}}_1, \tag{1.8}$$
$$\mathbf{R}_2 + m_2\mathbf{g} = m_2\ddot{\mathbf{r}}_2. \tag{1.9}$$

Adding Equations (1.8) and (1.9) gives

$$\mathbf{R}_1 + m_1\mathbf{g} + \mathbf{R}_2 + m_2\mathbf{g} = m_1\ddot{\mathbf{r}}_1 + m_2\ddot{\mathbf{r}}_2.$$

But by Newton's third law $\mathbf{R}_1 + \mathbf{R}_2 = \mathbf{0}$, so this equation simplifies to

$$m_1\mathbf{g} + m_2\mathbf{g} = m_1\ddot{\mathbf{r}}_1 + m_2\ddot{\mathbf{r}}_2.$$

This can be rearranged as

$$(m_1 + m_2)\,\mathbf{g} = (m_1 + m_2)\,\frac{m_1\ddot{\mathbf{r}}_1 + m_2\ddot{\mathbf{r}}_2}{m_1 + m_2}.$$

Substituting from Equation (1.7), we obtain

$$\ddot{\mathbf{r}}_G = \mathbf{g}, \tag{1.10}$$

which is the equation of motion of the point G.

This result may appear to be simple, but it is really quite surprising. It tells us that the balance point G — the centre of mass of the mace — behaves as if it were a particle acted on solely by the force of gravity. Thus if the initial velocity of G is vertically upwards, then G will simply move up and down in a vertical line. However, if the initial velocity has a horizontal component, then G will follow the parabolic trajectory of a projectile. In both cases, the other points on the mace may move along much more complicated trajectories. Figure 1.7 illustrates the simple parabolic trajectory of G and the more complicated trajectory of another point on the mace when there is a horizontal component to the initial velocity.

See *Unit 14* for details about projectiles. We assume here that air resistance can be neglected.

What does all this mean for the drum major? First, if he wants to hold the mace horizontally, then he should hold it at its balance point G, where he will not need to apply any torques to keep it level. Second, if he wants to be able to catch it after throwing it into the air, then catching it at G would be best, as G is the only point whose trajectory in the air he can easily predict.

So he knows where to hold and catch it. But how should he throw it? When he is stationary, it is clear that the initial upwards velocity of G should be vertical; but what if he is marching? Should he throw the mace upwards and slightly forwards? The answer is no, he should simply throw it upwards. This is because when the drum major is marching (at a constant velocity) holding the mace, the mace has a constant horizontal component of velocity which is the same as that of the drum major. Then the horizontal distance travelled by the mace, after being thrown upwards, will be the same as that travelled by the marching drum major. So the mace should return to hand level just as the drum major's hand gets there. If the mace were thrown slightly forwards, then the drum major would have to increase his marching pace to match, or else the mace would, embarrassingly, fall to the ground. However, when throwing the mace (vertically upwards), the drum major needs to make sure that he keeps his marching velocity constant in order to catch the mace safely. It would be a mistake, for example, to throw the mace while marching and then stop to wait for it to fall, or to change direction while the mace is in the air.

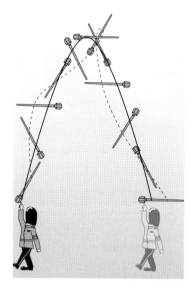

Figure 1.7

Vibrations of a nitrogen molecule

A nitrogen molecule consists of two nitrogen atoms, each of mass m, joined by a chemical bond, as illustrated in Figure 1.8(a). The atoms vibrate relative to each other along the direction of this bond. The molecule can be modelled as a pair of particles joined by a model spring, which exerts a force $\mathbf{H}_1$ on the left-hand particle, labelled A, and a force $\mathbf{H}_2$ on the right-hand particle, labelled B, as illustrated in Figure 1.8(b). Here we are concerned with the vibrations of the molecule in isolation and hence do not consider the effects of gravity (for example you could consider that the molecule is vibrating in deep space, far away from any gravitational influences). So the total force acting on the system is $\mathbf{F} = \mathbf{H}_1 + \mathbf{H}_2$.

You saw chemical bonds modelled in this way in *Unit 18.*

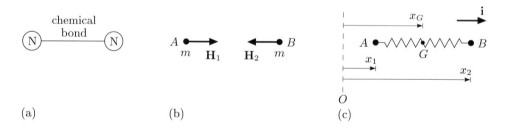

(a) (b) (c)

Figure 1.8

You saw how to model the vibrations of such a system in terms of normal modes in *Unit 18.* Here we want to look at what information we can glean from the motion of the centre G of the spring, which is the geometric centre of this symmetric system. We begin as usual by defining axes: we choose a fixed origin O and a direction $\mathbf{i}$ aligned with the spring. We measure x_1, x_2 and x_G along this axis, as shown in Figure 1.8(c).

As you will see later, the centre of the spring is the centre of mass of the system.

To derive the equation of motion of G, we start by expressing the position vector of G relative to O. One way to do this is to notice that, by symmetry, G is half-way between A and B, so $\mathbf{r}_G = (\mathbf{r}_1 + \mathbf{r}_2)/2$.

Applying Newton's second law to particles A and B in turn gives

$$\mathbf{H}_1 = m\ddot{\mathbf{r}}_1, \quad \mathbf{H}_2 = m\ddot{\mathbf{r}}_2.$$

Proceeding as before, we add together the above equations to obtain

$$\mathbf{H}_1 + \mathbf{H}_2 = m\ddot{\mathbf{r}}_1 + m\ddot{\mathbf{r}}_2.$$

But $\mathbf{H}_1$ and $\mathbf{H}_2$ are forces exerted by the same model spring, so by Newton's third law $\mathbf{H}_1 = -\mathbf{H}_2$. Hence the left-hand side of the above equation is zero, so

You saw this before, in Unit 18.

$$\mathbf{0} = m(\ddot{\mathbf{r}}_1 + \ddot{\mathbf{r}}_2).$$

We now write the right-hand side of this equation in the form of Newton's second law, i.e. a mass multiplied by the acceleration of a single point. To do this we differentiate $\mathbf{r}_G = (\mathbf{r}_1 + \mathbf{r}_2)/2$ twice to obtain $\ddot{\mathbf{r}}_G = (\ddot{\mathbf{r}}_1 + \ddot{\mathbf{r}}_2)/2$. Substituting for $\ddot{\mathbf{r}}_1 + \ddot{\mathbf{r}}_2$ in the above equation then gives

$$\underbrace{\mathbf{0}}_{\text{total force}} = \underbrace{2m}_{\text{total mass}} \times \underbrace{\ddot{\mathbf{r}}_G.}_{\text{acceleration}}$$

Now $\mathbf{r}_G = x_G\mathbf{i}$, since the motion is one-dimensional. So $\ddot{x}_G = 0$ and this can be integrated to give $\dot{x}_G = $ constant, i.e. G moves at a constant speed along the direction of the axis of the spring. The net result is that the geometric centre of the molecule moves just like a particle with no forces acting on it, i.e. it either remains at rest or travels with constant speed along a straight line (Newton's first law). It is worth emphasizing that the motion of G remains the same irrespective of how much the atoms at the ends of the bond vibrate.

Newton's first law was stated in Units 5 and 6.

1.2 Some general conclusions

Now let us try to extract some general principles from the three examples of two-particle systems discussed in the previous subsection.

The first point to note is that, when we obtained an expression for the total force on the system, certain forces on the components of the system cancelled out as a result of Newton's third law. The forces that cancel out in this way are known as **internal forces** of the system, while the remaining forces are referred to as **external forces**.

The internal forces for the three examples from the previous subsection are shown by white arrows in Figure 1.9, and the external forces by black arrows as usual. Notice that internal forces occur in equal and opposite pairs (i.e. each force in the pair has the same magnitude but opposite direction to the other). We have altered the notation of the previous subsection slightly in Figure 1.9 to reflect this.

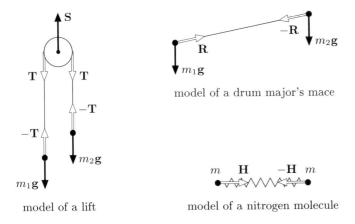

model of a lift

model of a drum major's mace

model of a nitrogen molecule

Here we use $\mathbf{g}$ for the vector acceleration due to gravity.

Figure 1.9

Exercise 1.2

Consider the system of weights, pulleys and strings shown in Figure 1.10(a). Assume that the pulleys are model pulleys (i.e. light and frictionless) and that the strings are model strings (i.e. light and inextensible). Modelling the weights as particles, we can therefore model the system and the forces acting on it as shown in Figure 1.10(b). Decide which of the forces are internal and which are external. Hence write down the total force acting on the whole system.

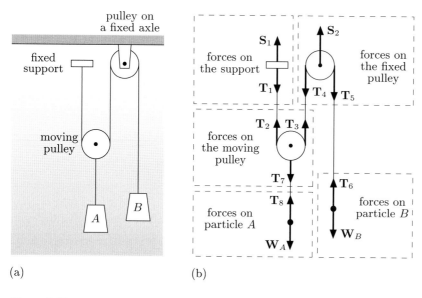

(a)   (b)

Figure 1.10

In all three examples of two-particle systems in the previous subsection, we not only obtained an expression for the total force $\mathbf{F}$ on the system, but also used Newton's second law to obtain an equation involving that force. In the lift example we obtained

$$\mathbf{F} = (m_1 + m_2)\frac{m_1\ddot{x}_1 + m_2\ddot{x}_2}{m_1 + m_2}\mathbf{i}.$$

See Equation (1.4).

If we write $\mathbf{r}_1 = x_1\mathbf{i}$ and $\mathbf{r}_2 = x_2\mathbf{i}$, so that $\mathbf{r}_1$ and $\mathbf{r}_2$ are the position vectors of the particles relative to the point P in Figure 1.2, we obtain

$$\mathbf{F} = (m_1 + m_2)\frac{m_1\ddot{\mathbf{r}}_1 + m_2\ddot{\mathbf{r}}_2}{m_1 + m_2}.$$

This is exactly the equation we obtained for the drum major's mace, where again $\mathbf{r}_1$ and $\mathbf{r}_2$ are the position vectors of the two particles. For the nitrogen molecule we obtained

$$\mathbf{0} = 2m\,\ddot{\mathbf{r}}_G,$$

where $\mathbf{r}_G$ is the position vector of the geometric centre of the position of the two particles, $\mathbf{r}_G = (\mathbf{r}_1 + \mathbf{r}_2)/2$. At first sight this looks different, but it is of the same form because there were no external forces acting (so $\mathbf{F} = \mathbf{0}$), both particles have the same mass (so $m_1 + m_2 = 2m$) and also

$$\frac{m_1\ddot{\mathbf{r}}_1 + m_2\ddot{\mathbf{r}}_2}{m_1 + m_2} = \frac{m\ddot{\mathbf{r}}_1 + m\ddot{\mathbf{r}}_2}{m + m} = \frac{\ddot{\mathbf{r}}_1 + \ddot{\mathbf{r}}_2}{2} = \ddot{\mathbf{r}}_G.$$

In summary, for each two-particle system the right-hand side of the equation is a product of the total mass of the system and a term of the form

$$\frac{m_1\ddot{\mathbf{r}}_1 + m_2\ddot{\mathbf{r}}_2}{m_1 + m_2},$$

which is the acceleration of the point G, with position vector

$$\mathbf{r}_G = \frac{m_1\mathbf{r}_1 + m_2\mathbf{r}_2}{m_1 + m_2},$$

within that system. We call this point the **centre of mass**.

In the case of symmetric systems (where the two particles have equal mass), such as the nitrogen molecule, the centre of mass is at the geometric centre. For systems where the particles are joined by a model rod, such as the drum major's mace, the centre of mass is at the balance point.

Exercise 1.3

The mass of the Earth is approximately 5.97×10^{24} kg and its diameter is about 1.27×10^4 km, while the mass of the Moon is approximately 7.39×10^{22} kg and its diameter is about 3.5×10^3 km. The mean distance from the centre of the Earth to the centre of the Moon is about 3.86×10^5 km. How far above the Earth's surface would you estimate the centre of mass of the Earth and the Moon to lie?

The equations obtained by applying Newton's second law to our examples, which led to the definition of centre of mass, are all of the form $\mathbf{F} = M\ddot{\mathbf{r}}_G$, where $\mathbf{F}$ is the total force on the system and M is its total mass. We should now verify that this equation holds for the centre of mass of *any* two-particle system.

Consider a general system consisting of two particles, labelled 1 and 2 in Figure 1.11, of masses m_1 and m_2, and with position vectors $\mathbf{r}_1$ and $\mathbf{r}_2$ relative to an origin O. In general, each particle is subject to internal and external forces. Let us denote the resultant of the external forces on each particle by $\mathbf{E}_1$ and $\mathbf{E}_2$, respectively. The internal force on each particle is exerted by the other particle by means of a model string, a model rod or a model spring, or in some other way. Let us denote the internal force exerted on particle 1 by particle 2 by $\mathbf{I}_{12}$ and, similarly, the internal force exerted on particle 2 by particle 1 by $\mathbf{I}_{21}$. The situation is illustrated in Figure 1.11.

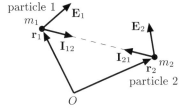

Figure 1.11

Applying Newton's second law to each particle, we obtain

$$\mathbf{E}_1 + \mathbf{I}_{12} = m_1\ddot{\mathbf{r}}_1, \quad \mathbf{E}_2 + \mathbf{I}_{21} = m_2\ddot{\mathbf{r}}_2.$$

We can add these equations to obtain

$$\mathbf{E}_1 + \mathbf{I}_{12} + \mathbf{E}_2 + \mathbf{I}_{21} = m_1\ddot{\mathbf{r}}_1 + m_2\ddot{\mathbf{r}}_2.$$

Since $\mathbf{I}_{12}$ and $\mathbf{I}_{21}$ are internal forces, we can apply Newton's third law to obtain $\mathbf{I}_{12} + \mathbf{I}_{21} = \mathbf{0}$. So the above equation simplifies to

$$\mathbf{F}^{\text{ext}} = m_1\ddot{\mathbf{r}}_1 + m_2\ddot{\mathbf{r}}_2, \tag{1.11}$$

where $\mathbf{F}^{\text{ext}} = \mathbf{E}_1 + \mathbf{E}_2$ is the sum of the external forces.

The centre of mass of this system is defined by the position vector

$$\mathbf{r}_G = \frac{m_1\mathbf{r}_1 + m_2\mathbf{r}_2}{m_1 + m_2} = \frac{m_1\mathbf{r}_1 + m_2\mathbf{r}_2}{M},$$

where $M = m_1 + m_2$ is the total mass of the system.

Differentiating twice gives

$$\ddot{\mathbf{r}}_G = \frac{m_1\ddot{\mathbf{r}}_1 + m_2\ddot{\mathbf{r}}_2}{M}. \tag{1.12}$$

From Equations (1.11) and (1.12), we have

$$\mathbf{F}^{\text{ext}} = M\ddot{\mathbf{r}}_G,$$

which is an important result worth restating.

Motion of the centre of mass of a two-particle system

The motion of the centre of mass G with position vector $\mathbf{r}_G$ of a two-particle system of total mass M subject to external forces with sum $\mathbf{F}^{\text{ext}}$ is given by

$$\mathbf{F}^{\text{ext}} = M\ddot{\mathbf{r}}_G. \tag{1.13}$$

Example 1.1

Two particles of masses m_1 and m_2 are attached to a model spring of natural length l_0 and stiffness k (as shown in Figure 1.12). The particle–spring system moves vertically. Determine the equation of motion of the centre of mass of the system.

What would be the effect on this equation of motion if the stiffness of the spring was doubled?

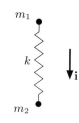

Figure 1.12

Solution

The spring forces are internal forces. The only external forces are the weights of the two particles, given by $m_1 g\mathbf{i}$ and $m_2 g\mathbf{i}$. Thus Equation (1.13) gives

$$(m_1 + m_2)g\mathbf{i} = (m_1 + m_2)\ddot{\mathbf{r}}_G, \tag{1.14}$$

where $\mathbf{r}_G$ is the position vector of the centre of mass of the system. This simplifies to $\ddot{\mathbf{r}}_G = g\mathbf{i}$, so the centre of mass moves as if it were a particle falling under gravity.

Since the spring forces are internal forces, they have no effect on the equation of motion (1.14), so changing the stiffness of the spring will have no effect on the equation of motion of the centre of mass of the system. ∎

*Exercise 1.4

Two objects of masses m_1 and m_2, connected by a light rigid rod, are sliding down an inclined plane in the direction of the axis of the rod, as shown in Figure 1.13. The coefficient of sliding friction between each object and the plane is μ'. The objects may be modelled as particles and the connecting rod as a model rod.

(a) Draw a force diagram for the system, and identify any internal forces.

(b) Determine the equation of motion for the centre of mass of this system.

(c) How would your solution to part (b) change in the following situations?

    (i) The rod is replaced by a light spring.

    (ii) The rod is removed, leaving just two disconnected objects.

(d) Compare your equation of motion in part (b) with that for a single particle of mass $m_1 + m_2$ sliding down the same inclined plane.

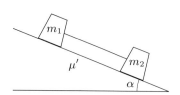

Figure 1.13

The two-particle system in Exercise 1.4 is actually a rigid body and does not rotate, so its motion is completely described by the equation of motion of its centre of mass. The drum major's mace is also a rigid body, but is subject to torques to make it rotate as the drum major twirls it. Nevertheless, the motion of the centre of mass still provides useful information for the drum major. In other cases, knowing about the motion of the centre of mass may not be directly useful. However, as the following example illustrates, it can form the basis for an analysis of the complete motion of such a system.

Example 1.2

Figure 1.14(a) shows two particles A and B, each of mass m, lying on a smooth horizontal surface and connected by a model spring of natural length $2l_0$ and stiffness k. Initially, the particles are at rest a distance $2l_0$ apart, so the spring is unstretched, and with centre of mass at the origin. Then a constant horizontal force $\mathbf{P}$ is applied to B in the direction AB, as shown in Figure 1.14(b). At time t, the particles are a distance $2d$ apart.

(a) Find the position of the centre of mass at time t.

(b) Find a differential equation for d.

(c) Find the x-coordinates of A and B at time t.

(d) Interpret your solution.

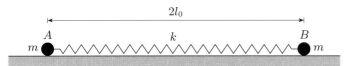

(a) the unstretched spring

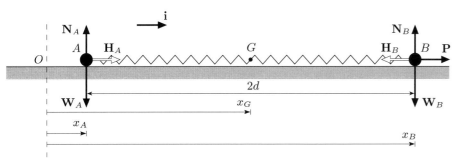

It is important to measure coordinates from a *fixed* point O. It is tempting to measure distances from the position of G or A or B, but as the whole system is moving none of these is appropriate.

(b) the stretched spring

Figure 1.14

Solution

(a) The force diagrams are shown in Figure 1.14(b). The two spring forces are internal forces, so Equation (1.13) gives

$$\mathbf{P} + \mathbf{N}_A + \mathbf{W}_A + \mathbf{N}_B + \mathbf{W}_B = 2m\ddot{x}_G\mathbf{i}.$$

But both particles are in vertical equilibrium, so $\mathbf{N}_A + \mathbf{W}_A = \mathbf{0}$ and $\mathbf{N}_B + \mathbf{W}_B = \mathbf{0}$. Cancelling terms and resolving in the $\mathbf{i}$-direction, we find that the centre of mass moves to the right with constant acceleration

$$\ddot{x}_G = \frac{|\mathbf{P}|}{2m}. \qquad (1.15)$$

Note that $\mathbf{N}_A$ and $\mathbf{W}_A$ are not internal forces, so we cannot invoke Newton's third law to obtain $\mathbf{N}_A + \mathbf{W}_A = \mathbf{0}$: this equation is true because the particles are not moving vertically.

Since the system starts from rest with the centre of mass at the origin, integrating twice gives

$$x_G = \frac{|\mathbf{P}|}{4m}t^2.$$

Alternatively, we can use the constant-acceleration equation $x = v_0 t + \frac{1}{2}a_0 t^2$ from *Unit 6*, with $v_0 = 0$ and $a_0 = \ddot{x}_G$.

(b) Applying Newton's second law to particle B gives

$$\mathbf{H}_B + \mathbf{P} = m\ddot{x}_B\mathbf{i}.$$

Now we need to model the forces. We are given that the force $\mathbf{P}$ acts in the direction AB, so $\mathbf{P} = |\mathbf{P}|\mathbf{i}$ and, by Hooke's law, we have

$$\mathbf{H}_B = -k(2d - 2l_0)\mathbf{i}.$$

Therefore we obtain

$$-2k(d - l_0)\mathbf{i} + |\mathbf{P}|\mathbf{i} = m\ddot{x}_B\mathbf{i}.$$

Resolving in the $\mathbf{i}$-direction and rearranging gives

$$m\ddot{x}_B + 2kd = 2kl_0 + |\mathbf{P}|. \tag{1.16}$$

To proceed further, we need to express the acceleration $\ddot{x}_B$ of particle B in terms of d and known parameters. We start by noting that throughout the motion the centre of mass is at the point

$$x_G\mathbf{i} = \frac{mx_A\mathbf{i} + mx_B\mathbf{i}}{2m} = \tfrac{1}{2}(x_A + x_B)\mathbf{i},$$

i.e. the centre of mass is always half-way between A and B.

This gives $x_B = x_G + d$, which we can differentiate twice to obtain $\ddot{x}_B = \ddot{x}_G + \ddot{d}$. Now we can use Equation (1.15) to obtain $\ddot{x}_B = |\mathbf{P}|/(2m) + \ddot{d}$, which is the desired expression for $\ddot{x}_B$ in terms of d and known parameters. Substituting this into Equation (1.16) and rearranging gives

$$m\ddot{d} + 2kd = 2kl_0 + |\mathbf{P}|/2, \tag{1.17}$$

which is the required differential equation for d.

(c) You should recognize Equation (1.17) as the differential equation for simple harmonic motion, which has solution

$$d = C_1\cos(\omega t) + C_2\sin(\omega t) + l_0 + |\mathbf{P}|/(4k),$$

where $\omega = \sqrt{2k/m}$ and the values of the constants C_1 and C_2 are determined by initial conditions. When $t = 0$, before the force $\mathbf{P}$ is applied, we have $d = l_0$ and $\dot{d} = 0$. This gives $C_1 = -|\mathbf{P}|/(4k)$ and $C_2 = 0$, so

$$d = -\frac{|\mathbf{P}|}{4k}\cos(\omega t) + l_0 + \frac{|\mathbf{P}|}{4k}.$$

We use $x_B = x_G + d$ together with $x_G = |\mathbf{P}|t^2/(4m)$ and the above expression for d, to obtain

$$x_B = \frac{|\mathbf{P}|}{4m}t^2 + \left(l_0 + \frac{|\mathbf{P}|}{4k} - \frac{|\mathbf{P}|}{4k}\cos(\omega t)\right).$$

Similarly $x_A = x_G - d$, so we have

$$x_A = \frac{|\mathbf{P}|}{4m}t^2 - \left(l_0 + \frac{|\mathbf{P}|}{4k} - \frac{|\mathbf{P}|}{4k}\cos(\omega t)\right).$$

(d) The equations for x_A and x_B show that particle A oscillates according to the function $(|\mathbf{P}|/(4k))\cos(\omega t)$ about a point a fixed distance $l_0 + |\mathbf{P}|/(4k)$ to the left of the moving position $x_G = |\mathbf{P}|t^2/(4m)$ of the centre of mass, and that particle B oscillates according to the function $-(|\mathbf{P}|/(4k))\cos(\omega t)$ about a point the same fixed distance to the right of the moving position of the centre of mass. The oscillations are simple harmonic with the same angular frequency $\omega = \sqrt{2k/m}$ and amplitude $|\mathbf{P}|/(4k)$, but are phase-opposed (in the terminology of *Unit 18*) because the terms (in large brackets above) describing the oscillations have different signs; this means that, relative to the centre of mass, the particles

If we started by applying Newton's second law to particle A, we would obtain the same differential equation for d.

See Unit 7.

are always moving in opposite directions. The situation is illustrated in Figure 1.15.

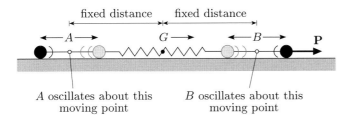

Figure 1.15 ■

Exercise 1.5

Suppose that the model spring in Example 1.2 is replaced by a light model rod of length $2l_0$. What can you say about the motion of the centre of mass of this new system, and about the motion of A and B? What forces are exerted by the rod on particles A and B?

(*Hint*: As for particle–spring models displaced from equilibrium, you may ignore the weights and normal reactions.)

*Exercise 1.6

Two particles A and B, each of mass m, move along the x-axis, and, although each exerts a force on the other, there are no external forces. Initially, A is at rest at the origin, while B is at $x = 3\,\text{m}$ and moving away from the origin with speed $6\,\text{m s}^{-1}$. If particle B returns to its initial position at time $t = 0.5\,\text{s}$, where is A at this time?

End-of-section Exercises

Exercise 1.7

Long ago and in a galaxy far, far away, an alien was alone in his spaceship, floating aimlessly through the void. He cursed his luck for running out of fuel, but then came up with a brilliant idea. Fortunately, he weighed half as much as the entire ship and he was quick on his (many) feet, so, starting from the back of the ship, he would run as fast as he could and hurl himself at the forward bulkhead. If he did this a few thousand times, he thought, the ship would gradually pick up speed and he would eventually arrive home. Comment on his chances of success.

Exercise 1.8

Two particles A and B, each of mass 50 kg, are at rest on a smooth horizontal surface and connected by a model string, which is stretched tightly between them. The breaking strain of the string is 10 N (i.e. it cannot sustain a tension greater than this value). A horizontal force **P** is applied to B in the direction AB, as shown in Figure 1.16. What is the greatest magnitude of the force **P** that can be applied to B before the string breaks?

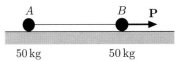

Figure 1.16

Exercise 1.9

Two particles A and B slide along a straight rough horizontal wire, and the coefficient of sliding friction between each of the particles and the wire is $\mu' = 0.4$. Particle A has mass 3 kg and particle B has mass 0.5 kg, and each particle exerts a force on the other. Find the acceleration of the centre of mass when both particles move along the wire in the same direction.

Exercise 1.10

Two particles move along a smooth straight horizontal track, and each exerts a force on the other. The first particle has mass 4 kg and experiences no external forces. The second particle has mass 1 kg and is pulled along the track by an external force of magnitude 20 N. It is found that the two particles accelerate along the track a fixed distance apart. Find the common acceleration of the particles and the magnitude of the internal forces.

2 Many-particle systems

In this section we shall generalize the ideas of Section 1 to systems of more than two particles. We shall also look at how to find the centre of mass of a variety of different systems and solid objects.

2.1 Motion of the centre of mass

We generalize here the results of Subsection 1.2 to systems with more than two particles. In fact, we consider a system of n particles, where n may be very large.

> **Definition**
>
> An n-**particle system** is a system modelled so that the total mass of the system is divided among n particles.

We assume that particle i has mass m_i and that its position vector is $\mathbf{r}_i$ (relative to some fixed origin O). We begin our discussion by extending the notion of the centre of mass to a system of n particles.

> **Definition**
>
> The **centre of mass** of an n-particle system, whose particles have masses $m_1, m_2, \ldots, m_n$, and position vectors $\mathbf{r}_1, \mathbf{r}_2, \ldots, \mathbf{r}_n$ relative to an origin O, has position vector
>
> $$\mathbf{r}_G = \frac{m_1 \mathbf{r}_1 + m_2 \mathbf{r}_2 + \cdots + m_n \mathbf{r}_n}{m_1 + m_2 + \cdots + m_n} = \frac{\sum_i m_i \mathbf{r}_i}{M} \qquad (2.1)$$
>
> relative to O, where $M = \sum_i m_i$ is the total mass of the system.

We write $\sum_i$ as a shorthand for $\sum_{i=1}^{n}$ throughout this unit.

Exercise 2.1

Determine the centre of mass of each of the following systems of particles, where each particle has the same mass m.

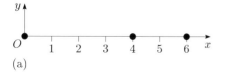

(a)

(b)

Each particle may be subject to a number of external forces, but these can always be added together to give a single resultant force, so we may assume that particle i is acted on by a single external force $\mathbf{E}_i$. The total external force on the whole system will then be

$$\mathbf{F}^{\text{ext}} = \mathbf{E}_1 + \mathbf{E}_2 + \cdots + \mathbf{E}_n = \sum_i \mathbf{E}_i. \tag{2.2}$$

In addition to the external forces, we assume that each particle exerts a force on every other (and that this force acts along the line joining them). Each particle is therefore acted on by $n-1$ internal forces. We denote the force acting on particle i due to particle j by $\mathbf{I}_{ij}$. Then (from Newton's third law) we have

$$\mathbf{I}_{ij} = -\mathbf{I}_{ji}. \tag{2.3}$$

It will make the summations that follow easier to write if we also introduce a term $\mathbf{I}_{ii}$ (the force exerted by the ith particle on itself), which we assume to be zero.

Now we apply Newton's second law to the ith particle and obtain

$$\underbrace{\mathbf{E}_i}_{\substack{\text{external force} \\ \text{on the } i\text{th particle}}} + \underbrace{\sum_j \mathbf{I}_{ij}}_{\substack{\text{sum of the internal} \\ \text{forces on the} \\ i\text{th particle}}} = \underbrace{m_i}_{\substack{\text{mass of the} \\ i\text{th particle}}} \times \underbrace{\ddot{\mathbf{r}}_i.}_{\substack{\text{acceleration of} \\ \text{the } i\text{th particle}}}$$

Adding together all of the equations like this, for all choices of i, we obtain

$$\underbrace{\sum_i \mathbf{E}_i}_{\substack{\text{sum of all the} \\ \text{external forces} \\ \text{on the system}}} + \underbrace{\sum_i \sum_j \mathbf{I}_{ij}}_{\substack{\text{sum of all the} \\ \text{internal forces} \\ \text{in the system}}} = \sum_i m_i \ddot{\mathbf{r}}_i. \tag{2.4}$$

The first term on the left-hand side is simply $\mathbf{F}^{\text{ext}}$, by Equation (2.2). The second term, involving a double summation, looks rather complicated. But it simply represents the sum of all the internal forces in the system. From Equation (2.3) we know that these forces cancel out in pairs, or are zero when $i = j$. The net result is that this term is zero. We now use Equation (2.1) to simplify the right-hand side of Equation (2.4), and we are left with the following important result.

Motion of the centre of mass of an n-particle system

The motion of the centre of mass $\mathbf{r}_G$ of an n-particle system of total mass M subject to external forces with sum $\mathbf{F}^{\text{ext}}$ is given by

$$\mathbf{F}^{\text{ext}} = M\ddot{\mathbf{r}}_G. \tag{2.5}$$

Notice that this formula is identical to the one for the two-particle case given by Equation (1.13).

Thus the centre of mass of an n-particle system moves as if it were a particle with mass the same as the total mass of the system and with all the external forces on the system applied to this particle.

Equation (2.5) is critical to the modelling of real objects as single particles. It tells us that an object composed of a very large number of components (modelled as particles) can be modelled by a single particle. However, if we do this, then the single-particle model will only predict the motion of the centre of mass. For example, consider the diver mentioned in the Introduction moving under gravity alone. As you know from *Unit 14*, the single-particle model predicts that the particle (i.e. the diver's centre of mass) moves along a parabolic path. This model does not give any information about the motion of any other part of the diver, which may move along a complicated path (see Figure 0.1).

2.2 Locating the centre of mass

In this subsection you will see how to find the centre of mass of a variety of systems and objects. One method for finding the centre of mass is to use the definition directly (Equation (2.1)). If the system is symmetric, then we can locate the centre of mass by finding the geometric centre (this was the method used in *Unit 5*).

Try the following exercise to find the centre of mass of two systems.

Exercise 2.2

Determine the centre of mass of each of the following systems of particles, where each particle has the same mass m.

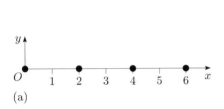
(a)

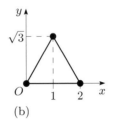
(b)

So far, we have looked at finding the centre of mass only of systems of particles. But you saw in *Unit 5* that sometimes it is more appropriate to model an object as a rigid body. To find the centre of mass of a rigid body, we simply suppose that the object is made up of a very large number of very small chunks of material, each of which can be modelled by a particle — i.e. we model the object as a system of particles. Then we can apply Equation (2.1) to find its centre of mass. However, this poses questions about how many particles we should use, what mass to give them and where to locate them.

In general, this is a difficult problem. But there are many objects whose physical properties can be used to help in this process. In particular, many objects are rigid and of *uniform density*, in that the mass of any small chunk of the object is proportional to its volume. Such an object modelled as a rigid body is said to be *homogeneous*.

Recall that *density* is mass per unit volume.

Definition

A **homogeneous rigid body** is a rigid body of uniform density.

The use of 'homogeneous' here is different from its use in the context of differential equations.

For a symmetric homogeneous rigid body, we can see at once that the centre of mass is at the geometric centre. We exploited this fact in *Unit 5* in locating the centres of mass of objects with some simple geometric shapes. Figure 2.1 shows six examples of symmetric homogeneous rigid bodies with their centres of mass G marked. Notice that the centre of mass in each case is located on an axis of symmetry — this is true in general of any symmetric homogeneous rigid body.

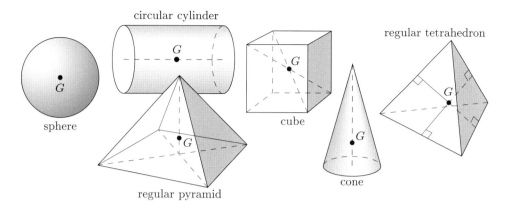

Figure 2.1

A homogeneous rigid body that is not symmetric can often be broken down into symmetric parts. The centre of mass of each symmetric part is at its geometric centre. If we model each part as a particle of appropriate mass located at its geometric centre, then we can use Equation (2.1) to find the centre of mass of the whole rigid body.

Example 2.1

Determine the centre of mass of the L-shaped piece of uniform cardboard shown in Figure 2.2.

Solution

Since the cardboard is uniform, its centre of mass must lie half-way through its thickness, so we can ignore the thickness and treat this as a two-dimensional problem. Thus we model the cardboard as a homogeneous two-dimensional rigid body. We know that its centre of mass must lie on the axis of symmetry shown in Figure 2.2. To find where on this axis it lies, we divide the L-shape into two parts, a square and a rectangle, as in Figure 2.3. Since we have homogeneity, their individual centres of mass must be at their geometric centres G_1 and G_2, which have position vectors

$$\mathbf{r}_{G_1} = \tfrac{1}{2}a\mathbf{i} + \tfrac{3}{2}a\mathbf{j} \quad \text{and} \quad \mathbf{r}_{G_2} = a\mathbf{i} + \tfrac{1}{2}a\mathbf{j}$$

with respect to O, where $\mathbf{i}$ and $\mathbf{j}$ are Cartesian unit vectors in the positive x- and y-directions. We now model each part as a particle: the square as a particle of mass m (say) at $\mathbf{r}_{G_1}$ and the rectangle as a particle of mass $2m$ (since the rectangle is twice the size of the square) at $\mathbf{r}_{G_2}$. Equation (2.1) then gives the centre of mass as

$$\mathbf{r}_G = \frac{m\left(\tfrac{1}{2}a\mathbf{i} + \tfrac{3}{2}a\mathbf{j}\right) + 2m\left(a\mathbf{i} + \tfrac{1}{2}a\mathbf{j}\right)}{3m} = \tfrac{5}{6}a\mathbf{i} + \tfrac{5}{6}a\mathbf{j},$$

which lies on the axis of symmetry (the line $y = x$) as expected. ■

*Exercise 2.3

The shape in Figure 2.2 can be divided into three squares as shown in Figure 2.4. Use this division of the shape to find its centre of mass.

It is often the case that a three-dimensional problem can be reduced to one in two dimensions, by taking account of certain uniformities or symmetries in the problem, as in Example 2.1. But even then there is no guarantee that we can divide the resulting plane figure into parts whose geometric centres we can find easily. Squares and rectangles are no problem, as Example 2.1 illustrates. But what about triangles?

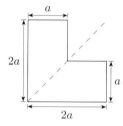

Figure 2.2

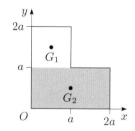

Figure 2.3

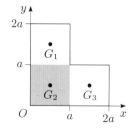

Figure 2.4

You saw other examples of this in *Unit 5*.

Figure 2.5(a) shows an isosceles triangle, and clearly its geometric centre lies on its axis of symmetry. Figure 2.5(b) shows the shape divided into a large number of very thin horizontal strips, and Figure 2.5(c) shows these strips pushed to the right to form another triangle. The centre of each strip lies on the broken line in Figure 2.5(c), so the geometric centre of this triangular shape lies on this line. Such a line passes through a vertex of the triangle and bisects the opposite side, and is known as a *median* of the triangle. This argument works for thin strips parallel to any of the three sides of the triangle. It follows that the geometric centre must lie on all three medians, i.e. the geometric centre must be the point of intersection of the medians, as shown in Figure 2.5(d). Any triangle may be constructed in this way, so this result holds for all triangles.

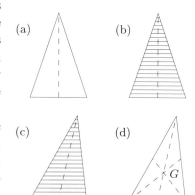

Figure 2.5

We can find the precise location of this point of intersection by using vectors. Figure 2.6 shows an arbitrary triangle OAB, and we know that the geometric centre G lies at the intersection of the medians AN and BM. It follows from the triangle rule for adding vectors that, for some numbers λ and μ, we have

$$\overrightarrow{OG} = \mathbf{a} + \lambda \overrightarrow{AN} = \mathbf{b} + \mu \overrightarrow{BM} . \tag{2.6}$$

But $\overrightarrow{AN} = -\mathbf{a} + \frac{1}{2}\mathbf{b}$ and $\overrightarrow{BM} = -\mathbf{b} + \frac{1}{2}\mathbf{a}$, so Equation (2.6) gives

$$\mathbf{a} + \lambda \left(-\mathbf{a} + \tfrac{1}{2}\mathbf{b}\right) = \mathbf{b} + \mu \left(-\mathbf{b} + \tfrac{1}{2}\mathbf{a}\right) .$$

Equating the coefficients of $\mathbf{a}$ and $\mathbf{b}$ gives

$$1 - \lambda = \tfrac{1}{2}\mu \quad \text{and} \quad 1 - \mu = \tfrac{1}{2}\lambda,$$

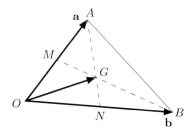

Figure 2.6

so $\lambda = \mu = \frac{2}{3}$. Thus the geometric centre lies on a median at the point two-thirds of the distance from the vertex to the centre of the opposite side, or, equivalently, one third of the way up a median from its base.

Now we mention one simple application of the centre of mass. There is a simple test to determine whether an object with a square base resting on a flat horizontal surface will topple over. Consider the situation shown in Figure 2.7. The forces acting on the object here are its weight and the normal reaction force due to the horizontal surface, as shown.

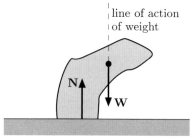

Figure 2.7

Recall from *Unit 5* that the weight acts through the centre of mass of the object. The point of action of the normal reaction force can be any point of contact between the object and the surface. If the object does not topple, then the equilibrium conditions of *Unit 5* apply, i.e. both the resultant force and the resultant torque must be zero. The condition that the resultant force must be zero fixes the magnitude of the normal reaction and can always be satisfied. For the resultant torque to be zero requires that the two forces have the same line of action. So the line of action of the weight of the object must pass through the base of the object, i.e. the centre of mass must be vertically above the base. This gives the following useful result.

Toppling condition

Consider an object with a square base resting on a flat horizontal surface. The object will topple over if and only if the centre of mass of the object is not vertically above the base.

Try to apply this result now in the following exercise.

Exercise 2.4

Figure 2.8(a) shows the design for a sculpture. It is to be made of concrete of uniform density, to be 1 m thick, 3 m high, and to have constant cross-sectional shape as shown in Figure 2.8(b), where $a = \frac{\sqrt{3}}{2} \simeq 0.866$ m. The sculpture is intended to rest on a horizontal surface, as shown in the figure. Will it topple over?

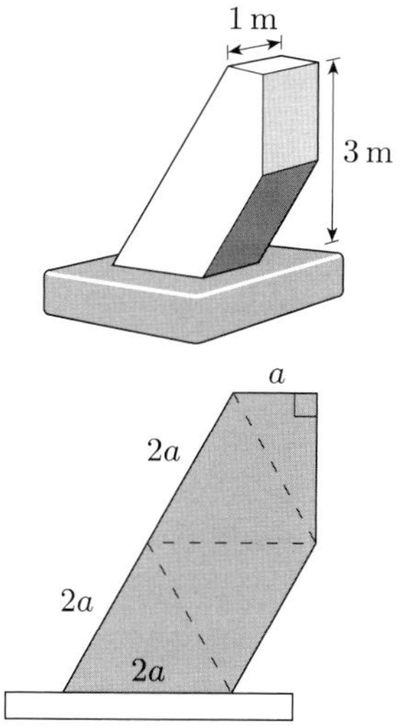

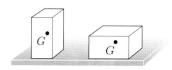

(a)

You have seen how to exploit the geometry of certain homogeneous rigid bodies to determine their centres of mass. In some cases, however, we may not be able to subdivide the object into parts whose geometric centres are known or easily found. In such cases we need to resort to integration to help us find the centre of mass, as you will see in *Unit 25*.

(b)

Figure 2.8

2.3 Potential energy

In this short subsection we look at another important application of the centre of mass — calculating potential energy.

Consider the homogeneous solid block shown in two positions in Figure 2.9. Clearly the block has a lower potential energy in the position shown on the right than in that shown on the left, but how are we to calculate it?

Figure 2.9

Let us return to the general system of particles introduced in Subsection 2.1, where the ith particle has mass m_i and position vector $\mathbf{r}_i$ (relative to some fixed origin O), but this time imagine the particles to lie in the Earth's gravitational field. Choose a Cartesian coordinate system x, y and z with origin at O and z-axis pointing vertically upwards, and take corresponding Cartesian unit vectors $\mathbf{i}$, $\mathbf{j}$ and $\mathbf{k}$. The height of the ith particle above the xy-plane is the $\mathbf{k}$-component of $\mathbf{r}_i$, given by $\mathbf{r}_i \cdot \mathbf{k}$, so the potential energy of the ith particle (relative to the datum O) is $m_i g(\mathbf{r}_i \cdot \mathbf{k})$. From Equation (2.1) we have

$$\sum_i m_i \mathbf{r}_i = M\mathbf{r}_G.$$

Taking the dot product of each side of this equation with $\mathbf{k}$, and then multiplying by g, we obtain

$$\sum_i m_i g(\mathbf{r}_i \cdot \mathbf{k}) = Mg(\mathbf{r}_G \cdot \mathbf{k}) = Mgh, \tag{2.7}$$

where h is the height of the centre of mass of the system above O. The left-hand side of this equation is the total potential energy of the system of particles, and the right-hand side is the potential energy of a single particle of mass M (equal to the total mass of the system) placed at the centre of mass. Equation (2.7) thus tells us that to find the potential energy of a system of particles or of a homogeneous rigid body of total mass M, all we need to do is to find the height h of the centre of mass above the datum and then use the formula Mgh.

Exercise 2.5

If the homogeneous solid block in Figure 2.9 has mass M, height $4h$, width h and depth h, calculate the change in its potential energy in the two positions shown in Figure 2.9.

End-of-section Exercises

Exercise 2.6

A uniform ball of mass M is dropped from rest and falls under gravity. What is the velocity of its centre of mass when the ball has fallen a distance h? What is the change in the potential energy when the ball has fallen a distance h?

Exercise 2.7

Find the centre of mass of the homogeneous rigid body shown in Figure 2.10. Will the object topple over when it is placed on a horizontal surface as shown on the right in Figure 2.10?

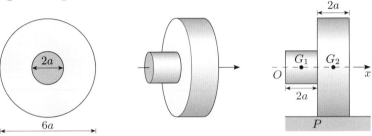

Figure 2.10

Exercise 2.8

Figure 2.11 shows the Great Pyramid of Cheops, with its centre of mass G a quarter of its height h above the square base. Originally the pyramid was 147 m high and built on a square base with sides 230 m. The stones of the pyramid are of limestone.

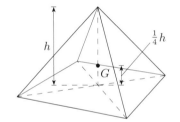

Figure 2.11

(a) Assuming that the density of limestone is approximately $2500 \, \text{kg m}^{-3}$, what is the approximate mass of the pyramid? (*Hint*: Recall that the volume of a pyramid is $\frac{1}{3} \times$ base area $\times$ vertical height.)

(b) Estimate the total energy required to lift all the stones of the pyramid into place.

(c) Given that a man can lift approximately 1000 kg of stones through a height of 1 m in a day, estimate how long a gang of 1000 men would have taken to lift all the stones of the pyramid into place.

3 Collisions

In this section we shall be concerned with the behaviour of objects when they collide. We begin in Subsection 3.1 by defining the concept of linear momentum, and we obtain a result that tells us when linear momentum is conserved. In Subsection 3.2 we go on to define and explore elastic and inelastic collisions.

3.1 Conservation of linear momentum

Suppose that two balls, A and B with position vectors $\mathbf{r}_1$ and $\mathbf{r}_2$ relative to a fixed origin, are moving far out in space, away from any outside influence, so there are no external forces. Let m_1 be the mass of ball A and let m_2 be the mass of ball B. The balls collide, and just after the collision A has velocity $\dot{\mathbf{R}}_1$ and B has velocity $\dot{\mathbf{R}}_2$, as shown in Figure 3.1. (We shall denote correspondingly the position vectors of A and B, relative to the origin, after the collision by $\mathbf{R}_1$ and $\mathbf{R}_2$.)

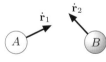

velocities shortly before impact

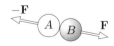

forces during impact

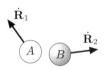

velocities shortly after impact

Figure 3.1

The system under consideration consists of the two balls A and B, which we model as two particles. The impact happens over a very small interval of time. During that time interval, B experiences a force $\mathbf{F}$ (due to A) and, by Newton's third law, A experiences an equal and opposite force $-\mathbf{F}$ (due to B). These forces may vary over the very small time interval when the balls are in contact, but the important point to appreciate is that they are internal forces. Thus, because there are no external forces, the discussion in Section 2 tells us that the centre of mass of the system moves with constant velocity before, during and after the collision. If we denote the velocity of the centre of mass before and after the collision by $\dot{\mathbf{r}}_G$ and $\dot{\mathbf{R}}_G$, respectively, we have $\dot{\mathbf{r}}_G = \dot{\mathbf{R}}_G$, where

$$\dot{\mathbf{r}}_G = \frac{m_1 \dot{\mathbf{r}}_1 + m_2 \dot{\mathbf{r}}_2}{m_1 + m_2} \quad \text{and} \quad \dot{\mathbf{R}}_G = \frac{m_1 \dot{\mathbf{R}}_1 + m_2 \dot{\mathbf{R}}_2}{m_1 + m_2}.$$

It follows that

$$m_1 \dot{\mathbf{r}}_1 + m_2 \dot{\mathbf{r}}_2 = m_1 \dot{\mathbf{R}}_1 + m_2 \dot{\mathbf{R}}_2. \tag{3.1}$$

The quantity

(mass of A) $\times$ (velocity of A) + (mass of B) $\times$ (velocity of B)

has been unchanged by the collision, and this leads us to make the following general definitions.

Definitions

The **linear momentum p** of a particle with position vector $\mathbf{r}$ is the product of its mass m and its velocity $\dot{\mathbf{r}}$, so

$$\mathbf{p} = m\dot{\mathbf{r}}.$$

The **linear momentum P** of an n-particle system is the sum of the linear momenta of the individual particles, so

$$\mathbf{P} = \sum_i m_i \dot{\mathbf{r}}_i = M\dot{\mathbf{r}}_G, \tag{3.2}$$

where m_i and $\mathbf{r}_i$ represent the mass and position of particle i, M is the total mass of the system and $\mathbf{r}_G$ is its centre of mass.

The SI units for the magnitude of linear momentum are $\mathrm{kg\,m\,s^{-1}}$.

Thus Equation (3.1) tells us that the linear momentum of our two-ball system with no external forces is the same before and after the collision, i.e. it is *conserved*.

We can link linear momentum to the motion of the centre of mass of a system, given by Equation (2.5) as $\mathbf{F}^{\text{ext}} = M\ddot{\mathbf{r}}_G$. Differentiating Equation (3.2) with respect to time gives $\dot{\mathbf{P}} = M\ddot{\mathbf{r}}_G$, so Equation (2.5) becomes

$$\mathbf{F}^{\text{ext}} = \dot{\mathbf{P}}. \tag{3.3}$$

This tells us that the sum of the external forces on an n-particle system is equal to the rate of change of linear momentum of the system. The case when there are no external forces is particularly simple, for then we have $\dot{\mathbf{P}} = \mathbf{0}$, so the linear momentum is constant throughout the motion.

As we observed above, the forces acting during a collision are *internal* forces, and so do not affect Equations (2.5) and (3.3). Therefore Equation (2.5) tells us that the motion of the centre of mass of an n-particle system is unaffected by any collisions between the particles. Equation (3.3) tells us that the rate of change of linear momentum of the system is also unaffected by any collisions.

In the case where there is no net external force, Equation (3.3) also tells us that the linear momentum remains constant despite any collisions, as you saw in the two-ball example. Let us now consider what Equation (3.3) tells us about the linear momentum (rather than its rate of change) when our two-ball system is subject to external forces. With this aim, suppose now that the two balls are in the Earth's gravitational field, as shown in Figure 3.2.

In this case there is a net external force, the combined weight of the balls, so $\mathbf{F}^{\text{ext}} = (m_1 + m_2)\mathbf{g}$, which is constant, and Equation (3.3) becomes $(m_1 + m_2)\mathbf{g} = \dot{\mathbf{P}}$. The collision occurs over a very small time interval of length T. If we integrate this equation with respect to time over this time interval, we obtain

$$\int_0^T (m_1 + m_2)\mathbf{g}\, dt = \int_0^T \dot{\mathbf{P}}\, dt = [\mathbf{P}]_0^T,$$

and it follows that $(m_1 + m_2)T\mathbf{g} = \mathbf{P}_{\text{after}} - \mathbf{P}_{\text{before}}$. If we suppose that the collision is instantaneous, so $T = 0$ (i.e. if we take the limit as $T \to 0$), then $\mathbf{P}_{\text{after}} = \mathbf{P}_{\text{before}}$; in other words, the linear momentum is conserved.

This result generalizes to any n-particle system. Suppose that we have such a system on which the resultant of the external forces is $\mathbf{F}^{\text{ext}}$. Over a very small time interval of length T, we can take $\mathbf{F}^{\text{ext}}$ to be constant, so integrating Equation (3.3) with respect to time gives

$$\int_0^T \mathbf{F}^{\text{ext}}\, dt = \int_0^T \dot{\mathbf{P}}\, dt = [\mathbf{P}]_0^T,$$

so $\mathbf{F}^{\text{ext}}T = \mathbf{P}_{\text{after}} - \mathbf{P}_{\text{before}}$. Hence, for an instantaneous collision, with $T = 0$ (i.e. if we take the limit as $T \to 0$), we have $\mathbf{P}_{\text{after}} = \mathbf{P}_{\text{before}}$.

This means that, in the presence of external forces, the total linear momentum of an n-particle system may change over time, but the instantaneous collisions of the particles within the system have no effect on the total linear momentum.

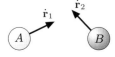

velocities shortly before impact

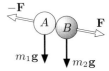

forces during impact

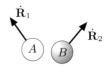

velocities shortly after impact

Figure 3.2

Principle of conservation of linear momentum

The total linear momentum of an n-particle system is not affected by (instantaneous) collisions among the particles. Furthermore, in the absence of external forces, the total linear momentum of the system remains constant.

By modelling a rigid body as a system of particles (as we did in Section 2), this principle can be extended to systems involving rigid bodies and/or particles. In particular, it means that if two rigid bodies collide, then the collision causes no change to the total linear momentum of the two rigid bodies.

Example 3.1

A railway truck A of mass $50\,000\,\text{kg}$ rolls down a slight incline and collides with a stationary truck B of mass $30\,000\,\text{kg}$. After the collision, the trucks are coupled together (so that A and B have the same velocity). If the speed of A immediately before the collision is $2\,\text{m\,s}^{-1}$, what is the speed of the trucks immediately after the collision (assuming that the collision is instantaneous)?

Solution

We ignore the motion of the wheels and model the trucks as rigid bodies. Let v be the speed of the trucks after impact. Then, using the notation $\mathbf{P}_{\text{before}}$ and $\mathbf{P}_{\text{after}}$ for the total linear momentum before and after impact, we have

$$|\mathbf{P}_{\text{before}}| = 50\,000 \times 2,$$
$$|\mathbf{P}_{\text{after}}| = (50\,000 + 30\,000) \times v.$$

It follows from the principle of conservation of linear momentum that $80\,000v = 100\,000$ and therefore $v = 1.25\,\mathrm{m\,s^{-1}}$. ∎

Exercise 3.1

A railway engine of mass M, moving on a straight horizontal track, collides with a stationary truck of mass m. The truck becomes attached to the engine, and both move off together. Express the speed v of the engine and truck immediately after the collision in terms of M, m and the speed u of the engine immediately prior to the collision.

3.2 Elastic and inelastic collisions

Sometimes in a collision between objects, the total kinetic energy of the system before and after the collision remains the same, i.e. is conserved. However, some of the kinetic energy may be transformed into other forms of energy by the collision. We use different terms for the two types of collision.

> **Definitions**
>
> If the kinetic energy of a system is the same before and after a collision within the system, then the collision is said to be **elastic**; otherwise, it is said to be **inelastic**.

Notice that here we use the terms 'elastic' and 'inelastic' in a technical sense which is somewhat different from their everyday usage.

Example 3.2

Suppose that a snooker ball A, of mass m, moving with speed $5\,\mathrm{m\,s^{-1}}$ in a straight line across a smooth snooker table, collides elastically with a similar ball B, of the same mass, at rest. Suppose that A hits B head on, i.e. they both move along the same straight line after impact as A was moving along before impact. Modelling each ball as a particle, predict the speeds of the balls after the collision.

Solution

Define an x-axis along the line of motion of the balls, with positive direction in the direction of motion of A before the collision. Then the velocities of A and B before the collision can be written as $\dot{\mathbf{r}}_1 = \dot{x}_1\mathbf{i}$ and $\dot{\mathbf{r}}_2 = \dot{x}_2\mathbf{i}$, and their velocities after the collision as $\dot{\mathbf{R}}_1 = \dot{X}_1\mathbf{i}$ and $\dot{\mathbf{R}}_2 = \dot{X}_2\mathbf{i}$, where $\mathbf{i}$ is a unit vector in the positive x-direction.

By the principle of conservation of linear momentum, we have

$$m\dot{x}_1\mathbf{i} + m\dot{x}_2\mathbf{i} = m\dot{X}_1\mathbf{i} + m\dot{X}_2\mathbf{i}.$$

Dividing by m and resolving in the $\mathbf{i}$-direction gives

$$\dot{x}_1 + \dot{x}_2 = \dot{X}_1 + \dot{X}_2,$$

which, since $\dot{x}_1 = 5\,\mathrm{m\,s}^{-1}$ and $\dot{x}_2 = 0\,\mathrm{m\,s}^{-1}$, gives

$$\dot{X}_1 + \dot{X}_2 = 5. \tag{3.4}$$

The kinetic energies of the balls A and B before impact are $\frac{1}{2}m\dot{x}_1^2 = \frac{25}{2}m$ and $\frac{1}{2}m\dot{x}_2^2 = 0$, and the kinetic energies after impact are $\frac{1}{2}m\dot{X}_1^2$ and $\frac{1}{2}m\dot{X}_2^2$. Since the collision is elastic, kinetic energy is conserved, so we have

$$\tfrac{25}{2}m = \tfrac{1}{2}m\dot{X}_1^2 + \tfrac{1}{2}m\dot{X}_2^2,$$

hence

$$\dot{X}_1^2 + \dot{X}_2^2 = 25. \tag{3.5}$$

From Equation (3.4), $\dot{X}_2 = 5 - \dot{X}_1$. Substituting for $\dot{X}_2$ in Equation (3.5), we obtain

$$\dot{X}_1^2 + (5 - \dot{X}_1)^2 = 25,$$

which simplifies to

$$\dot{X}_1(\dot{X}_1 - 5) = 0.$$

So there are two possibilities: either $\dot{X}_1 = 5$ or $\dot{X}_1 = 0$. Substituting $\dot{X}_1 = 5$ into Equation (3.4) gives $\dot{X}_2 = 0$, which is physically impossible (since B is in front of A). So $\dot{X}_1 = 0$ and $\dot{X}_2 = 5$ (again from Equation (3.4)). In other words, after the collision ball A comes to rest, while ball B moves across the table with a speed equal to the original speed of ball A. ∎

Exercise 3.2 ──────────────────────────────────

A railway truck of mass $15\,000\,\mathrm{kg}$ is moving at $4\,\mathrm{m\,s}^{-1}$ along a straight track and collides with a stationary truck of mass $10\,000\,\mathrm{kg}$. After impact the trucks move together along the track.

(a) What is their combined speed after impact?

(b) Is the collision elastic?

In Example 3.2 and Exercise 3.2, the motion before and after impact was along the same straight line. Also only one object was moving before impact. In the next example there is still only one object moving before impact, but the directions of motion of the two objects after impact are along different straight lines. This sort of collision, referred to as an *oblique* collision, occurs, for example, when one ball strikes a glancing blow on another, as illustrated in Figure 3.3.

Figure 3.3

Example 3.3

A white snooker ball A, moving parallel to the sides of the table with speed u, collides obliquely with the stationary black ball B (which is equidistant from two of the end pockets), as shown in Figure 3.4. As a result, the black ball moves off at an angle of $\frac{\pi}{4}$ to the original direction of motion of the white ball, and ends up in the pocket at the top of Figure 3.4. If the collision is elastic and each ball has mass m, find the speeds of the balls after impact and decide if the white ball is likely to enter a pocket.

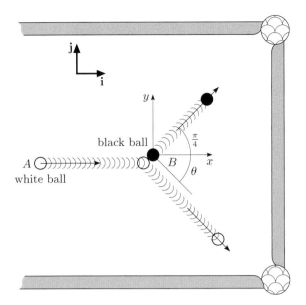

Figure 3.4

Solution

We choose axes as shown in the figure, with origin at the original position of the black ball. Modelling the balls as particles and using $\dot{\mathbf{r}}_1$, $\dot{\mathbf{r}}_2$ and $\dot{\mathbf{R}}_1$, $\dot{\mathbf{R}}_2$ for the velocities of A, B just before and just after impact, respectively, we have

$$\dot{\mathbf{r}}_1 = u\mathbf{i} \quad \text{and} \quad \dot{\mathbf{r}}_2 = \mathbf{0},$$

where $\mathbf{i}$ and $\mathbf{j}$ are Cartesian unit vectors in the positive x- and y-directions, respectively. We are told that the direction of motion of the black ball after impact is at an angle of $\frac{\pi}{4}$ to the x-axis, so

$$\dot{\mathbf{R}}_2 = \left(|\dot{\mathbf{R}}_2|\cos\tfrac{\pi}{4}\right)\mathbf{i} + \left(|\dot{\mathbf{R}}_2|\sin\tfrac{\pi}{4}\right)\mathbf{j} = \tfrac{1}{\sqrt{2}}|\dot{\mathbf{R}}_2|\mathbf{i} + \tfrac{1}{\sqrt{2}}|\dot{\mathbf{R}}_2|\mathbf{j} = V\mathbf{i} + V\mathbf{j},$$

where $V = \frac{1}{\sqrt{2}}|\dot{\mathbf{R}}_2|$. Also, if θ is the angle made with the x-axis by the white ball's direction of motion after impact, then

We measure the angles in an anticlockwise direction from the positive x-axis as usual, so (from Figure 3.4) we expect θ to be negative.

$$\dot{\mathbf{R}}_1 = \left(|\dot{\mathbf{R}}_1|\cos\theta\right)\mathbf{i} + \left(|\dot{\mathbf{R}}_1|\sin\theta\right)\mathbf{j} = V_x\mathbf{i} + V_y\mathbf{j},$$

where $V_x = |\dot{\mathbf{R}}_1|\cos\theta$ and $V_y = |\dot{\mathbf{R}}_1|\sin\theta$ denote the components of the white ball's velocity after impact.

The principle of conservation of linear momentum gives

$$mu\mathbf{i} = m(V_x\mathbf{i} + V_y\mathbf{j}) + m(V\mathbf{i} + V\mathbf{j}).$$

Resolving in the $\mathbf{i}$- and $\mathbf{j}$-directions in turn and dividing by m, leads to

$$V_x = u - V \quad \text{and} \quad V_y = -V. \tag{3.6}$$

As the collision is elastic, kinetic energy is conserved, so we have

$$\tfrac{1}{2}mu^2 = \tfrac{1}{2}m(V_x^2 + V_y^2) + \tfrac{1}{2}m(\sqrt{2}V)^2.$$

If we substitute the values for V_x and V_y obtained in Equations (3.6) and divide by $\frac{1}{2}m$, then this equation becomes

$$u^2 = (u - V)^2 + V^2 + 2V^2,$$

which simplifies to $uV = 2V^2$.

We know that $V \neq 0$, therefore $V = \frac{1}{2}u$, and Equations (3.6) give $V_x = \frac{1}{2}u$, $V_y = -\frac{1}{2}u$. Hence the speeds of the white ball and the black ball after impact are, respectively,

$$|\dot{\mathbf{R}}_1| = \sqrt{V_x^2 + V_y^2} = \frac{1}{\sqrt{2}}u \quad \text{and} \quad |\dot{\mathbf{R}}_2| = \sqrt{2}V = \frac{1}{\sqrt{2}}u.$$

Also, $\tan\theta = \left(|\dot{\mathbf{R}}_1|\sin\theta\right) \Big/ \left(|\dot{\mathbf{R}}_1|\cos\theta\right) = V_y/V_x = -1$ and hence $\theta = -\frac{\pi}{4}$, so the white ball moves off at an angle of $\frac{\pi}{4}$ to its original direction of motion, towards the bottom pocket shown in Figure 3.4.

However, although the white ball is travelling in the general direction of the bottom pocket, notice from Figure 3.4 that its diagonal motion does not start at exactly the same point as that of the black ball, but rather slightly below and to the left of it. So although it goes close to the bottom pocket, we need to know more about the size of snooker balls, the dimensions of snooker tables and the geometry of snooker table pockets before we can make any firm conclusion about whether it enters the bottom pocket. (Even with all this information, we still could not be sure because our two-particle model takes no account of aspects of the physical situation such as the rolling motion of the balls.)   ∎

Exercise 3.3 ───────────────────────────────────

A white snooker ball, travelling with speed u, collides with a stationary green ball. As a result, the green ball moves off at an angle of $\frac{\pi}{3}$ to the original direction of motion of the white ball. Modelling the balls as particles of equal mass m, and assuming that the collision is elastic, find the velocity of each ball after the collision. Also determine the direction of motion of the white ball after the collision.

Exercise 3.4 ───────────────────────────────────

A particle of mass m_1 travels in the positive x-direction with speed u. Another particle of mass m_2 travels in the positive y-direction with the same speed u. The particles collide and then move off together with the same velocity. Find the velocity of the particles after the collision. Is the collision elastic?

End-of-section Exercise

Exercise 3.5 ───────────────────────────────────

A particle of mass m_1 collides with a particle of mass m_2. Their velocities are $\mathbf{v}_1$ and $\mathbf{v}_2$, respectively, before impact, and $\mathbf{V}_1$ and $\mathbf{V}_2$, respectively, after impact.

(a) If $m_1 = m_2 = 3$, $\mathbf{v}_1 = 2\mathbf{i}$, $\mathbf{v}_2 = \mathbf{0}$, $\mathbf{V}_1 = \mathbf{i} + \mathbf{j}$ and $\mathbf{V}_2 = \mathbf{i} - \mathbf{j}$, show that the collision is elastic.

(b) If $m_1 = 1$, $m_2 = 3$, $\mathbf{v}_1 = 2\mathbf{i} + \mathbf{j}$, $\mathbf{v}_2 = \mathbf{j}$ and $\mathbf{V}_1 = \mathbf{V}_2 = \frac{1}{2}\mathbf{i} + \mathbf{j}$, show that the collision is inelastic, and find the decrease in kinetic energy due to the collision.

4 Newton's law of restitution

Here we look at the relationship between the relative velocities of objects before and after collisions.

Although some collisions are elastic, usually we expect there to be some transfer of energy when objects collide. So most collisions are inelastic. To obtain information about velocities after an inelastic collision, where kinetic energy is not conserved, we can use *Newton's law of restitution*, a law that is well supported by empirical evidence.

The starting point for this law is the experimental observation that if you drop a ball onto a flat fixed horizontal solid surface, then the height to which the ball rebounds appears to be a fixed fraction of the original height.

If the ball is dropped from a height H and rebounds to a height h, then it appears that

$$h = cH,$$

where c is a constant (with $0 \leq c \leq 1$) depending both on the material of the ball and on that of the surface. If $c = 1$, then the ball rebounds to its original height; if $c = 0$, then the ball does not bounce. A steel ball dropped onto a steel plate would provide an example of a collision where c is close to 1; on the other hand, a ball of a material like putty would hardly bounce, so c would be almost zero.

If we model the ball as a particle of mass m, then (relative to a datum at the surface) the potential energy of the ball as it is dropped is mgH, and its potential energy at the top of the first bounce is $mgh = cmgH$. So, with each successive bounce, a fixed fraction of the ball's energy is lost (we shall see later where it has gone). Suppose that the velocities are $\dot{x}\mathbf{i}$ and $\dot{X}\mathbf{i}$ just before and after the first impact, as shown in Figure 4.1. We can apply the law of conservation of mechanical energy to the one-dimensional motion of the ball before impact and after impact (but not during impact, as then there is an extra force due to the impact). The law applied to the motion before impact gives

$$\tfrac{1}{2}m\dot{x}^2 = mgH,$$

and after impact gives

$$\tfrac{1}{2}m\dot{X}^2 = mgh = cmgH.$$

Therefore $\dot{X}^2 = c\dot{x}^2$, so $\dot{X} = -\sqrt{c}\dot{x}$ (since the velocity changes direction). We normally replace the constant $\sqrt{c}$ by e, which is known as the *coefficient of restitution* between the ball and the surface, so

$$\dot{X} = -e\dot{x}.$$

This means that the velocity of the ball after impact is $-e$ times its velocity before impact.

This result holds not only for balls bouncing on surfaces, but also for any instantaneous collision between any two objects moving along the same line, in which case it takes the form

relative velocity after impact
$= -e \times$ relative velocity before impact.   (4.1)

Notice that if $e = 1$, then the speed is the same before and after impact, and hence so is the kinetic energy. Therefore $e = 1$ corresponds to an elastic collision, while $e < 1$ corresponds to an inelastic one.

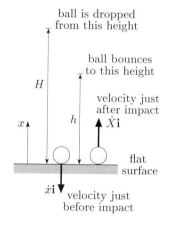

Figure 4.1

The law of conservation of mechanical energy for one-dimensional motion was discussed in *Unit 8*.

Exercise 4.1

Suppose that there is a collision between a ball A, of mass m_1, which is moving with velocity $\dot{\mathbf{r}}_1$, and a ball B, of mass m_2, which is moving with velocity $\dot{\mathbf{r}}_2$. Suppose also that both balls are moving along the same straight line, and that the coefficient of restitution between the balls is e.

(a) Find the velocities of the balls after impact in terms of the velocities before impact.

(b) Use your results to provide an alternative solution to Example 3.2.

Exercise 4.2

A ball of mass m_1 moves with speed u across a smooth table and collides head on with a stationary ball of mass m_2 (so the motion before and after impact takes place along the same straight line). Given that the coefficient of restitution between the balls is e, and assuming that the balls can be modelled as particles, show that the kinetic energy lost from the system due to the collision is

$$\frac{m_1 m_2 (1 - e^2) u^2}{2(m_1 + m_2)}.$$

Consider a ball bouncing on a smooth fixed horizontal solid surface. When the ball is dropped onto the surface, the only forces acting on the ball at the moment of impact are the weight of the ball and the normal reaction of the surface on the ball. These forces are vertical and act along the line of motion, so their effect changes the velocity of the ball but not its line of motion, which remains vertical. Suppose now that the ball is not dropped but is thrown so that it strikes the surface at an angle, as in Figure 4.2. At the moment of impact, the forces acting on the ball are still just the weight and the normal reaction, and these are both vertical. So the impact affects just the vertical component of the ball's velocity — there is no force with a horizontal component to affect the horizontal component of the ball's velocity. If the velocities before and after impact are $\dot{\mathbf{r}} = \dot{x}\mathbf{i} + \dot{y}\mathbf{j}$ and $\dot{\mathbf{R}} = \dot{X}\mathbf{i} + \dot{Y}\mathbf{j}$, where $\mathbf{i}$ and $\mathbf{j}$ are horizontal and vertical Cartesian unit vectors, then we have $\dot{X} = \dot{x}$. Also, applying Equation (4.1) to the vertical components of the velocity, we have $\dot{Y} = -e\dot{y}$, where e is the coefficient of restitution between the ball and the surface. The kinetic energy just before impact is $\frac{1}{2}m\left(\dot{x}^2 + \dot{y}^2\right)$, and the kinetic energy just after impact is $\frac{1}{2}m\left(\dot{X}^2 + \dot{Y}^2\right) = \frac{1}{2}m\left(\dot{x}^2 + e^2\dot{y}^2\right)$.

As before, these ideas can be extended to collisions between any two objects, one or both of which may be moving, provided that the areas of contact between the objects during impact are both smooth (i.e. frictionless) and lie on the same tangent plane, as illustrated in Figure 4.3. In our mathematical models of colliding objects, the objects are often spheres or planes, in which case the proviso about the areas of contact lying on the same tangent plane is automatically satisfied, but the ideas can be applied to collisions between objects of other shapes too. We shall also need to assume that neither object is rotating, or at least that any rotation can be ignored — this assumption is reasonable in many cases. (The assumption that an object can be modelled as a particle implies that any rotation of the object can be ignored — see *Unit 6.*)

As for the ball bouncing obliquely on a surface, only the component of the velocity perpendicular to the tangent plane of contact is affected by the collision. At a point of contact, the direction perpendicular to the common tangent plane is referred to as the **common normal**; this is illustrated in Figure 4.3.

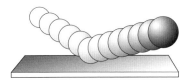

Figure 4.2

There is no friction as the surface is smooth.

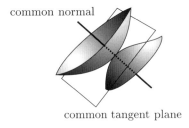

common normal

common tangent plane

Figure 4.3

If there is significant rotation, then other forces come into play and affect the results.

Thus we have the following result, which as we noted earlier is well supported by empirical evidence.

Newton's law of restitution

In an (instantaneous) collision between two smooth non-rotating objects, where the area of contact at the moment of impact lies on a common tangent plane, the velocities parallel to the tangent plane remain unchanged before and after impact. Also we have

$$\begin{pmatrix} \text{relative velocity component} \\ \text{parallel to the common} \\ \text{normal after impact} \end{pmatrix} = -e \times \begin{pmatrix} \text{relative velocity component} \\ \text{parallel to the common} \\ \text{normal before impact} \end{pmatrix},$$

where e is the **coefficient of restitution** for a collision between the two objects.

To see how we can make use of this law, suppose that two smooth balls A and B of the same radius, of masses m_1 and m_2, are moving along a smooth horizontal surface before colliding. Assume that any rotation can be ignored. The situation is illustrated in Figure 4.4, which also shows the common tangent plane at the point of impact and Cartesian unit vectors $\mathbf{i}$ and $\mathbf{j}$ in the direction of the tangent plane and perpendicular to it (in the direction of the common normal). Figure 4.4 also shows the velocities of the balls before and after impact.

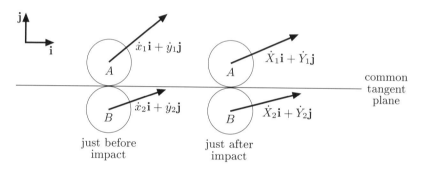

Figure 4.4

From Newton's law of restitution, we have

$$\dot{x}_1\mathbf{i} = \dot{X}_1\mathbf{i}, \quad \dot{x}_2\mathbf{i} = \dot{X}_2\mathbf{i}, \quad (\dot{Y}_1 - \dot{Y}_2)\mathbf{j} = -e(\dot{y}_1 - \dot{y}_2)\mathbf{j}, \tag{4.2}$$

where e is the coefficient of restitution for the balls. Also, the principle of conservation of linear momentum gives

$$m_1(\dot{x}_1\mathbf{i} + \dot{y}_1\mathbf{j}) + m_2(\dot{x}_2\mathbf{i} + \dot{y}_2\mathbf{j}) = m_1(\dot{X}_1\mathbf{i} + \dot{Y}_1\mathbf{j}) + m_2(\dot{X}_2\mathbf{i} + \dot{Y}_2\mathbf{j}). \tag{4.3}$$

Resolving in the $\mathbf{j}$-direction in Equations (4.2) and (4.3) gives

$$\dot{Y}_1 - \dot{Y}_2 = -e(\dot{y}_1 - \dot{y}_2),$$
$$m_1\dot{y}_1 + m_2\dot{y}_2 = m_1\dot{Y}_1 + m_2\dot{Y}_2.$$

These equations can be solved for $\dot{Y}_1$ and $\dot{Y}_2$ to give

$$\dot{Y}_1 = \frac{(m_1 - em_2)\dot{y}_1 + m_2(1 + e)\dot{y}_2}{m_1 + m_2},$$

$$\dot{Y}_2 = \frac{m_1(1 + e)\dot{y}_1 + (m_2 - em_1)\dot{y}_2}{m_1 + m_2}.$$

You solved the equivalent equations using xs rather than ys in Exercise 4.1.

So, given e and the velocities before impact, we can find the velocities after impact.

127

Example 4.1

Figure 4.5 shows the head of a golf club A just before and just after it strikes a golf ball B. Just before impact the ball is stationary and the head of the club is moving horizontally with speed u. The mass of A is $9m$ and the mass of B is m, the coefficient of restitution between the club and the ball is 0.8, and the face of the club is inclined at an angle α as shown in the figure. Model the club head and the ball as smooth objects and ignore any rotational effects. Estimate the loss of kinetic energy caused by the collision.

The 'spin' imparted to a golf ball by a golf club can be very important, as any golfer will tell you.

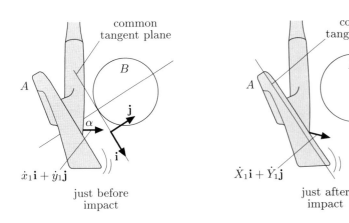

Figure 4.5

Solution

Choosing the Cartesian unit vectors as shown in Figure 4.5, we can write the velocity of A just before impact as

$$\dot{x}_1\mathbf{i} + \dot{y}_1\mathbf{j} = (u\sin\alpha)\mathbf{i} + (u\cos\alpha)\mathbf{j},$$

while the velocity of B just before impact is $\mathbf{0}$.

By Newton's law of restitution, we have

$$\dot{X}_1\mathbf{i} = \dot{x}_1\mathbf{i}, \quad \dot{X}_2\mathbf{i} = \dot{x}_2\mathbf{i}, \quad (\dot{Y}_1 - \dot{Y}_2)\mathbf{j} = -e(\dot{y}_1 - \dot{y}_2)\mathbf{j}.$$

Resolving in the $\mathbf{i}$- and $\mathbf{j}$-directions, and substituting in known values, we obtain

$$\dot{X}_1 = \dot{x}_1 = u\sin\alpha,$$
$$\dot{X}_2 = \dot{x}_2 = 0,$$
$$\dot{Y}_1 - \dot{Y}_2 = -0.8(u\cos\alpha - 0) = -0.8u\cos\alpha. \tag{4.4}$$

Also, the principle of conservation of linear momentum gives Equation (4.3), which, resolving in the $\mathbf{j}$-direction, using known values and dividing through by m, gives

$$9u\cos\alpha = 9\dot{Y}_1 + \dot{Y}_2. \tag{4.5}$$

Solving Equations (4.4) and (4.5) for $\dot{Y}_1$ and $\dot{Y}_2$, we obtain

$$\dot{Y}_1 = 0.82u\cos\alpha, \quad \dot{Y}_2 = 1.62u\cos\alpha.$$

We now have enough information to be able to compare the kinetic energy just after impact with the kinetic energy just before impact. The kinetic energy of the system just before impact is $\frac{1}{2}(9m)u^2 = 4.5mu^2$. The velocity of the club head just after impact is $\dot{X}_1\mathbf{i} + \dot{Y}_1\mathbf{j} = (u\sin\alpha)\mathbf{i} + (0.82u\cos\alpha)\mathbf{j}$, and the velocity of the ball just after impact is $\dot{X}_2\mathbf{i} + \dot{Y}_2\mathbf{j} = 0\mathbf{i} + (1.62u\cos\alpha)\mathbf{j}$, so that their combined kinetic energy just after impact is

$$\frac{1}{2}(9m)(u^2\sin^2\alpha + (0.82)^2u^2\cos^2\alpha) + \frac{1}{2}m(1.62)^2u^2\cos^2\alpha$$
$$= (4.5\sin^2\alpha + 4.338\cos^2\alpha)mu^2$$
$$= (4.5 - 0.162\cos^2\alpha)mu^2.$$

So the model estimates that the kinetic energy of the system has decreased by $0.162mu^2\cos^2\alpha$. ∎

In *Unit 8* we showed that the total mechanical energy of certain one-particle systems is conserved, but in this section we have shown that the mechanical energy decreases in an inelastic collision. What has happened to this energy?

It is a basic assumption of physics that the total energy of a system is conserved. So either our model is inadequate, or some of the mechanical energy has been converted into another form of energy. Actually, it is a bit of both. During a collision, a little of the mechanical energy is converted into sound energy, and some is converted into heat energy; but much of the 'missing' energy still exists in the form of mechanical energy — it is just that our particle model is too crude to detect it.

You met heat energy in Unit 14.

For the golf ball, some of the 'missing' energy is in the spinning motion of the ball.

Exercise 4.3

Two smooth non-rotating balls A and B of equal mass m slide on a frictionless horizontal table and undergo an inelastic collision with coefficient of restitution $e = 0$. Before the collision, A has speed u while B is stationary. After the collision, B moves off at an angle $\frac{\pi}{4}$ measured clockwise from the direction of approach of A. Let $\mathbf{i}$ be the unit vector in the direction of motion of B. Let $\mathbf{j}$ be the unit vector obtained by rotating $\mathbf{i}$ through $\frac{\pi}{2}$ anticlockwise in the plane of the horizontal table. Find the velocities of both balls after the collision.

Such a collision is sometimes called a plastic collision.

(*Hint*: The vector $\mathbf{j}$ lies in the common tangent plane for the collision.)

End-of-section Exercise

Exercise 4.4

A rubber ball is dropped from rest onto a horizontal floor, and after bouncing twice it rebounds to half its original height. Calculate the coefficient of restitution between the ball and the floor.

Outcomes

After studying this unit you should be able to:
- find the centre of mass of a system of particles;
- determine the motion of the centre of mass of a system of particles;
- find the centre of mass of certain homogeneous rigid bodies;
- use the centre of mass to calculate the potential energy of a homogeneous rigid body;
- apply the principle of conservation of linear momentum to collisions between objects;
- apply Newton's law of restitution to collisions between objects.

Solutions to the exercises

Section 1

1.1 **(a)** Resolving the forces into components gives $\mathbf{T}_2 = -|\mathbf{T}_2|\mathbf{i}$ and $\mathbf{T}_4 = -|\mathbf{T}_4|\mathbf{i}$. Resolving Equations (1.1) and (1.2) in the **i**-direction then gives

$$m_1 g - |\mathbf{T}_2| = m_1 \ddot{x}_1,$$
$$m_2 g - |\mathbf{T}_4| = m_2 \ddot{x}_2.$$

To progress further we need to relate $\ddot{x}_1$ and $\ddot{x}_2$, and to relate $|\mathbf{T}_2|$ and $|\mathbf{T}_4|$. Using the assumption that the cable is inextensible gives $x_1 + x_2 = \text{constant}$, as quoted in the question. Differentiating this twice gives the desired relation between the accelerations of the lift and the counterweight: $\ddot{x}_1 = -\ddot{x}_2$. To find relationships between the magnitudes of the tension forces, we use the assumptions that the cable is a model string and the pulley is a model pulley to obtain $|\mathbf{T}_2| = |\mathbf{T}_1|$ (model string), $|\mathbf{T}_1| = |\mathbf{T}_3|$ (model pulley) and $|\mathbf{T}_3| = |\mathbf{T}_4|$ (model string again). Putting these together gives $|\mathbf{T}_2| = |\mathbf{T}_4|$, which we can substitute into the above equations to obtain

$$m_1 g - |\mathbf{T}_2| = -m_1 \ddot{x}_2,$$
$$m_2 g - |\mathbf{T}_2| = m_2 \ddot{x}_2.$$

Eliminating $|\mathbf{T}_2|$ by subtracting the first equation from the second gives

$$m_2 g - m_1 g = m_2 \ddot{x}_2 + m_1 \ddot{x}_2.$$

Rearrangement gives the acceleration of the lift:

$$\ddot{x}_2 = \frac{(m_2 - m_1)g}{m_1 + m_2}. \tag{S.1}$$

(b) Substituting for $\ddot{x}_2$ in Equation (1.2) gives

$$m_2 g\,\mathbf{i} + \mathbf{T}_4 = m_2 \left(\frac{(m_2 - m_1)g}{m_1 + m_2} \right) \mathbf{i}.$$

Rearranging gives

$$\mathbf{T}_4 = m_2 g \left(\frac{m_2 - m_1}{m_1 + m_2} - 1 \right) \mathbf{i}$$
$$= m_2 g \left(\frac{m_2 - m_1 - m_1 - m_2}{m_1 + m_2} \right) \mathbf{i}$$
$$= -\frac{2 m_1 m_2 g}{m_1 + m_2} \mathbf{i}.$$

From part (a) we have $|\mathbf{T}_1| = |\mathbf{T}_2| = |\mathbf{T}_3| = |\mathbf{T}_4|$, so the magnitude of the tension in the cable is $2 m_1 m_2 g/(m_1 + m_2)$.

(c) Resolving Equation (1.3) in the **i**-direction gives

$$-|\mathbf{S}| + |\mathbf{T}_1| + |\mathbf{T}_3| = 0.$$

From part (a) we have $|\mathbf{T}_1| = |\mathbf{T}_2| = |\mathbf{T}_3| = |\mathbf{T}_4|$, so

$$|\mathbf{S}| = 2|\mathbf{T}_2| = \frac{4 m_1 m_2 g}{m_1 + m_2}.$$

(d) Substituting the given values $m_1 = 1000\,\text{kg}$ and $m_2 = 1065\,\text{kg}$ into the equation for the acceleration of the lift (Equation (S.1)) gives

$$\ddot{x}_2 = 65g/2065 \simeq 0.31\,\text{m s}^{-2}.$$

The speed of the lift after the lift has travelled $100\,\text{m}$ can be calculated using the constant acceleration formula $v^2 = v_0^2 + 2ax$, where v_0 is the initial speed of the lift (zero in this case). Substituting in the values gives

$$v^2 \simeq 0^2 + 2 \times 0.31 \times 100 = 62.$$

So the speed of the lift after travelling $100\,\text{m}$ is $\sqrt{62} \simeq 7.9\,\text{m s}^{-1}$. This is more than fast enough to give the occupant a nasty bump! This explains why such a design is impractical: a lift that travels with constant acceleration (either up or down) could be quite dangerous.

1.2 The internal forces are $\mathbf{T}_1$, $\mathbf{T}_2$, $\mathbf{T}_3$, $\mathbf{T}_4$, $\mathbf{T}_5$, $\mathbf{T}_6$, $\mathbf{T}_7$ and $\mathbf{T}_8$. The external forces are $\mathbf{S}_1$, $\mathbf{S}_2$, $\mathbf{W}_A$ and $\mathbf{W}_B$. The total force is $\mathbf{F} = \mathbf{S}_1 + \mathbf{S}_2 + \mathbf{W}_A + \mathbf{W}_B$.

1.3 Since the radii of the Earth and the Moon are small compared with their distance apart, we can model each as a particle so that we have a two-particle system.

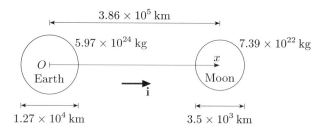

If we choose an x-axis joining the centre of the Earth to the centre of the Moon, as shown in the figure, with the centre of the Earth at the origin, then using the definition of centre of mass we have, working in kilometres,

$$\mathbf{r}_G = \frac{m_{\text{Earth}} \mathbf{r}_{\text{Earth}} + m_{\text{Moon}} \mathbf{r}_{\text{Moon}}}{m_{\text{Earth}} + m_{\text{Moon}}}$$
$$= \frac{(5.97 \times 10^{24}) \times \mathbf{0} + (7.39 \times 10^{22}) \times (3.86 \times 10^5)\mathbf{i}}{5.97 \times 10^{24} + 7.39 \times 10^{22}}$$
$$\simeq 4720\mathbf{i}.$$

So the distance from the centre of the Earth to the centre of mass of the Earth/Moon system is about $4720\,\text{km}$; but the radius of the Earth is about $6350\,\text{km}$, so the centre of mass of this system is about $1630\,\text{km}$ *below* the Earth's surface.

1.4 **(a)** The force diagram is shown below.

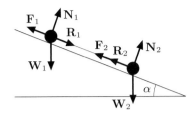

The only internal forces are those due to the rod, $\mathbf{R}_1$ and $\mathbf{R}_2$. The remaining forces — the weights $\mathbf{W}_1$ and $\mathbf{W}_2$, the normal reaction forces $\mathbf{N}_1$ and $\mathbf{N}_2$, and the friction forces $\mathbf{F}_1$ and $\mathbf{F}_2$ — are all external forces.

(b) We define axes as shown below, with origin at the initial position of the upper particle.

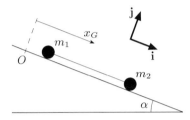

Equation (1.13), $\mathbf{F}^{\text{ext}} = M\ddot{\mathbf{r}}_G$, gives
$$\mathbf{W}_1 + \mathbf{W}_2 + \mathbf{N}_1 + \mathbf{N}_2 + \mathbf{F}_1 + \mathbf{F}_2$$
$$= (m_1 + m_2)\ddot{\mathbf{r}}_G, \tag{S.2}$$
where $\mathbf{r}_G = x_G\mathbf{i}$ is the position vector of the centre of mass relative to O. We have
$$\mathbf{W}_1 = m_1 g((\sin\alpha)\mathbf{i} - (\cos\alpha)\mathbf{j}),$$
$$\mathbf{W}_2 = m_2 g((\sin\alpha)\mathbf{i} - (\cos\alpha)\mathbf{j}),$$
$$\mathbf{N}_1 = |\mathbf{N}_1|\mathbf{j}, \quad \mathbf{N}_2 = |\mathbf{N}_2|\mathbf{j},$$
$$\mathbf{F}_1 = -|\mathbf{F}_1|\mathbf{i}, \quad \mathbf{F}_2 = -|\mathbf{F}_2|\mathbf{i}.$$
Also, $|\mathbf{F}_1| = \mu'|\mathbf{N}_1|$ and $|\mathbf{F}_2| = \mu'|\mathbf{N}_2|$.
Thus Equation (S.2) becomes
$$m_1 g((\sin\alpha)\mathbf{i} - (\cos\alpha)\mathbf{j}) + m_2 g((\sin\alpha)\mathbf{i} - (\cos\alpha)\mathbf{j})$$
$$+|\mathbf{N}_1|\mathbf{j} + |\mathbf{N}_2|\mathbf{j} - \mu'|\mathbf{N}_1|\mathbf{i} - \mu'|\mathbf{N}_2|\mathbf{i} = (m_1 + m_2)\ddot{x}_G\mathbf{i}.$$
Resolving in the $\mathbf{i}$- and $\mathbf{j}$-directions in turn gives
$$(m_1 + m_2)g\sin\alpha - \mu'(|\mathbf{N}_1| + |\mathbf{N}_2|)$$
$$= (m_1 + m_2)\ddot{x}_G, \tag{S.3}$$
$$-(m_1 + m_2)g\cos\alpha + |\mathbf{N}_1| + |\mathbf{N}_2| = 0. \tag{S.4}$$
From Equation (S.4) we have
$$|\mathbf{N}_1| + |\mathbf{N}_2| = (m_1 + m_2)g\cos\alpha.$$
Substituting this into Equation (S.3) gives
$$(m_1 + m_2)g(\sin\alpha - \mu'\cos\alpha) = (m_1 + m_2)\ddot{x}_G,$$
which simplifies to
$$\ddot{x}_G = g(\sin\alpha - \mu'\cos\alpha). \tag{S.5}$$
This is the required equation of motion for the centre of mass.

(c) Changing the rod to a light spring would change only the internal forces; the external forces would remain the same. Similarly, removing the rod would not

change the external forces. So in both cases the equation of motion of the centre of mass will be as in part (b).

(d) You saw in *Unit 6* (e.g. Example 3.2 and Exercise 3.4) that the equation of motion of a particle sliding down an inclined plane is
$$a = g(\sin\alpha - \mu'\cos\alpha),$$
where a is the acceleration of the particle and α is the angle of incline. This is identical to Equation (S.5) with $\ddot{x}_G$ replaced by a. Thus the motion of the centre of mass of a two-particle system sliding down an inclined plane is the same as the motion of a single particle sliding down the plane.

1.5 The equation $\mathbf{P} = 2m\ddot{x}_G\mathbf{i}$ still holds, so that $\ddot{x}_G = |\mathbf{P}|/(2m)$. But now d is constant, so $x_A = x_G - d$ and $x_B = x_G + d$ give $\ddot{x}_A = \ddot{x}_G = \ddot{x}_B$. Hence A, B and G all move with the same fixed acceleration $|\mathbf{P}|/(2m)$. The system moves as a rigid body and there is no oscillatory motion.

We denote the forces on particles A and B due to the model rod by $\mathbf{R}_A$ and $\mathbf{R}_B$. Applying Newton's second law to particle A gives
$$\mathbf{R}_A = m\ddot{x}_A\mathbf{i} = m\ddot{x}_G\mathbf{i} = \tfrac{1}{2}|\mathbf{P}|\mathbf{i}.$$
Also, since $\mathbf{R}_B = -\mathbf{R}_A$, we have $\mathbf{R}_B = -\tfrac{1}{2}|\mathbf{P}|\mathbf{i}$. So the forces exerted by the rod on A and B have half the magnitude of $\mathbf{P}$ and are directed from each particle towards the centre of the rod.

1.6 There are no external forces, so from Equation (1.13) we have $\ddot{\mathbf{r}}_G = \mathbf{0}$, and it follows that $\dot{x}_G = c$ (a constant). Now
$$x_G = \frac{mx_A + mx_B}{m + m} = \frac{x_A + x_B}{2},$$
where $\mathbf{r}_A = x_A\mathbf{i}$ and $\mathbf{r}_B = x_B\mathbf{i}$ are the position vectors of A and B. So
$$\dot{x}_G = \frac{\dot{x}_A + \dot{x}_B}{2} = c.$$
Initially, we have $\dot{x}_A = 0$ and $\dot{x}_B = 6$, so $c = 3$. Integrating the equation $\dot{x}_G = 3$ with respect to time gives $x_G = 3t + 1.5$ (because the centre of mass is initially at $x = 1.5$). Substituting $t = 0.5$ into this gives $x_G = (3 \times 0.5) + 1.5 = 3$ and $x_B = 3$, therefore we must also have $x_A = 3$, i.e. the particles collide at $t = 0.5$.

1.7 Not a chance! If we consider the ship and the alien as a two-particle system, then, from Newton's third law, any force that the alien exerts on the ship is met by an equal and opposite force from the ship on the alien. In other words, nothing the alien does can affect the external forces acting on the system, so he cannot change the motion of the centre of mass of the two-particle system.

1.8 We can use notation similar to that of Example 1.2, using $x_G\mathbf{i}$ as the position vector of the centre of mass G (which is mid-way between A and B), and $x_A\mathbf{i}$, and $x_B\mathbf{i}$ as the position vectors of A and B, all with respect to a horizontal x-axis with origin at the position of A before the force is applied. As in Example 1.2, the motion is in a horizontal plane, so the vertical forces must sum to zero. From Equation (1.13) we have

$$\mathbf{P} = \mathbf{F}^{\text{ext}} = (m_A + m_B)\ddot{\mathbf{r}}_G = 100\ddot{x}_G\mathbf{i}.$$

The string is taut and inextensible, so A, B and the centre of mass have the same acceleration, and in particular $\ddot{x}_B\mathbf{i} = \ddot{x}_G\mathbf{i}$. Let $\mathbf{T}$ be the force exerted by the string on B. Then applying Newton's second law to B we have

$$\mathbf{P} + \mathbf{T} = m_B\ddot{x}_B\mathbf{i} = 50\ddot{x}_G\mathbf{i} = \tfrac{1}{2}\mathbf{P}.$$

It follows that $\mathbf{T} = -\tfrac{1}{2}\mathbf{P}$, so, if the string is not to break, the magnitude of $\mathbf{P}$ must not exceed $20\,\text{N}$.

1.9 Choose the wire to lie along the x-axis, and suppose that the particles are moving in the positive direction. The forces acting on each particle are its weight $\mathbf{W}$, the normal reaction $\mathbf{N}$ of the wire and friction $\mathbf{F}$ (which acts at right angles to the other two). We have $\mathbf{N} = -\mathbf{W}$ and $|\mathbf{F}| = \mu'|\mathbf{N}|$. If particle A has mass m_A and particle B has mass m_B, then the friction force on A is $\mathbf{F}_A = -\mu'm_Ag\mathbf{i}$ and the friction force on B is $\mathbf{F}_B = -\mu'm_Bg\mathbf{i}$. Since the normal reactions and weights cancel each other out, the total external force is $\mathbf{F}^{\text{ext}} = \mathbf{F}_A + \mathbf{F}_B = -\mu'(m_A + m_B)g\mathbf{i}$. Hence, by Equation (1.13), we have

$$-\mu'(m_A + m_B)g\mathbf{i} = (m_A + m_B)\ddot{\mathbf{r}}_G,$$

giving $\ddot{\mathbf{r}}_G = -\mu'g\mathbf{i} = -0.4g\mathbf{i}$. So the centre of mass accelerates at $0.4g\,\text{m s}^{-2}$ in the direction opposite to that of the motion of the particles. (Notice that the masses of the particles do not affect this result.)

1.10 We choose the x-axis to lie along the track in the direction of the external force. Using Equation (1.13) with $\mathbf{F}^{\text{ext}} = 20\mathbf{i}$ and $M = 5\,\text{kg}$, we have $20\mathbf{i} = 5\ddot{\mathbf{r}}_G$, so $\ddot{\mathbf{r}}_G = 4\mathbf{i}$. Therefore the common acceleration of the particles is $4\,\text{m s}^{-2}$. Applying Newton's second law to the first particle, we obtain

$$\text{internal force} = 4 \times 4\mathbf{i} = 16\mathbf{i},$$

so the internal forces have magnitude $16\,\text{N}$.

Section 2

2.1 (a) If we let $\mathbf{i}$ denote a unit vector in the positive x-direction, then we have particles of mass m at the points $\mathbf{r}_1 = \mathbf{0}$, $\mathbf{r}_2 = 4\mathbf{i}$ and $\mathbf{r}_3 = 6\mathbf{i}$, relative to O. From Equation (2.1) we have

$$\mathbf{r}_G = \frac{m\mathbf{r}_1 + m\mathbf{r}_2 + m\mathbf{r}_3}{m + m + m} = \frac{0 + 4\mathbf{i} + 6\mathbf{i}}{3} = \tfrac{10}{3}\mathbf{i}.$$

(b) Similarly,

$$\mathbf{r}_G = \frac{\mathbf{0} + \mathbf{i} + 4\mathbf{i} + 5\mathbf{i} + 6\mathbf{i}}{5} = \tfrac{16}{5}\mathbf{i}.$$

2.2 (a) Let $\mathbf{i}$ be a unit vector in the positive x-direction. The most obvious way to calculate the centre of mass is to use Equation (2.1), giving

$$\mathbf{r}_G = \frac{m \times \mathbf{0} + m \times 2\mathbf{i} + m \times 4\mathbf{i} + m \times 6\mathbf{i}}{m + m + m + m} = \frac{12m\mathbf{i}}{4m},$$

so $\mathbf{r}_G = 3\mathbf{i}$.

Alternatively, in this case, the centre of mass can also be found by inspection, since the system is symmetric about the point $(3,0)$. So this is the centre of mass, i.e. $\mathbf{r}_G = 3\mathbf{i}$.

(b) To find the position vector of the centre of mass, relative to O, consider Cartesian unit vectors $\mathbf{i}$ and $\mathbf{j}$ in the positive x- and y-directions. Now use Equation (2.1):

$$\mathbf{r}_G = \frac{m\mathbf{r}_1 + m\mathbf{r}_2 + m\mathbf{r}_3}{m + m + m}$$
$$= \frac{\mathbf{0} + 2\mathbf{i} + (\mathbf{i} + \sqrt{3}\mathbf{j})}{3} = \mathbf{i} + \tfrac{1}{\sqrt{3}}\mathbf{j}.$$

Alternatively you could have used symmetry. In this case notice that the particles are at the corners of an equilateral triangle (the fact that $\left(\sqrt{3}\right)^2 + 1^2 = 4$ tells us that the sloping sides are each of length 2). So the centre of mass is at the geometric centre of the triangle. If you know that the geometric centre of an equilateral triangle is one third of the way up the perpendicular from a base to an apex, then you can write down the equation immediately as $\mathbf{r}_G = \mathbf{i} + \tfrac{1}{3}\left(\sqrt{3}\mathbf{j}\right) = \mathbf{i} + \tfrac{1}{\sqrt{3}}\mathbf{j}$. (This result is proved later, on page 116.)

2.3 The squares are of equal size and hence of equal mass, m say, with centres of mass at

$$\mathbf{r}_{G_1} = \tfrac{1}{2}a\mathbf{i} + \tfrac{3}{2}a\mathbf{j}, \ \mathbf{r}_{G_2} = \tfrac{1}{2}a\mathbf{i} + \tfrac{1}{2}a\mathbf{j}, \ \mathbf{r}_{G_3} = \tfrac{3}{2}a\mathbf{i} + \tfrac{1}{2}a\mathbf{j}.$$

Hence, using Equation (2.1), the centre of mass of the whole shape is $\mathbf{r}_G$ at position vector

$$\frac{m\left(\tfrac{1}{2}a\mathbf{i} + \tfrac{3}{2}a\mathbf{j}\right) + m\left(\tfrac{1}{2}a\mathbf{i} + \tfrac{1}{2}a\mathbf{j}\right) + m\left(\tfrac{3}{2}a\mathbf{i} + \tfrac{1}{2}a\mathbf{j}\right)}{3m}$$
$$= \tfrac{5}{6}a\mathbf{i} + \tfrac{5}{6}a\mathbf{j},$$

which, as expected, is the same as the result we obtained in Example 2.1.

2.4 The uniform density and constant cross-sectional area mean that the problem reduces to a two-dimensional one. One way to find the centre of mass of the two-dimensional cross-section is to divide it into triangles as in Figure 2.8(b), and to find the centre of mass of each.

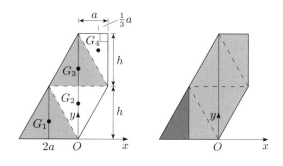

Relative to the origin at O shown above, the position vectors of the centres of mass G_1, G_2, G_3 and G_4 are

$$\mathbf{r}_{G_1} = -a\mathbf{i} + \tfrac{1}{3}h\mathbf{j}, \quad \mathbf{r}_{G_2} = \tfrac{2}{3}h\mathbf{j},$$

$$\mathbf{r}_{G_3} = \tfrac{4}{3}h\mathbf{j}, \quad \mathbf{r}_{G_4} = \tfrac{2}{3}a\mathbf{i} + \tfrac{5}{3}h\mathbf{j},$$

where h is half the height of the sculpture (as shown), and $\mathbf{i}$ and $\mathbf{j}$ are Cartesian unit vectors in the positive x- and y-directions.

If we model the equilateral triangles as particles of mass m (say) at G_1, G_2 and G_3, then the fourth triangle can be modelled as a particle of mass $\tfrac{1}{2}m$ at G_4. Then Equation (2.1) gives the centre of mass of the cross-section $\mathbf{r}_G$ as

$$\frac{m(-a\mathbf{i} + \tfrac{1}{3}h\mathbf{j}) + m(\tfrac{2}{3}h\mathbf{j}) + m(\tfrac{4}{3}h\mathbf{j}) + \tfrac{1}{2}m(\tfrac{2}{3}a\mathbf{i} + \tfrac{5}{3}h\mathbf{j})}{m + m + m + \tfrac{1}{2}m}$$

$$= \frac{-\tfrac{2}{3}a\mathbf{i} + \tfrac{19}{6}h\mathbf{j}}{\tfrac{7}{2}} = -\tfrac{4}{21}a\mathbf{i} + \tfrac{19}{21}h\mathbf{j}.$$

Since $\mathbf{r}_G$ lies to the left of O, we find that the sculpture will not topple over.

Alternatively, you could notice that the lightly shaded part of the cross-section on the right above is symmetric about the y-axis and so its centre of mass will lie on the y-axis. Hence the whole cross-section, with the darker shaded triangle added, must have its centre of mass to the left of O, so that the sculpture will not topple over.

2.5 Taking a datum at ground level, the height of the centre of mass above the datum is $2h$ when upright and $\tfrac{1}{2}h$ when lying down. So the change in potential energy is $Mg \times 2h - Mg \times \tfrac{1}{2}h = \tfrac{3}{2}Mgh$.

2.6 The total external force on the ball is its weight $M\mathbf{g}$, so, from Equation (2.5), we have

$$M\mathbf{g} = M\ddot{\mathbf{r}}_G,$$

which gives $\ddot{\mathbf{r}}_G = \mathbf{g}$, so the centre of mass of the ball accelerates downwards with the acceleration due to gravity. Taking this as the direction of the x-axis, we have $\mathbf{r}_G = x_G\mathbf{i}$ and

$$\ddot{x}_G = g.$$

So the acceleration is constant and we may use the constant acceleration formula $v^2 = v_0^2 + 2a_0x$ from *Unit 6*. In this case we have

$$\dot{x}_G^2 = [\dot{x}_G(0)]^2 + 2gh = 2gh,$$

since the ball starts from rest. So the velocity of the ball after falling a distance h is $\sqrt{2gh}$.

(Notice that these equations are exactly what we would have obtained if we had modelled the ball as a particle.) The change in the potential energy is $-Mgh$.

2.7 The solid shape is composed of two cylinders with radii a and $3a$, each with thickness $2a$. The centre of mass lies on the axis of symmetry (the x-axis in Figure 2.10). The positions of the centres of mass of the two cylinders, G_1 and G_2, relative to O are given by

$$\mathbf{r}_{G_1} = a\mathbf{i} \quad \text{and} \quad \mathbf{r}_{G_2} = 3a\mathbf{i}.$$

The volume of the smaller cylinder is given by

$$V_1 = \pi a^2 \times 2a = 2\pi a^3,$$

while the volume of the larger cylinder is given by

$$V_2 = \pi(3a)^2 \times 2a = 18\pi a^3.$$

If the density of the material is ρ, then the corresponding masses are

$$m_1 = 2\pi\rho a^3 \quad \text{and} \quad m_2 = 18\pi\rho a^3.$$

From Equation (2.1) we have

$$\mathbf{r}_G = \frac{2\pi\rho a^3(a\mathbf{i}) + 18\pi\rho a^3(3a\mathbf{i})}{20\pi\rho a^3} = \tfrac{14}{5}a\mathbf{i}.$$

The centre of mass is a little to the left of G_2, as we would expect. The object will not topple over because $14a/5 > 2a$, so the centre of mass is to the right of the point P in Figure 2.10 (the leftmost point of contact with the surface).

2.8 (a) The volume V of a pyramid is given by

$$V = \tfrac{1}{3} \times \text{base area} \times \text{vertical height},$$

so in this case we have

$$V = \tfrac{1}{3} \times (230)^2 \times 147 = 2\,592\,100\,\text{m}^3.$$

Hence the total mass is approximately

$$2\,592\,100 \times 2500 \simeq 6.48 \times 10^9\,\text{kg}.$$

(b) The centre of mass is a quarter of the height above the base, which in this case is $h/4$. The total energy required to lift all the stones from ground level is

$$Mg(h/4) = (6.48 \times 10^9) \times 9.81 \times 147/4$$
$$\simeq 2.34 \times 10^{12}\,\text{J}.$$

(c) According to the question, the energy a man can expend in a day is $1000g$ J. So the total number of days required by 1000 men is approximately

$$\frac{2.34 \times 10^{12}}{1000 \times 9.81 \times 1000} \simeq 2.4 \times 10^5 \text{ days}.$$

A gang of 1000 men would therefore take about 652 years. (This figure is certainly a low estimate, since it takes no account of friction in the system used to lift the stones, nor the time taken to construct the lifting mechanism. However, we can be reasonably sure that it would have taken 1000 men more than 600 years to lift the stones to the appropriate heights, which gives some idea of the scale of the enterprise.)

Section 3

3.1 If we take $\mathbf{i}$ to be a unit vector in the direction of motion, then the total linear momentum of the system just before the collision is $\mathbf{P}_{\text{before}} = Mu\mathbf{i} + m\mathbf{0} = Mu\mathbf{i}$, and the total linear momentum just after the collision is $\mathbf{P}_{\text{after}} = (M + m)v\mathbf{i}$. If the collision is instantaneous, then the principle of conservation of linear momentum tells us that

$$Mu\mathbf{i} = (M + m)v\mathbf{i}.$$

Resolving in the $\mathbf{i}$-direction and rearranging, we obtain

$$v = Mu/(M + m).$$

3.2 **(a)** We define an x-axis along the track in the direction of motion of the first truck before impact. Let the trucks have masses m_1 and m_2, and velocities before impact $\dot{\mathbf{r}}_1 = \dot{x}_1\mathbf{i}$ and $\dot{\mathbf{r}}_2 = \dot{x}_2\mathbf{i}$. Then the total linear momentum before impact is

$$m_1\dot{x}_1\mathbf{i} + m_2\dot{x}_2\mathbf{i} = 15\,000 \times 4\mathbf{i} + 10\,000 \times \mathbf{0} = 60\,000\mathbf{i}.$$

After impact, the combined mass of $25\,000\,\text{kg}$ moves with speed V say, so the linear momentum is $25\,000V\mathbf{i}$. By the principle of conservation of linear momentum,

$$60\,000\mathbf{i} = 25\,000V\mathbf{i},$$

therefore $V = 2.4\,\text{m s}^{-1}$.

(b) The kinetic energy before impact is

$$\tfrac{1}{2}m_1\dot{x}_1^2 + \tfrac{1}{2}m_2\dot{x}_2^2 = \tfrac{1}{2}15\,000(4)^2 = 120\,000\,\text{J},$$

while after impact the kinetic energy is

$$\tfrac{1}{2}25\,000(2.4)^2 = 72\,000\,\text{J},$$

so the collision is not elastic.

3.3 Choose the positive x-direction to be along the direction of motion of the white ball before the collision, and the positive y-direction to correspond to a positive $\mathbf{j}$-component for the velocity of the green ball after the collision, where $\mathbf{i}$ and $\mathbf{j}$ are Cartesian unit vectors in the positive x- and y- directions. The situation is illustrated in the figure below.

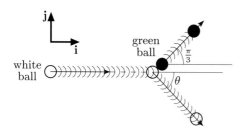

If $\dot{\mathbf{R}}_1$ and $\dot{\mathbf{R}}_2$ are the velocities of the white and green balls, respectively, after the collision, then we have

$$\dot{\mathbf{R}}_1 = (|\dot{\mathbf{R}}_1|\cos\theta)\mathbf{i} + (|\dot{\mathbf{R}}_1|\sin\theta)\mathbf{j} = U_x\mathbf{i} + U_y\mathbf{j},$$

where $U_x = |\dot{\mathbf{R}}_1|\cos\theta$ and $U_y = |\dot{\mathbf{R}}_1|\sin\theta$, and

$$\dot{\mathbf{R}}_2 = (|\dot{\mathbf{R}}_2|\cos\tfrac{\pi}{3})\mathbf{i} + (|\dot{\mathbf{R}}_2|\sin\tfrac{\pi}{3})\mathbf{j}$$
$$= \tfrac{1}{2}V\mathbf{i} + \tfrac{\sqrt{3}}{2}V\mathbf{j},$$

where $V = |\dot{\mathbf{R}}_2|$ is the speed of the green ball. Also, if $\dot{\mathbf{r}}_1$ and $\dot{\mathbf{r}}_2$ are the velocities of the white and green balls before the collision, then we have

$$\dot{\mathbf{r}}_1 = u\mathbf{i} \quad \text{and} \quad \dot{\mathbf{r}}_2 = \mathbf{0}.$$

Therefore, by the principle of conservation of linear momentum,

$$mu\mathbf{i} = m(U_x\mathbf{i} + U_y\mathbf{j}) + m(\tfrac{1}{2}V\mathbf{i} + \tfrac{\sqrt{3}}{2}V\mathbf{j}).$$

Resolving in the $\mathbf{i}$- and $\mathbf{j}$-directions and dividing by m gives

$$u = U_x + \tfrac{1}{2}V,$$
$$0 = U_y + \tfrac{\sqrt{3}}{2}V.$$

This gives the velocity of the white ball after the collision in terms of the speed of the green ball after the

collision as

$$U_x = u - \tfrac{1}{2}V,$$
$$U_y = -\tfrac{\sqrt{3}}{2}V.$$

To determine the remaining unknown, V, we use the fact that the collision is elastic; so kinetic energy is conserved and we have

$$\tfrac{1}{2}mu^2 = \tfrac{1}{2}m(U_x^2 + U_y^2) + \tfrac{1}{2}mV^2$$
$$= \tfrac{1}{2}m\left((u - \tfrac{1}{2}V)^2 + (-\tfrac{\sqrt{3}}{2}V)^2\right) + \tfrac{1}{2}mV^2,$$

which, after simplifying and dividing by $\tfrac{1}{2}m$, becomes $uV = 2V^2$. Since $V \neq 0$, we have $V = \tfrac{1}{2}u$. Therefore

$$U_x = \tfrac{3}{4}u,$$
$$U_y = -\tfrac{\sqrt{3}}{4}u,$$

and so the velocities of the balls after impact are

$$\dot{\mathbf{R}}_1 = u\left(\tfrac{3}{4}\mathbf{i} - \tfrac{\sqrt{3}}{4}\mathbf{j}\right) \quad \text{and} \quad \dot{\mathbf{R}}_2 = u\left(\tfrac{1}{4}\mathbf{i} + \tfrac{\sqrt{3}}{4}\mathbf{j}\right).$$

Also, $\tan\theta = U_y/U_x = -\tfrac{1}{\sqrt{3}}$, so $\theta = -\pi/6$. So the white ball moves off at an angle $\pi/6$ below the x-axis.

3.4 Suppose that the velocity of the particles immediately after the collision is $\mathbf{V}$. Then, from the principle of conservation of linear momentum, we have

$$m_1 u\mathbf{i} + m_2 u\mathbf{j} = (m_1 + m_2)\mathbf{V}.$$

It follows that

$$\mathbf{V} = \frac{u(m_1\mathbf{i} + m_2\mathbf{j})}{m_1 + m_2} = \frac{m_1 u}{m_1 + m_2}\mathbf{i} + \frac{m_2 u}{m_1 + m_2}\mathbf{j}.$$

The kinetic energy before impact is $\tfrac{1}{2}(m_1 + m_2)u^2$, while the kinetic energy after impact is

$$\tfrac{1}{2}(m_1 + m_2)\left[\left(\frac{m_1 u}{m_1 + m_2}\right)^2 + \left(\frac{m_2 u}{m_1 + m_2}\right)^2\right]$$
$$= \tfrac{1}{2}\frac{m_1^2 + m_2^2}{m_1 + m_2}u^2.$$

The collision is therefore not elastic. (The loss of kinetic energy is $m_1 m_2 u^2/(m_1 + m_2)$.)

3.5 **(a)** If $m_1 = m_2 = 3$, $\mathbf{v}_1 = 2\mathbf{i}$, $\mathbf{v}_2 = \mathbf{0}$ and $\mathbf{V}_1 = \mathbf{i} + \mathbf{j}$, $\mathbf{V}_2 = \mathbf{i} - \mathbf{j}$, then the kinetic energy just before impact is

$$\tfrac{1}{2}m_1|\mathbf{v}_1|^2 + \tfrac{1}{2}m_2|\mathbf{v}_2|^2 = \tfrac{1}{2}(3 \times 4 + 3 \times 0) = 6,$$

and the kinetic energy just after impact is

$$\tfrac{1}{2}m_1|\mathbf{V}_1|^2 + \tfrac{1}{2}m_2|\mathbf{V}_2|^2 = \tfrac{1}{2}(3 \times 2 + 3 \times 2) = 6.$$

Therefore the collision is elastic.

(b) We are given $m_1 = 1$, $m_2 = 3$, $\mathbf{v}_1 = 2\mathbf{i} + \mathbf{j}$, $\mathbf{v}_2 = \mathbf{j}$ and $\mathbf{V}_1 = \mathbf{V}_2 = \tfrac{1}{2}\mathbf{i} + \mathbf{j}$, so the kinetic energy just before impact is

$$\tfrac{1}{2}m_1|\mathbf{v}_1|^2 + \tfrac{1}{2}m_2|\mathbf{v}_2|^2 = \tfrac{1}{2}(1 \times 5 + 3 \times 1) = 4,$$

and the kinetic energy just after impact is

$$\tfrac{1}{2}m_1|\mathbf{V}_1|^2 + \tfrac{1}{2}m_2|\mathbf{V}_2|^2$$
$$= \tfrac{1}{2}(1 \times 1.25 + 3 \times 1.25) = 2.5.$$

As there is a loss of kinetic energy, the collision is inelastic. The decrease in kinetic energy is 1.5 joules.

Section 4

4.1 (a) Take the positive x-axis to be in the direction of motion of ball A before impact, and let $\mathbf{i}$ be a unit vector in this direction. Then we can write the velocities of the balls before impact as $\dot{\mathbf{r}}_1 = \dot{x}_1\mathbf{i}$ and $\dot{\mathbf{r}}_2 = \dot{x}_2\mathbf{i}$, and after impact as $\dot{\mathbf{R}}_1 = \dot{X}_1\mathbf{i}$ and $\dot{\mathbf{R}}_2 = \dot{X}_2\mathbf{i}$. Modelling the balls as particles, we can use the principle of conservation of linear momentum to obtain

$$m_1\dot{x}_1\mathbf{i} + m_2\dot{x}_2\mathbf{i} = m_1\dot{X}_1\mathbf{i} + m_2\dot{X}_2\mathbf{i}.$$

Also, Equation (4.1) gives the relative velocity after impact as

$$\dot{X}_1\mathbf{i} - \dot{X}_2\mathbf{i} = -e(\dot{x}_1\mathbf{i} - \dot{x}_2\mathbf{i}).$$

Resolving both equations in the $\mathbf{i}$-direction gives

$$m_1\dot{x}_1 + m_2\dot{x}_2 = m_1\dot{X}_1 + m_2\dot{X}_2,$$
$$\dot{X}_1 - \dot{X}_2 = -e(\dot{x}_1 - \dot{x}_2).$$

Eliminating $\dot{X}_1$ between these equations, we obtain

$$m_1\dot{x}_1 + m_2\dot{x}_2 = m_1(\dot{X}_2 - e(\dot{x}_1 - \dot{x}_2)) + m_2\dot{X}_2$$
$$= (m_1 + m_2)\dot{X}_2 - em_1(\dot{x}_1 - \dot{x}_2),$$

so

$$\dot{X}_2 = \frac{m_1(1+e)\dot{x}_1 + (m_2 - em_1)\dot{x}_2}{m_1 + m_2}.$$

Therefore

$$\dot{X}_1 = \dot{X}_2 - e(\dot{x}_1 - \dot{x}_2)$$
$$= \frac{(m_1 - em_2)\dot{x}_1 + m_2(1+e)\dot{x}_2}{m_1 + m_2}.$$

So the velocities after impact are

$$\dot{\mathbf{R}}_1 = \frac{(m_1 - em_2)\dot{x}_1 + m_2(1+e)\dot{x}_2}{m_1 + m_2}\,\mathbf{i},$$
$$\dot{\mathbf{R}}_2 = \frac{m_1(1+e)\dot{x}_1 + (m_2 - em_1)\dot{x}_2}{m_1 + m_2}\,\mathbf{i}.$$

(b) The situation here is the same as in Example 3.2 with $m_1 = m_2 = m$, $\dot{x}_1 = 5\,\mathrm{m\,s^{-1}}$, $\dot{x}_2 = 0\,\mathrm{m\,s^{-1}}$ and $e = 1$ (since the collision is elastic), so we have

$$\dot{X}_1 = \frac{(m-m)5 + m(1+1)0}{m+m} = 0\,\mathrm{m\,s^{-1}},$$
$$\dot{X}_2 = \frac{m(1+1)5 + (m-m)0}{m+m} = 5\,\mathrm{m\,s^{-1}},$$

as in Example 3.2.

4.2 Let U and V be the speeds after the collision of the balls of masses m_1 and m_2, respectively. If we let $\mathbf{i}$ be a unit vector in the direction of motion, then the principle of conservation of linear momentum gives

$$m_1 u\mathbf{i} = m_1 U\mathbf{i} + m_2 V\mathbf{i},$$

so, resolving in the $\mathbf{i}$-direction, we obtain

$$m_1 u = m_1 U + m_2 V.$$

Equation (4.1) gives the relative velocity after impact as

$$V\mathbf{i} - U\mathbf{i} = -e(\mathbf{0} - u\mathbf{i}),$$

so, resolving in the $\mathbf{i}$-direction, we obtain

$$V - U = -e(0 - u) = eu.$$

Solving these equations for U and V, we find that

$$U = \frac{m_1 - em_2}{m_1 + m_2}u \quad \text{and} \quad V = \frac{m_1(1+e)}{m_1 + m_2}u.$$

The change in kinetic energy is

$$\tfrac{1}{2}m_1 u^2 - \left(\tfrac{1}{2}m_1 U^2 + \tfrac{1}{2}m_2 V^2\right) = \frac{m_1 m_2(1 - e^2)u^2}{2(m_1 + m_2)},$$

using the values for U and V found above.

(Notice that when $e = 1$, no kinetic energy is lost from the system and the collision is elastic.)

4.3 We choose Cartesian unit vectors as shown in the figure below, which also shows the common tangent plane at the moment of impact, and the velocities of A and B just before and just after impact.

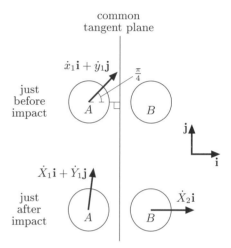

Using the fact that A has speed u just before impact while B is stationary, from the figure we see that

$$\dot{x}_1\mathbf{i} + \dot{y}_1\mathbf{j} = \left(u\cos\tfrac{\pi}{4}\right)\mathbf{i} + \left(u\sin\tfrac{\pi}{4}\right)\mathbf{j} = \tfrac{1}{\sqrt{2}}u\mathbf{i} + \tfrac{1}{\sqrt{2}}u\mathbf{j},$$
$$\dot{x}_2\mathbf{i} + \dot{y}_2\mathbf{j} = \mathbf{0}.$$

So, by Newton's law of restitution and noticing that the common normal is parallel to $\mathbf{i}$, we have

$$\dot{X}_1 - \dot{X}_2 = -e(\dot{x}_1 - \dot{x}_2) = -e\tfrac{1}{\sqrt{2}}u,$$
$$\dot{Y}_1 = \dot{y}_1 = \tfrac{1}{\sqrt{2}}u, \quad \dot{Y}_2 = \dot{y}_2 = 0.$$

Since $e = 0$, we have $\dot{X}_1 = \dot{X}_2$. Now, using the principle of conservation of linear momentum, we obtain

$$m(\dot{x}_1\mathbf{i} + \dot{y}_1\mathbf{j}) + m(\dot{x}_2\mathbf{i} + \dot{y}_2\mathbf{j})$$
$$= m(\dot{X}_1\mathbf{i} + \dot{Y}_1\mathbf{j}) + m(\dot{X}_2\mathbf{i} + \dot{Y}_2\mathbf{j}),$$

so, resolving in the $\mathbf{i}$-direction and dividing by m, we have

$$\dot{x}_1 + \dot{x}_2 = \dot{X}_1 + \dot{X}_2,$$

and hence $\dot{X}_1 + \dot{X}_2 = \tfrac{1}{\sqrt{2}}u$. Therefore, since $\dot{X}_1 = \dot{X}_2$, we have $\dot{X}_1 = \dot{X}_2 = \tfrac{1}{2\sqrt{2}}u$, and the velocities just after impact are

$$\dot{X}_1\mathbf{i} + \dot{Y}_1\mathbf{j} = \tfrac{1}{2\sqrt{2}}u\mathbf{i} + \tfrac{1}{\sqrt{2}}u\mathbf{j},$$
$$\dot{X}_2\mathbf{i} + \dot{Y}_2\mathbf{j} = \tfrac{1}{2\sqrt{2}}u\mathbf{i}.$$

(In the question you were told that the common tangent plane at the moment of impact is perpendicular to the subsequent direction of motion of B. This piece of information is, in fact, redundant. Ball B was orig-inally *stationary*, so after impact it must move in the direction perpendicular to the common tangent plane, i.e. in the direction of the common normal.)

4.4 Let the ball start from height h_1. By using con-servation of energy we have $mgh_1 = \frac{1}{2}mv_1^2$, where v_1 is the speed of the ball just before the first bounce. The speed of the ball just after the first bounce is given by $v_2 = ev_1$, using Newton's law of restitution. By con-servation of energy, we have $mgh_2 = \frac{1}{2}mv_2^2$, where h_2 is the maximum height after the first bounce. Putting these together, we have

$$mgh_2 = \tfrac{1}{2}mv_2^2 = \tfrac{1}{2}m(ev_1)^2 = e^2 \times mgh_1,$$

i.e. $h_2 = e^2h_1$.

Similarly, we find that the height h_3 after the second bounce is related to the height before the second bounce by $h_3 = e^2h_2$, so $h_3 = e^4h_1$. But we are told that $h_3 = \frac{1}{2}h_1$, so $e^4 = \frac{1}{2}$ and hence

$$e = \frac{1}{\sqrt[4]{2}} \simeq 0.84.$$

UNIT 20 Circular motion

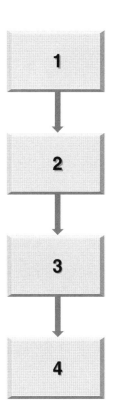

Study guide for Unit 20

This unit is about the motion of a particle in a circle. It builds on several ideas from earlier units, mainly:

- polar coordinates (*Unit 4*);
- vectors (*Unit 4*);
- torque (*Unit 5*);
- Newton's second law (*Unit 6*).

Some of the ideas in this unit are extended in *Unit 27* from the motion of a particle to the motion of a rigid body, and in *Unit 28* to the elliptical orbits of planets.

You should study the sections of this unit in the order in which they are presented. Sections 1 and 4 will each take about one study session. Section 2 is longer and will need two study sessions. Section 3 is somewhat shorter and should take only half a study session.

Introduction

The theme of this unit is rotational motion. We shall concentrate mainly on analysing the circular motion of a particle. This can be used to model a wide range of situations, such as a child on a swing, the pendulum of a clock and a chair-o-plane roundabout (see Figure 0.1) at the fairground.

Figure 0.1

Many fairground rides depend for their thrills on the forces involved in circular motion. We shall be able to use our model of the chair-o-plane, for example, to answer such questions as the following.

- Will a child swing out at a greater angle than a heavier adult?
- Will the people on the outside swing out at a greater angle than those on the inside?
- How does the angle at which people swing out depend on the speed of rotation of the roundabout?

These questions will be answered in Subsection 2.5.

Before we are able to answer questions such as these, we need to investigate the motion of a particle moving in a circle. In Section 1 we derive expressions for the velocity and acceleration of a particle moving in a circle. In Section 2 we apply Newton's second law to uniform circular motion, i.e. motion in a circle with constant speed. In Section 3 this is extended to non-uniform circular motion. Section 4 starts to look beyond circular motion to the concepts that are needed to analyse more general rotational motion.

1   Describing circular motion

Consider an object following a circular path at constant speed. This might be a particle, attached to an inextensible string, swung round in a circle; or a vehicle following a circular path on a 'bowl' racetrack or part of a circle when cornering. In this section we shall analyse this motion. We do so first in Cartesian coordinates and subsequently in polar coordinates, after an intervening subsection revising the differentiation of vector functions.

1.1   *Circular motion in Cartesian coordinates*

In this subsection we take a first look at circular motion, using Cartesian coordinates. Some simple features of the motion will be derived, which can be compared with more general results derived later.

You saw in *Unit 1* that the point $(\cos\theta, \sin\theta)$ lies on a circle of radius 1 and centre $(0,0)$. More generally, $(R\cos\theta, R\sin\theta)$ lies on a circle of radius R and centre $(0,0)$. If t denotes time and α is a constant, then a particle with position

$$(R\cos(\alpha t), R\sin(\alpha t))$$

We use $\langle r, \theta\rangle$ to denote a general point in polar coordinates and $\langle R, \theta\rangle$ to denote a point on the circle of radius R, i.e. R is a constant.

at time t will move on a circle of radius R with centre $(0,0)$. The line joining the particle's position to $(0,0)$ makes an angle $\theta = \alpha t$ with the positive x-axis and this angle is changing with time at a constant rate α, i.e. $\dot\theta = \alpha$. The quantity $\omega = |\alpha| = |\dot\theta|$ is the **angular speed** of the particle (the definition $\omega = |\dot\theta|$ applies even when $\dot\theta$ is not constant).

The angular speed has units of radians per second.

The motion considered in this subsection, where $\dot\theta$ is constant, is called **uniform circular motion**. If the motion is circular and $\dot\theta$ is not constant, then the motion is called **non-uniform circular motion**.

To study the mechanics of an object moving in a circle at constant angular speed, we need to know its velocity and acceleration. Choosing Cartesian unit vectors $\mathbf{i}$ and $\mathbf{j}$ as shown in Figure 1.1, the position vector of the particle is given by

$$\mathbf{r} = R\cos(\alpha t)\mathbf{i} + R\sin(\alpha t)\mathbf{j}. \tag{1.1}$$

We have

$$\begin{aligned}|\mathbf{r}| &= \sqrt{R^2\cos^2(\alpha t) + R^2\sin^2(\alpha t)}\\ &= R,\end{aligned}$$

the radius of the circle.

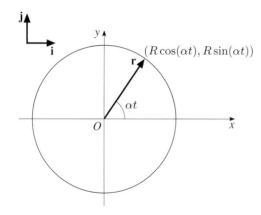

Figure 1.1

Before looking at the general case of a particle moving uniformly in a circle, try the following exercise.

Exercise 1.1

A particle has position vector $\mathbf{r}$ at time t given by

$$\mathbf{r}(t) = 3\cos(4t)\mathbf{i} + 3\sin(4t)\mathbf{j}.$$

(a) Find the velocity vector $\dot{\mathbf{r}}(t)$ and the acceleration vector $\ddot{\mathbf{r}}(t)$ of the particle at time t.

(b) What is the magnitude of the acceleration vector $\ddot{\mathbf{r}}(t)$?

(c) Show that $\ddot{\mathbf{r}}(t)$ is of the form $-c\mathbf{r}(t)$, where c is a positive constant.

Now consider again the case of a particle with position vector given by Equation (1.1), and differentiate to obtain the particle's velocity

$$\mathbf{v} = \dot{\mathbf{r}} = -\alpha R \sin(\alpha t)\mathbf{i} + \alpha R \cos(\alpha t)\mathbf{j}$$

$$= \alpha R(-\sin(\alpha t)\mathbf{i} + \cos(\alpha t)\mathbf{j}). \tag{1.2}$$

Note that R is a constant (the radius of the circle).

What can we deduce about the velocity from this expression? First, $\mathbf{v}$ has magnitude

$$|\mathbf{v}| = \sqrt{\alpha^2 R^2 \sin^2(\alpha t) + \alpha^2 R^2 \cos^2(\alpha t)} = |\alpha|R = \omega R.$$

So the object moves with speed ωR. Since both ω and R are independent of t, the speed of the particle is constant. (The *velocity* is not constant because its direction is changing.) Secondly, notice that

$$\mathbf{r} \cdot \mathbf{v} = \left(R\cos(\alpha t)\mathbf{i} + R\sin(\alpha t)\mathbf{j}\right) \cdot \left(-\alpha R \sin(\alpha t)\mathbf{i} + \alpha R \cos(\alpha t)\mathbf{j}\right)$$

$$= -\alpha R^2 \cos(\alpha t)\sin(\alpha t) + \alpha R^2 \cos(\alpha t)\sin(\alpha t)$$

$$= 0.$$

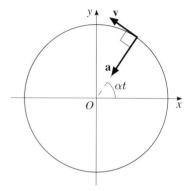

Figure 1.2

You saw in *Unit 4* that if the dot product of two non-zero vectors is zero, then they are perpendicular. So the particle's velocity $\mathbf{v}$ is perpendicular to its position vector $\mathbf{r}$. This is illustrated in Figure 1.2, which shows that the velocity $\mathbf{v}$ is tangential to the circle that the particle is tracing.

Differentiating the velocity vector $\mathbf{v}$ (Equation (1.2)) gives the acceleration

$$\mathbf{a} = \ddot{\mathbf{r}} = \alpha R(-\alpha \cos(\alpha t)\mathbf{i} - \alpha \sin(\alpha t)\mathbf{j})$$

$$= -\alpha^2 R(\cos(\alpha t)\mathbf{i} + \sin(\alpha t)\mathbf{j})$$

$$= -\alpha^2 \mathbf{r}$$

$$= -\omega^2 \mathbf{r}. \tag{1.3}$$

Since this vector is a negative multiple of $\mathbf{r}$, the acceleration is towards the centre of the circle (see Figure 1.2). The magnitude of the acceleration is $\omega^2 R$. Since $|\mathbf{v}| = \omega R$, the magnitude of the acceleration can also be written as $|\mathbf{v}|^2/R$. This form is useful if we know the speed of the particle, rather than its angular speed.

The main results derived above are summarized below.

Motion in a circle at constant angular speed

For a particle moving in a circle of radius R with constant angular speed ω:

- the speed (the magnitude of the velocity) is a constant, $|\mathbf{v}| = \omega R$;
- the direction of the velocity is tangential to the circle;
- the acceleration has constant magnitude, $|\mathbf{a}| = \omega^2 R = |\mathbf{v}|^2/R$;
- the direction of the acceleration is towards the centre of the circle.

If a particle follows a circle of radius R at a constant speed $|\mathbf{v}|$, then it has a constant angular speed $|\mathbf{v}|/R$, and these results apply.

Since a particle moving in a circle in this way has a non-zero acceleration, it must be subject to some force, say $\mathbf{F}$. By Newton's second law, this force must act in the same direction as the acceleration $\mathbf{a}$, i.e. towards the centre of the circle. Such a force might be provided by a string attaching the particle to the centre of the circle. Alternatively, if the particle is constrained to move in a circle by following a track, the track must exert a sideways force on the object (the force acting towards the centre of the circle). If the particle has mass m, then Newton's second law gives $\mathbf{F} = m\mathbf{a} = -m\omega^2 \mathbf{r}$. The force is towards the centre of the circle and has magnitude $m\omega^2 R$, or $m|\mathbf{v}|^2/R$.

The results listed in the summary box on page 140 are sufficient to solve some problems involving circular motion, such as the following exercise.

Exercise 1.2

A miniature locomotive of mass 40 kilograms is following a circular track of diameter 200 metres at constant speed. It completes one circuit in 50 seconds. What is the magnitude of the sideways force exerted by the track on the locomotive?

In the form of motion discussed in this subsection, we have a particle subject to a force at right angles to its direction of motion. The effect of this force is not to change the magnitude of the particle's velocity (the speed remains constant), but to change the *direction* of the velocity. In general, forces in the direction of motion change the speed, while forces at right angles to the direction of motion change the direction.

Exercise 1.2 was tractable because a single force is causing the circular motion. In order to solve more complicated problems involving circular motion, we need to be able to resolve forces radially and tangentially. For this we need appropriate unit vectors. The radial and tangential unit vectors are introduced in Subsection 1.3, but first we revise the differentiation of vector functions, which was introduced in *Unit 6*.

1.2   Differentiation of vector functions

In *Unit 6* you saw that, if $\mathbf{f}(t) = f_1(t)\mathbf{i} + f_2(t)\mathbf{j} + f_3(t)\mathbf{k}$ is a vector function of t, where $\mathbf{i}$, $\mathbf{j}$, $\mathbf{k}$ are the (constant) Cartesian unit vectors, then

$$\dot{\mathbf{f}}(t) = \dot{f}_1(t)\mathbf{i} + \dot{f}_2(t)\mathbf{j} + \dot{f}_3(t)\mathbf{k}. \tag{1.4}$$

We can use this result to obtain rules for differentiating sums and products of vectors.

Example 1.1

If the scalar c and the vector $\mathbf{f}$ are both functions of the scalar variable t, show that

$$\frac{d}{dt}(c\mathbf{f}) = \frac{dc}{dt}\mathbf{f} + c\frac{d\mathbf{f}}{dt}.$$

For ease of reading, we frequently write $\mathbf{f}$, f_i, etc., rather than $\mathbf{f}(t)$, $f_i(t)$, etc., i.e. omitting explicit reference to the variable t.

Solution

We write the vector function $\mathbf{f}$ in Cartesian component form as

$$\mathbf{f} = f_1\mathbf{i} + f_2\mathbf{j} + f_3\mathbf{k},$$

so

$$c\mathbf{f} = (cf_1)\mathbf{i} + (cf_2)\mathbf{j} + (cf_3)\mathbf{k}.$$

To differentiate $c\mathbf{f}$, we apply Equation (1.4) and differentiate the three components cf_1, cf_2 and cf_3. These are products of scalar functions and so we can use the rule for differentiating the product of two scalar functions, giving

$$\frac{d}{dt}(cf_i) = \frac{dc}{dt}f_i + c\frac{df_i}{dt} \quad (i = 1, 2, 3).$$

Therefore

$$\frac{d}{dt}(c\mathbf{f}) = \left(\frac{dc}{dt}f_1 + c\frac{df_1}{dt}\right)\mathbf{i} + \left(\frac{dc}{dt}f_2 + c\frac{df_2}{dt}\right)\mathbf{j} + \left(\frac{dc}{dt}f_3 + c\frac{df_3}{dt}\right)\mathbf{k}$$

$$= \frac{dc}{dt}(f_1\mathbf{i} + f_2\mathbf{j} + f_3\mathbf{k}) + c\left(\frac{df_1}{dt}\mathbf{i} + \frac{df_2}{dt}\mathbf{j} + \frac{df_3}{dt}\mathbf{k}\right)$$

$$= \frac{dc}{dt}\mathbf{f} + c\frac{d\mathbf{f}}{dt},$$

which is the required result. ∎

*Exercise 1.3

If the vectors $\mathbf{f}$ and $\mathbf{g}$ are both functions of the scalar variable t, show that

$$\frac{d}{dt}(\mathbf{f}\cdot\mathbf{g}) = \frac{d\mathbf{f}}{dt}\cdot\mathbf{g} + \mathbf{f}\cdot\frac{d\mathbf{g}}{dt}.$$

We can similarly derive the rules for differentiating the other possible combinations of scalar and vector functions.

> **Rules for differentiating vector functions**
>
> If the scalar c and the vectors $\mathbf{f}$ and $\mathbf{g}$ are functions of the scalar variable t, then
>
> $$\frac{d}{dt}(\mathbf{f} + \mathbf{g}) = \frac{d\mathbf{f}}{dt} + \frac{d\mathbf{g}}{dt},$$
>
> $$\frac{d}{dt}(c\mathbf{f}) = \frac{dc}{dt}\mathbf{f} + c\frac{d\mathbf{f}}{dt},$$
>
> $$\frac{d}{dt}(\mathbf{f}\cdot\mathbf{g}) = \frac{d\mathbf{f}}{dt}\cdot\mathbf{g} + \mathbf{f}\cdot\frac{d\mathbf{g}}{dt},$$
>
> $$\frac{d}{dt}(\mathbf{f}\times\mathbf{g}) = \frac{d\mathbf{f}}{dt}\times\mathbf{g} + \mathbf{f}\times\frac{d\mathbf{g}}{dt}.$$

The rules for differentiating products bear a strong resemblance to the rule for differentiating the product of two scalar functions. Note that in the rule for differentiating a cross product the order of the factors in each term is important.

These rules will prove useful in the next subsection.

Exercise 1.4

Differentiate $\mathbf{f}\cdot\mathbf{f}$, where $\mathbf{f}$ is a vector function of the scalar variable t.

In the above exercise you showed that

$$\frac{d}{dt}(\mathbf{f}\cdot\mathbf{f}) = 2\mathbf{f}\cdot\frac{d\mathbf{f}}{dt}.$$

This leads to an important result for a vector of *constant magnitude*. If $\mathbf{e}$ is such a vector, then $\mathbf{e}\cdot\mathbf{e} = |\mathbf{e}|^2 = \text{constant}$. So

$$\frac{d}{dt}(\mathbf{e}\cdot\mathbf{e}) = 0.$$

Using the result of Exercise 1.4, this leads directly to

$$\mathbf{e}\cdot\frac{d\mathbf{e}}{dt} = 0.$$

Hence, if a non-zero vector $\mathbf{e}$ has constant magnitude, its derivative $d\mathbf{e}/dt$ is always either zero or perpendicular to $\mathbf{e}$.

1.3   Circular motion in polar coordinates

If position is given in Cartesian coordinates (x, y), then it is natural to write the position vector $\mathbf{r}$ in terms of the Cartesian unit vectors $\mathbf{i}$ and $\mathbf{j}$, i.e.

$$\mathbf{r}(t) = x(t)\mathbf{i} + y(t)\mathbf{j}. \qquad (1.5)$$

Then the velocity and acceleration vectors are

$$\mathbf{v}(t) = \dot{\mathbf{r}}(t) = \dot{x}(t)\mathbf{i} + \dot{y}(t)\mathbf{j}, \qquad (1.6)$$

$$\mathbf{a}(t) = \dot{\mathbf{v}}(t) = \ddot{\mathbf{r}}(t) = \ddot{x}(t)\mathbf{i} + \ddot{y}(t)\mathbf{j}. \qquad (1.7)$$

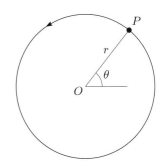

Figure 1.3

The ease of derivation of Equations (1.6) and (1.7) from Equation (1.5) is due to the fact that $\mathbf{i}$ and $\mathbf{j}$ are constant vectors. Only the coordinates x and y, which are functions of time t, vary during the motion.

However, for a particle P moving in a circle (as shown in Figure 1.3), it is convenient to use polar coordinates $\langle r, \theta \rangle$, with an origin O at the centre of the circle, to describe the position vector $\mathbf{r}$ of the particle. With this choice of coordinate system, the coordinate r is a constant for circular motion (being the radius of the circle) and only the coordinate θ is a function of time t. However, in order to discuss the motion of a particle in a vector context using polar coordinates, we need to introduce two orthogonal unit vectors $\mathbf{e}_r$ and $\mathbf{e}_\theta$ (see Figure 1.4). In the same way that $\mathbf{i}$ and $\mathbf{j}$ are unit vectors in the directions of increasing x and increasing y, respectively, $\mathbf{e}_r$ is a unit vector in the direction of increasing r (the **radial direction**) and $\mathbf{e}_\theta$ is a unit vector in the direction of increasing θ (the **tangential direction**). Although the vectors $\mathbf{e}_r$ and $\mathbf{e}_\theta$ have constant magnitude (they are *unit* vectors), their directions depend on the position of the particle P, and hence on the time t. This is illustrated in Figure 1.5, which shows two different positions of P (moving in a circle).

You met polar coordinates in *Units 1* and *4*.

Two vectors are **orthogonal** if they are perpendicular to each other.

In contexts where the motion is not circular — and sometimes even when it is — the direction of increasing θ is called the **transverse direction**.

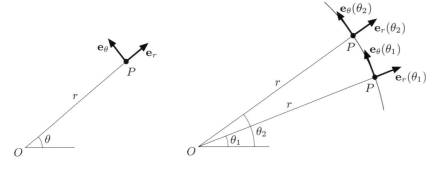

Figure 1.4   *Figure 1.5*

Before we obtain expressions for the position, velocity and acceleration of the particle P in terms of $\mathbf{e}_r$ and $\mathbf{e}_\theta$, we need to express each of $\mathbf{e}_r$ and $\mathbf{e}_\theta$ as a linear combination of $\mathbf{i}$ and $\mathbf{j}$. Take the Cartesian coordinate system to have its origin at O, the centre of the circle, and take the positive x-axis to lie along the line from O from which the polar coordinate θ is measured, as shown in Figure 1.6. First let us consider $\mathbf{e}_r$. From Figure 1.6, the x-component of the *unit* vector $\mathbf{e}_r$ is $\cos \theta$, whereas its y-component is $\sin \theta$, so

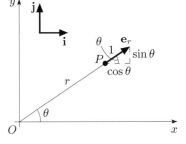

Figure 1.6

$$\mathbf{e}_r = (\cos \theta)\mathbf{i} + (\sin \theta)\mathbf{j}. \qquad (1.8)$$

Exercise 1.5

Find an expression for the unit vector $\mathbf{e}_\theta$ in terms of $\mathbf{i}$, $\mathbf{j}$ and θ.

In Exercise 1.5 you showed that

$$\mathbf{e}_\theta = (-\sin\theta)\mathbf{i} + (\cos\theta)\mathbf{j}. \tag{1.9}$$

Equations (1.8) and (1.9) show that $\mathbf{e}_r$ and $\mathbf{e}_\theta$ are functions of the polar coordinate angle θ.

Exercise 1.6

Show explicitly that the vectors

$$\mathbf{e}_r = (\cos\theta)\mathbf{i} + (\sin\theta)\mathbf{j}, \quad \mathbf{e}_\theta = (-\sin\theta)\mathbf{i} + (\cos\theta)\mathbf{j},$$

form an orthogonal pair of unit vectors, i.e. that they satisfy the conditions

$$\mathbf{e}_r \cdot \mathbf{e}_r = 1, \quad \mathbf{e}_\theta \cdot \mathbf{e}_\theta = 1, \quad \mathbf{e}_r \cdot \mathbf{e}_\theta = 0.$$

We also need to express the time derivatives $\dot{\mathbf{e}}_r$ and $\dot{\mathbf{e}}_\theta$ in terms of $\mathbf{e}_r$ and $\mathbf{e}_\theta$. Differentiating Equation (1.8) with respect to time (since θ is a function of time) using the Chain Rule, we obtain

$$\dot{\mathbf{e}}_r = (-\sin\theta)\dot\theta\mathbf{i} + (\cos\theta)\dot\theta\mathbf{j} = \dot\theta((-\sin\theta)\mathbf{i} + (\cos\theta)\mathbf{j}) = \dot\theta\mathbf{e}_\theta,$$

where we have used the expression for $\mathbf{e}_\theta$ given by Equation (1.9).

Exercise 1.7

By differentiating Equation (1.9) with respect time and using Equation (1.8), show that

$$\dot{\mathbf{e}}_\theta = -\dot\theta\mathbf{e}_r.$$

Since $\mathbf{e}_r$ and $\mathbf{e}_\theta$ are orthogonal, $\dot{\mathbf{e}}_r = \dot\theta\mathbf{e}_\theta$ is perpendicular to $\mathbf{e}_r$ and, in addition, $\dot{\mathbf{e}}_\theta = -\dot\theta\mathbf{e}_r$ is perpendicular to $\mathbf{e}_\theta$. These are special cases of the result proved after Exercise 1.4 that the derivative of a non-zero vector of constant magnitude is always either zero or perpendicular to that vector.

Plane polar unit vectors $\mathbf{e}_r$ and $\mathbf{e}_\theta$

Given a plane polar coordinate system and a two-dimensional Cartesian coordinate system with the same origin O, where the positive x-axis corresponds to the axis from which the polar coordinate θ is measured, then the plane polar unit vectors $\mathbf{e}_r$ and $\mathbf{e}_\theta$ are related to the Cartesian unit vectors $\mathbf{i}$ and $\mathbf{j}$ by

$$\mathbf{e}_r = (\cos\theta)\mathbf{i} + (\sin\theta)\mathbf{j}, \tag{1.8}$$

$$\mathbf{e}_\theta = (-\sin\theta)\mathbf{i} + (\cos\theta)\mathbf{j}. \tag{1.9}$$

The derivatives with respect to time of the plane polar unit vectors are

$$\dot{\mathbf{e}}_r = \dot\theta\mathbf{e}_\theta, \tag{1.10}$$

$$\dot{\mathbf{e}}_\theta = -\dot\theta\mathbf{e}_r. \tag{1.11}$$

We are now in a position to obtain expressions for the position $\mathbf{r}$, the velocity $\mathbf{v} = \dot{\mathbf{r}}$ and the acceleration $\mathbf{a} = \dot{\mathbf{v}} = \ddot{\mathbf{r}}$ of a particle P moving in a circle of radius R, say (see Figure 1.7), in terms of the unit vectors $\mathbf{e}_r$ and $\mathbf{e}_\theta$. For any point on the circle $r = R$, the position vector of P is in the direction of $\mathbf{e}_r$ and so can be expressed as

$$\mathbf{r} = R\mathbf{e}_r. \tag{1.12}$$

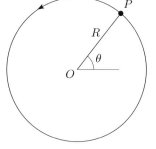

Figure 1.7

Differentiating Equation (1.12) with respect to time, and remembering that R is a constant, we have

$$\dot{\mathbf{r}} = R\dot{\mathbf{e}}_r.$$

Using Equation (1.10), this may be written as

$$\dot{\mathbf{r}} = R\dot{\theta}\mathbf{e}_\theta. \tag{1.13}$$

Exercise 1.8

By differentiating Equation (1.13) with respect to time, remembering that θ and $\mathbf{e}_\theta$ are functions of time but that R is a constant, show that the acceleration of a particle moving in a circle of radius R is

$$\ddot{\mathbf{r}} = -R\dot{\theta}^2\mathbf{e}_r + R\ddot{\theta}\mathbf{e}_\theta. \tag{1.14}$$

It is useful to collect together the results that apply whenever the motion is circular (both uniform circular motion (considered in Section 2) and non-uniform circular motion (considered in Section 3)).

Position, velocity and acceleration in plane polar coordinates for circular motion

In plane polar coordinates, the position, velocity and acceleration of a particle moving in the circle $r = R$ are

$$\mathbf{r} = R\mathbf{e}_r, \tag{1.12}$$

$$\dot{\mathbf{r}} = R\dot{\theta}\mathbf{e}_\theta, \tag{1.13}$$

$$\ddot{\mathbf{r}} = -R\dot{\theta}^2\mathbf{e}_r + R\ddot{\theta}\mathbf{e}_\theta. \tag{1.14}$$

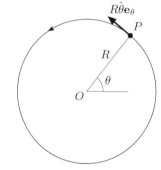

Figure 1.8   Velocity

It is geometrically clear (see Figure 1.8) that the velocity of a particle moving in a circle is tangential to the circle and Equation (1.13) confirms this. On the other hand (see Figure 1.9), the acceleration has a radial component $-R\dot{\theta}^2\mathbf{e}_r$ (arising from the rate of change of the direction of the velocity) as well as a tangential component $R\ddot{\theta}\mathbf{e}_\theta$ (arising from the rate of change of the speed). Furthermore, the component of the acceleration in the radial direction is *negative*, which indicates that the acceleration of a particle moving in a circle has a component of magnitude $R\dot{\theta}^2$ directed *inwards*, towards the centre of the circle. This inward component is commonly called the **centripetal acceleration**, but you must remember that the acceleration for circular motion in general also has a non-zero tangential component.

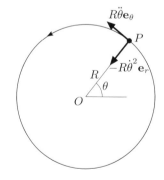

Figure 1.9   Acceleration

The above boxed results are the generalization of the results of Subsection 1.1 to motion where the angular speed is not constant. If the angular speed is constant (i.e. the circular motion is *uniform*), then $\dot{\theta}$ = constant and $\ddot{\theta} = 0$, so Equation (1.14) reduces to $\ddot{\mathbf{r}} = -R\dot{\theta}^2\mathbf{e}_r$ and the acceleration is solely towards the centre of the circle, as you saw in Subsection 1.1.

End-of-section Exercises

Exercise 1.9

A particle is moving on a unit circle centred on the origin O, i.e. on the circle $r = 1$. Its polar coordinate angle θ at time t is given by $\theta(t) = t^2$. Find the velocity and acceleration of the particle at time t.

---

2 Uniform circular motion

The previous section derived formulae that apply whenever an object is moving in a circle. This section considers the special case where the angular rate of rotation is constant, i.e. **uniform circular motion**. Non-uniform circular motion is studied in Section 3.

2.1 First examples

We begin with a summary of results from Section 1 specialized to the case of uniform circular motion, i.e. the case where $\ddot{\theta} = 0$.

Kinematics of uniform circular motion

Consider a particle moving in a circle of radius R, with centre at the origin O, having a constant rate of rotation $\dot{\theta}$ and hence a constant angular speed $\omega = |\dot{\theta}|$.

(a) The velocity of the particle is

$$\dot{\mathbf{r}} = R\dot{\theta}\mathbf{e}_\theta, \tag{2.1}$$

i.e. the velocity of the particle is purely tangential and has constant magnitude $v = |\dot{\mathbf{r}}| = R|\dot{\theta}| = R\omega$.

(b) The acceleration of the particle is

$$\ddot{\mathbf{r}} = -R\dot{\theta}^2\mathbf{e}_r = -R\omega^2\mathbf{e}_r = -\frac{v^2}{R}\mathbf{e}_r, \tag{2.2}$$

i.e. the acceleration is directed towards the centre of the circle and has constant magnitude $|\ddot{\mathbf{r}}| = R\dot{\theta}^2 = R\omega^2 = v^2/R$.

(c) The time taken for one complete revolution of the circle is

$$T = \frac{2\pi}{\omega}. \tag{2.3}$$

This follows from ωt being the magnitude of the angle measured from the x-axis at time t, and the period being defined as the time for this angle to equal 2π.

---

*Exercise 2.1 ⎯⎯⎯⎯⎯⎯⎯⎯⎯⎯⎯⎯⎯⎯⎯

A fly sits at the tip of the minute hand of a clock. The hand has length 0.5 metres and can be assumed to move with constant angular speed. Find the angular speed, the speed and the magnitude of the acceleration of the fly.

If there are no forces acting on a particle, then, by Newton's first law, it will either remain at rest or move with constant speed in a straight line. Therefore, if the particle moves on a circular path, there must be some force or forces causing it to do so, even when the circular motion is uniform. In Subsection 1.1 you saw that a particle moving on a circle of radius R with constant angular speed ω and constant speed v is being accelerated towards the centre of the circle with an acceleration of magnitude $R\omega^2 = v^2/R$. If the particle has mass m, then Newton's second law states that there must be a force

$$\mathbf{F} = m\ddot{\mathbf{r}} = -mR\omega^2\mathbf{e}_r = -\frac{mv^2}{R}\mathbf{e}_r$$

acting on the particle. This force is directed towards the circle's centre and has constant magnitude. There is no tangential component of the acceleration and so there is no component of the total force (i.e. resultant force) acting on the particle in this direction.

Similarly, there is no component of the resultant force acting at right angles to the plane of the motion. To be able to use this fact to solve problems we need to introduce a third unit vector $\mathbf{k}$, which is perpendicular to the plane of motion and whose direction is chosen so that the unit vectors $\mathbf{e}_r$, $\mathbf{e}_\theta$ and $\mathbf{k}$ form a right-handed system. An example of such a right-handed system is shown in Figure 2.1.

You met the term right-handed system in *Unit 4*.

Example 2.1

Two particles A and B, of equal mass m, are connected by a model string that passes through a small smooth hole in a smooth horizontal table. Particle A is on the surface of the table, while particle B is suspended beneath the table. Particle A describes circles of radius R with constant angular speed ω, as a result of which particle B is static. Find the angular speed of particle A.

Solution

Without loss of generality, we can assume that particle A moves in an anticlockwise direction, when viewed from above the table. We shall describe the motion of particle A using a polar coordinate system in the plane of the table surface with origin at O, where O is the centre of the circle described by particle A. The situation, together with the force diagrams for the two particles, is shown in Figure 2.1. $\mathbf{T}_1$ and $\mathbf{T}_2$ are the tension forces due to the string on particles A and B, respectively, $\mathbf{W}_1$ and $\mathbf{W}_2$ are the weights of particles A and B, respectively, and $\mathbf{N}$ is the normal reaction of the table on particle A (there is no friction force since the table is smooth).

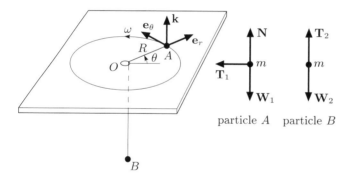

Figure 2.1

First consider particle B. There are two forces acting on this particle: the tension force $\mathbf{T}_2 = |\mathbf{T}_2|\mathbf{k}$ due to the string and its weight $\mathbf{W}_2 = -mg\mathbf{k}$, where $\mathbf{k}$ is a unit vector pointing vertically upwards. Since particle B is static, the total force acting on it is zero, so

$$\mathbf{T}_2 + \mathbf{W}_2 = \mathbf{0},$$

that is,

$$|\mathbf{T}_2|\mathbf{k} - mg\mathbf{k} = \mathbf{0}.$$

Hence, resolving in the $\mathbf{k}$-direction, we obtain $|\mathbf{T}_2| = mg$.

Now consider particle A. There are three forces acting on the particle: the tension force $\mathbf{T}_1 = -|\mathbf{T}_1|\mathbf{e}_r$ due to the string, the normal reaction $\mathbf{N} = |\mathbf{N}|\mathbf{k}$ of the table on the particle and its weight $\mathbf{W}_1 = -mg\mathbf{k}$. Applying Newton's second law to particle A gives

The vectors $\mathbf{e}_r$, $\mathbf{e}_\theta$ and $\mathbf{k}$ are mutually perpendicular, so we can resolve in these directions in the same way as for the Cartesian unit vectors $\mathbf{i}$, $\mathbf{j}$ and $\mathbf{k}$.

$$m\ddot{\mathbf{r}} = \mathbf{T}_1 + \mathbf{N} + \mathbf{W}_1,$$

that is,

$$-mR\omega^2\mathbf{e}_r = -|\mathbf{T}_1|\mathbf{e}_r + |\mathbf{N}|\mathbf{k} - mg\mathbf{k}.$$

Resolving in the direction of $\mathbf{e}_r$ gives

$$|\mathbf{T}_1| = mR\omega^2.$$

Since we have a model string and a smooth hole, $|\mathbf{T}_1| = |\mathbf{T}_2|$ and so $mR\omega^2 = mg$. Thus $\omega^2 = g/R$ and $\omega = \sqrt{g/R}$. Hence the angular speed of particle A is $\sqrt{g/R}$. ■

Exercise 2.2

A particle P of mass m moves in a circle with constant angular speed ω on a smooth horizontal table. It is attached to an end of a model string of length l. The other end of the string is fixed to a point on the table. What is the tension in the string?

*Exercise 2.3

A particle A of mass m lies on a smooth horizontal table and is attached, by a model string that passes through a smooth hole in the table to a particle B of mass $2m$ that is suspended below the table. Particle A describes a circle of radius 40 cm with constant speed on the table, so particle B remains at rest. Calculate the speed v of particle A.

Exercise 2.4

A child places a small toy on a playground roundabout and spins the roundabout so that it describes one complete revolution every two seconds. The toy stays at the same point relative to the roundabout while the latter rotates. The coefficient of static friction between the toy and the roundabout is $\mu = \frac{1}{2}$. By modelling the toy as a particle and the roundabout as a horizontal disc rotating uniformly about its centre, show that the greatest possible distance of the toy from the centre of the roundabout is about 0.5 metres.

2.2 Geostationary satellites

An interesting application of uniform circular motion concerns communications satellites. Some of the most important satellites are those with *geostationary orbits*, i.e. those satellites which maintain a fixed position relative to the Earth's rotating surface. Signals can be sent to and from such a satellite without the need to adjust continually the orientations of the transmitter and the receiver. In order that the geostationary satellite should maintain its position, it must have a circular orbit in the equatorial plane and an orbital period of one sidereal day, so its angular speed is $\omega = 2\pi/T$, where $T = 1$ day $= 23.9343 \times 60 \times 60$ seconds. Hence $\omega \simeq 7.292 \times 10^{-5}\,\text{rad s}^{-1}$.

The sidereal day is the time required for a complete rotation of the Earth relative to a particular star. You will examine this later in Example 4.1.

The force causing the circular motion, in this case, is the gravitational force of attraction on the satellite due to the presence of the Earth. This force is attractive and directed towards the centre of the Earth. Empirical evidence has shown that it is well modelled by

$$\mathbf{F} = -\frac{GmM}{|\mathbf{r}|^3}\mathbf{r}, \qquad (2.4)$$

where m is the mass of the satellite, M is the mass of the Earth, $\mathbf{r}$ is the position vector of the satellite with respect to the centre of the Earth (as shown in Figure 2.2) and G is a constant, known as the **gravitational constant**, whose value in SI units is $G = 6.673 \times 10^{-11}\,\text{N m}^2\,\text{kg}^{-2}$.

Figure 2.2

Equation (2.4) is a special case of *Newton's law of universal gravitation,* which models the gravitational force between any two particles.

> **Newton's law of universal gravitation**
>
> The gravitational force of attraction exerted on a particle of mass m_1 by a particle of mass m_2 is
>
> $$\mathbf{F} = -\frac{Gm_1m_2}{|\mathbf{r}|^3}\mathbf{r}, \qquad\qquad (2.5)$$
>
> where $\mathbf{r}$ is the position vector of the particle of mass m_1, relative to the particle of mass m_2, and $G = 6.673 \times 10^{-11}\,\mathrm{N\,m^2\,kg^{-2}}$ is the gravitational constant.

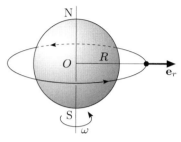

Figure 2.3

To use Newton's law of universal gravitation to model the gravitational force on a geostationary satellite, we assume that we can model the Earth and the satellite as particles (evidence shows that this assumption is reasonable). Using polar coordinates in the equatorial plane, with origin at the centre of the Earth, the position vector of the satellite can be written as $\mathbf{r} = R\mathbf{e}_r$, where R is the radius of the orbit (see Figure 2.3). So Equation (2.4) can be written as

$$\mathbf{F} = -\frac{GmM}{R^2}\mathbf{e}_r.$$

Applying Newton's second law to the satellite, we obtain

$$-mR\omega^2\mathbf{e}_r = -\frac{GmM}{R^2}\mathbf{e}_r,$$

which leads to

$$R = \sqrt[3]{\frac{GM}{\omega^2}}.$$

Now the mass of the Earth is $M = 5.977 \times 10^{24}$ kilograms. Substituting the values of G, M and ω into the above equation, we obtain

$$R \simeq 4.217 \times 10^7 \text{ metres.}$$

The equatorial radius of the Earth is 6378.2 kilometres and so all geostationary satellites must orbit approximately $35\,800$ kilometres above the Earth's surface.

Exercise 2.5

A good approximation for planetary motion is to assume that a planet orbits in uniform circular motion around the Sun under the action of their mutual gravitational attraction. Model the Sun and the planet as particles, take the origin at the centre of mass of the Sun, and take R to be the radius of the planet's orbit around this origin, so the position of the planet is $\mathbf{r} = R\mathbf{e}_r$. Newton's law of universal gravitation then tells us that a good model of the gravitational force on the planet is

$$\mathbf{F} = -\frac{GmM}{R^2}\mathbf{e}_r,$$

where m is the mass of the planet and M is the mass of the Sun. Verify that the square of the period T of the orbit is proportional to the cube of the radius of the orbit, i.e. $T^2 \propto R^3$.

2.3   Conical pendulums

So far in this section we have considered examples of motion where the force causing the circular motion is in the plane of the motion. In the following two exercises you are asked to consider examples where this is not the case.

*Exercise 2.6

A *conical pendulum* is a pendulum whose bob traces out a horizontal circle, rather than a vertical circle. The pendulum can be modelled as a particle of mass m, joined by a light model rod of length l to a fixed point. As the particle traces out a horizontal circle below the fixed point, the rod traces out a cone whose semi-vertical angle α is the inclination of the rod to the vertical (see Figure 2.4). Assume that, for any given angle α, the bob performs uniform circular motion.

(a) Determine the tension in the rod.

(b) Find an expression for the angular speed ω of the bob in terms of g, l and α, and for the angle of inclination α in terms of g, l and ω.

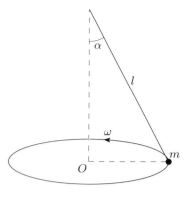

Figure 2.4

You saw in Exercise 2.6 that the angular speed of a conical pendulum is given by $\omega = \sqrt{g/(l\cos\alpha)}$, where l is the length of the pendulum rod and α is the angle the rod makes with the vertical. For a fixed l, this means that ω depends solely on α. As α increases, so does ω (since $\cos\alpha$ decreases), and $\omega \to \infty$ as $\alpha \to \frac{\pi}{2}$.

The fact that the angular speed of a conical pendulum depends on the angle made with the vertical is used in the design of *governors* of steam engines, which regulate the supply of steam to the engine (see Figure 2.5). A model of a governor is illustrated in Figure 2.6. It consists of two light rods AB and AC, freely hinged at A to a vertical shaft AG that is rotated by the engine. At the other ends of the rods are two equal weights at B and C.

Two other light rods DE and DF are freely hinged to the rods AB and AC, and to a collar at D that can slide freely up and down the shaft AG. A lever is attached to the collar at D and operates a valve that admits steam to the engine — as the collar rises the amount of steam is decreased.

So when the angular speed of the shaft increases as more steam enters the engine, the weights at B and C rise and pull the collar at D up the shaft. This shuts off some of the steam entering the engine and the speed of rotation is decreased. Similarly, when the speed of rotation decreases, the collar at D falls and more steam is admitted to the engine.

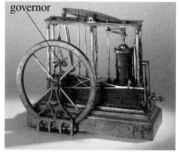

Figure 2.5   Courtesy of the Science Museum Science and Society Picture Library.

Exercise 2.7

A simple model of a steam governor assumes that, in Figure 2.6, the points B and E coincide, and the points C and F coincide, i.e. that the rods DE and DF are freely hinged at B and C. From the symmetry of Figure 2.6, we need model only one half of the governor, i.e. two rods and one weight, and one half-collar at D. We model the rods and the shaft as light model rods, the weight as a particle P and the half-collar as another particle.

Assume that the half-collar particle remains in smooth contact with the shaft, so there is no friction and the only force on the half-collar particle due to the shaft is the normal reaction.

Also assume that there are no friction forces at any of the hinges, that both particles have the same mass m and that both rods have the same length l.

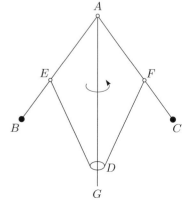

Figure 2.6

The particle P rotates about the shaft in a horizontal circle with constant angular speed ω. The model is shown in Figure 2.7. Because both rods have the same length, each rod makes the same angle α with the vertical.

(a) Determine the tensions in the rods.

(b) Find an expression for the angular speed ω in terms of g, l and α, and for the angle α of inclination in terms of g, l and ω.

(*Hint*: For fixed values of ω and α, the half-collar particle does not move.)

Figure 2.7

2.4 Cornering

In this subsection we look at the application of the formulae for circular motion to the real-world problem in the following example.

Example 2.2

Consider a vehicle of mass m moving at constant speed v around a circular bend of radius R as shown in Figure 2.8(a). Suppose that the road has a horizontal surface, i.e. it is not banked or cambered.

(a) If the coefficient of static friction between the vehicle and the road is μ, what is the maximum constant speed v at which the vehicle can go around the corner without slipping?

(b) Suppose that the vehicle is driven around a roundabout on a circle of radius 15 metres at a constant speed of $10\,\mathrm{m\,s^{-1}}$ without skidding. What does this imply about the coefficient of static friction?

It may seem odd to use the coefficient of *static* friction here. However, there is no *sideways* motion between the tyres and the road.

Solution

(a) Model the vehicle as a particle, at position X. Choose the $\mathbf{e}_r$, $\mathbf{e}_\theta$ and $\mathbf{k}$ coordinate system shown in Figure 2.8.

The forces acting on the vehicle are not all in one plane, so it is hard to draw a complete force diagram. Figure 2.8(b) shows the forces in a vertical plane through the vehicle and the centre of the circle, which are the weight $\mathbf{W}$, the normal reaction $\mathbf{N}$ and the sideways friction force $\mathbf{F}$. There are other forces acting on the vehicle, e.g. air resistance and the force propelling the vehicle. For the purposes of this model, we shall lump them together as one force $\mathbf{C}$, whose magnitude is unknown but whose direction is along the direction of travel, i.e. tangential to the circle and perpendicular to the plane shown in Figure 2.8(b).

The vehicle is being treated as a particle, so $\mathbf{W}$ is the weight of the vehicle together with its occupants. The normal reaction $\mathbf{N}$ is the resultant of the separate forces acting at each tyre/road contact.

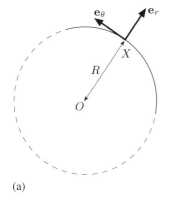

(a)

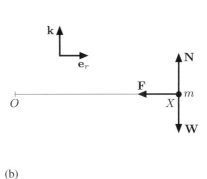

(b)

Figure 2.8   Vehicle following a circular bend at constant speed
(a) viewed from above   (b) viewed from the side, showing a vertical plane through OX and the forces acting in this plane.

Applying Newton's second law to the vehicle gives

$$\mathbf{N} + \mathbf{W} + \mathbf{F} + \mathbf{C} = m\mathbf{a}. \tag{2.6}$$

Now we model the forces that appear in this equation. By inspection of Figure 2.8(b), we have $\mathbf{W} = -mg\mathbf{k}$, $\mathbf{N} = |\mathbf{N}|\mathbf{k}$ and $\mathbf{F} = -|\mathbf{F}|\mathbf{e}_r$. By definition, the force $\mathbf{C}$ is tangential to the circle, so $\mathbf{C} = |\mathbf{C}|\mathbf{e}_\theta$. Since the vehicle is moving in a circular path at constant speed, the acceleration is $\mathbf{a} = (-v^2/R)\mathbf{e}_r$. Now we can resolve Equation (2.6) in each of three orthogonal directions.

Resolving Equation (2.6) in the $\mathbf{e}_\theta$-direction gives

$$|\mathbf{C}| = 0, \tag{2.7}$$

resolving Equation (2.6) in the $\mathbf{k}$-direction gives

$$|\mathbf{N}| - mg = 0, \tag{2.8}$$

and resolving Equation (2.6) in the $\mathbf{e}_r$-direction gives

$$-|\mathbf{F}| = -\frac{mv^2}{R}. \tag{2.9}$$

From Equation (2.7) we see that the forces tangential to the circle must balance, since we have uniform circular motion. This justifies the modelling assumption that we can lump them all together.

From Equation (2.8) we obtain $|\mathbf{N}| = mg$, so, by the force model for static friction, we have

$$|\mathbf{F}| \leq \mu|\mathbf{N}| = \mu mg.$$

But from Equation (2.9) we obtain $|\mathbf{F}| = mv^2/R$, which we can substitute into this inequality to obtain

$$\frac{mv^2}{R} \leq \mu mg,$$

that is,

$$v^2 \leq \mu Rg. \tag{2.10}$$

So the maximum (constant) speed at which the circular bend can be negotiated without skidding is $v = \sqrt{\mu Rg}$.

(b) We have $v = 10\,\mathrm{m\,s^{-1}}$ and $R = 15$ metres. So, from expression (2.10), we require that

$$\mu \geq \frac{v^2}{Rg} = \frac{100}{15 \times 9.81} \simeq 0.68.$$

So the coefficient of static friction must be at least 0.68 to avoid skidding. ∎

Exercise 2.8

Suppose that the coefficient of static friction between a particular car and the road in dry conditions is 1.3, and assume that the car follows a circular path at constant speed.

(a) At what speed could the car be driven around a roundabout on a circular path of radius 10 metres in dry conditions without skidding?

(b) What would be the smallest radius of the roundabout that would enable the car to drive around it in dry conditions at $15\,\mathrm{m\,s^{-1}}$?

(c) Suppose that when conditions are wet, the coefficient of static friction between the car and the road is reduced by a factor of 2. What would be the smallest radius of the roundabout that would enable the car to be driven around it in wet conditions at $15 \ \mathrm{m\,s^{-1}}$?

Some motor racing venues consist of 'bowls' with steeply sloping sides. Even conventional roads may have cambered bends. If a bend has a slope facing in towards the centre of the bend, this reduces the reliance on friction when cornering. The following example shows how to calculate the magnitude of this effect.

Example 2.3

We revisit Example 2.2, but the assumption that the road is flat and horizontal is replaced with the assumption that the track is banked at an angle α towards the centre of the circle.

(a) What is the minimum coefficient of friction μ such that the vehicle can go around the corner without slipping, in terms of the parameters v, R and g introduced in Example 2.2 and α?

(b) A car is travelling at $80 \, \mathrm{m\,s^{-1}}$ around a circle of radius 500 metres on a track banked at an angle α towards the centre of the circle. In wet conditions, the coefficient of static friction between the tyres and the track may be as low as 0.4. What is the minimum angle of bank which would allow the car to avoid skidding up the slope in wet conditions?

Solution

(a) As in Example 2.2, we model the vehicle as a particle of mass m moving at a constant speed v around a circular bend of radius R.

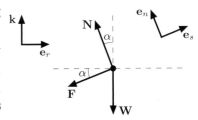

Figure 2.9

The forces acting on the vehicle are its weight $\mathbf{W}$, the normal reaction $\mathbf{N}$ of the road on the vehicle and the friction force $\mathbf{F}$, as shown in Figure 2.9. As before, we model all the forces acting tangentially to the circle (i.e. in the direction of motion or opposed to the direction of motion) as a single resultant force $\mathbf{C}$. The force $\mathbf{C}$ is perpendicular to the plane shown in Figure 2.9.

Also shown in Figure 2.9 is the choice of axes for this problem. On the left-hand side of Figure 2.9 is shown the radial $\mathbf{e}_r$ and vertical $\mathbf{k}$ unit vectors that we used for Example 2.2. In this problem it is better to use a unit vector $\mathbf{e}_s$ pointing along the slope and a unit vector $\mathbf{e}_n$ perpendicular to the slope, as shown on the right of Figure 2.9.

We apply Newton's second law to the vehicle to obtain

$$\mathbf{W} + \mathbf{N} + \mathbf{F} + \mathbf{C} = m\mathbf{a}. \tag{2.11}$$

Now we model the forces acting on the vehicle. The friction force acts down the slope because we are investigating the point at which the vehicle starts to skid up the slope. So $\mathbf{F} = -|\mathbf{F}|\mathbf{e}_s$. The normal reaction $\mathbf{N} = |\mathbf{N}|\mathbf{e}_n$ is normal to the slope and the force $\mathbf{C}$ is, by definition, along the direction of motion, i.e. $\mathbf{C} = |\mathbf{C}|\mathbf{e}_\theta$. The weight can be resolved using the method described in *Unit 4*:

$$\mathbf{W} = mg \cos(\tfrac{\pi}{2} + \alpha)\mathbf{e}_s + mg \cos(\pi + \alpha)\mathbf{e}_n,$$
$$= -mg \sin \alpha \, \mathbf{e}_s - mg \cos \alpha \, \mathbf{e}_n.$$

153

Now that the forces have been resolved, we proceed to resolve the acceleration so that we can resolve Equation (2.11). Since the motion is uniform and circular, we have $\mathbf{a} = -(v^2/R)\mathbf{e}_r$, so we need to express $\mathbf{e}_r$ in terms of $\mathbf{e}_s$ and $\mathbf{e}_n$. We do this using the method from *Unit 4* again:

$$\begin{aligned}
\mathbf{e}_r &= \cos\alpha\,\mathbf{e}_s + \cos(\tfrac{\pi}{2} + \alpha)\mathbf{e}_n, \\
&= \cos\alpha\,\mathbf{e}_s - \sin\alpha\,\mathbf{e}_n.
\end{aligned}$$

So the acceleration of the vehicle is given by

$$\mathbf{a} = -\frac{v^2}{R}\left(\cos\alpha\,\mathbf{e}_s - \sin\alpha\,\mathbf{e}_n\right).$$

Resolving Equation (2.11) in the $\mathbf{e}_\theta$-direction gives $|\mathbf{C}| = 0$ as before.

Resolving Equation (2.11) in the $\mathbf{e}_s$-direction yields

$$-|\mathbf{F}| - mg\sin\alpha = -\frac{mv^2}{R}\cos\alpha,$$

which gives a formula for the magnitude of the friction force,

$$|\mathbf{F}| = \frac{mv^2}{R}\cos\alpha - mg\sin\alpha.$$

Resolving Equation (2.11) in the $\mathbf{e}_n$-direction yields

$$|\mathbf{N}| - mg\cos\alpha = \frac{mv^2}{R}\sin\alpha,$$

which gives the magnitude of the normal reaction as

$$|\mathbf{N}| = mg\cos\alpha + \frac{mv^2}{R}\sin\alpha.$$

For the car not to skid up the slope, we must have $|\mathbf{F}| \le \mu|\mathbf{N}|$, i.e.

$$\frac{mv^2}{R}\cos\alpha - mg\sin\alpha \le \mu\left(mg\cos\alpha + \frac{mv^2}{R}\sin\alpha\right).$$

This can be simplified by multiplying through by $R/(m\cos\alpha)$ to obtain

$$v^2 - Rg\tan\alpha \le \mu Rg + \mu v^2\tan\alpha. \tag{2.12}$$

So the condition on μ for the vehicle not to slip up the slope is

$$\mu \ge \frac{v^2 - Rg\tan\alpha}{Rg + v^2\tan\alpha}.$$

Note that $R/(m\cos\alpha)$ is positive, since R and m are positive and $0 \le \alpha < \pi/2$.

Note that $Rg + v^2\tan\alpha$ is always positive.

(b) Starting from Equation (2.12), we rearrange it to make $\tan\alpha$ the subject:

$$Rg\tan\alpha + \mu v^2\tan\alpha \ge v^2 - \mu Rg.$$

This gives

$$\tan\alpha \ge \frac{v^2 - \mu Rg}{Rg + \mu v^2}. \tag{2.13}$$

Note that the denominator is always positive.

Substituting $v = 80\,\mathrm{m\,s^{-1}}$, $R = 500$ metres, $\mu = 0.4$ and $g = 9.81\mathrm{m\,s^{-2}}$ gives

$$\tan\alpha \ge \frac{80^2 - 0.4 \times 500 \times 9.81}{500 \times 9.81 + 0.4 \times 80^2} \simeq 0.595.$$

Hence the minimum angle is $\alpha \simeq 0.54$. (We know that α must be between 0 and $\frac{\pi}{2}$.) So the minimum necessary angle for the banking is about $31°$. ■

To answer Question 2, note from Figure 2.11 that as R increases, the graph of $y = R + l \sin \alpha$ is translated upwards (assuming that all other parameters are fixed). This moves the point of intersection of the two graphs to the right. So larger R corresponds to an angle α closer to $\alpha = \pi/2$. The answer to Question 2 is therefore that people on the outside do swing out further than those on the inside.

To answer Question 3, consider what happens to the point of intersection of the two graphs as ω increases. In this case, g/ω^2 decreases and, for a given α, the curve $y = (g/\omega^2) \tan \alpha$ becomes less steep. This has the effect of moving the point of intersection of the graphs to the right and hence increases the angle α of inclination. So the answer to Question 3 is that increasing the angular speed ω of the roundabout increases the angle of inclination α: as ω tends to infinity, the angle α tends to $\pi/2$, i.e. the chains are almost horizontal if the roundabout has a very large angular speed.

(It can also be deduced from the graphs that the angle α of inclination increases as the length l of the chains increases.)

The next exercise asks you to consider another fairground ride.

Exercise 2.12

A fairground ride consists of a large wheel that, once it has reached a steady state, rotates at a uniform angular speed in a vertical plane. The seats in which passengers sit are located on the rim of the wheel with the bases of the seats facing in towards the centre of the wheel. Model a passenger as a particle of mass m in a seat rotating in a circle of radius R in a vertical plane at constant angular speed ω, as shown in Figure 2.12.

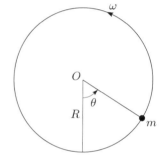

Figure 2.12

(a) Determine the equation of motion of the passenger. Hence find expressions for the radial and tangential components of the reaction force acting on the passenger due to the seat.

Although the passengers are constrained in their seats, we want to determine the minimum rate of rotation such that the constraints would not be necessary. (Assume that the seats have sides so that passengers cannot slip out of them sideways.)

(b) Find the minimum angular speed ω so that the passengers would not fall out, even if they were not constrained.

(*Hint*: Recall from *Unit 14* that a particle leaves a surface when the reaction force of the surface on the particle has a zero component normal to the surface.)

End-of-section Exercises

Exercise 2.13

A particle of mass m is joined by a model spring of stiffness k and natural length l_0 to a fixed point on a smooth horizontal table. The particle is moving in a circle on the table, the circle being centred on the fixed point, with a constant angular speed ω (where $\omega < \sqrt{k/m}$). Find the length of the model spring in terms of m, k, l_0 and ω.

Exercise 2.14

A model string ACB has a particle of mass m attached at one end A and a particle of mass $2m$ attached at the other end B. The string is threaded through a smooth fixed ring C. The particle B is at rest vertically below the ring C and the particle A is rotating in a horizontal circle of radius R with constant angular speed ω, as shown in Figure 2.13.

(a) Find the angle α of inclination of AC to the vertical.

(b) Find, in terms of R and g, the angular speed ω of particle A.

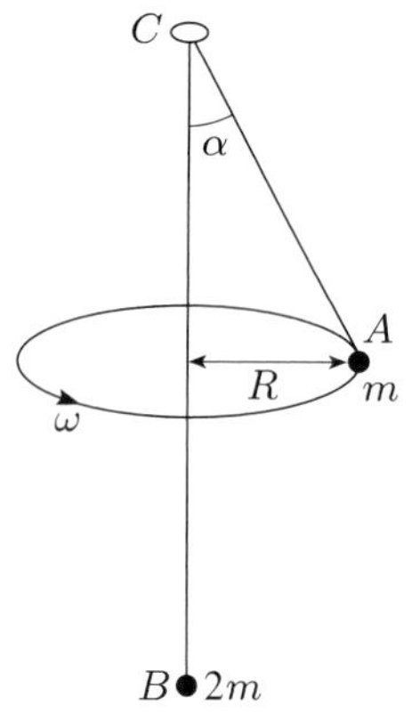

Figure 2.13

Exercise 2.15

A car is driven horizontally around a circular track of radius 400 metres, which is banked at $35°$ to the horizontal and towards the centre of the track. The coefficient of static friction between the tyres and the track is 0.45. At what range of speeds can the car be driven without skidding?

Exercise 2.16

A stunt motorcyclist is considering riding around the inside of a cylinder of radius 8 metres. The axis of the cylinder is horizontal and the motorcycle will follow a vertical circle. Assuming that he rides at a constant speed, how fast does he need to ride to avoid falling away from the inside of the cylinder?

Exercise 2.17

The motorcyclist described in Exercise 2.16 is concerned about skidding as he executes the stunt. He estimates that the coefficient of static friction μ between the tyres and the cylinder wall is 0.8. Assume that the motorcycle follows a vertical circle of radius 8 metres at a constant speed.

(a) Use the fact that there is no acceleration tangential to the circle to express the magnitude $|\mathbf{F}|$ of the friction force in terms of the mass (m say) of the motorcycle.

(b) Use $|\mathbf{F}| \leq \mu|\mathbf{N}|$ to derive a condition that must be satisfied if the motorcycle is to avoid skidding. Hence find the minimum speed at which the motorcyclist must ride to avoid skidding.

(*Hint*: Recall from *Units 1* and *7* that an expression of the form $f(\alpha) = B\cos\alpha + C\sin\alpha$ can be rewritten as $\sqrt{B^2 + C^2}\cos(\alpha + \phi)$ for a suitable choice of ϕ. Hence, since the largest value taken by $\cos(\alpha + \phi)$ is 1 (whatever the value of ϕ), the largest value taken by $f(\alpha)$ is $\sqrt{B^2 + C^2}$.)

3 Non-uniform circular motion

In this section we look at **non-uniform circular motion**, i.e. circular motion in which the angular rate of rotation is not constant. This section builds on the previous section. We shall continue to make use of the plane polar unit vectors $\mathbf{e}_r$ and $\mathbf{e}_\theta$. Most of the section is concerned with the motion of a simple pendulum. You examined the motion of such a pendulum in *Unit 8*. In the text of that unit you modelled the motion using a second-order differential equation obtained by examining the mechanical energy of the system. In the multimedia package for *Unit 14*, you modelled the motion using Newton's second law and Cartesian unit vectors. Here we use Newton's second law and plane polar unit vectors to obtain an equation for the varying angular speed of the pendulum.

We model the pendulum as a particle P of mass m attached to a light model rod of length l. The other end of the rod is attached to a fixed point O and the particle moves in a vertical circle about this fixed point, as shown in Figure 3.1. The angle θ made by the rod with the vertical is measured anticlockwise from the downward vertical. We want to find expressions for the rate of rotation $\dot{\theta}$ and for the tension in the rod in terms of θ.

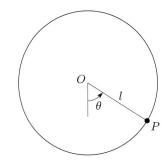

Figure 3.1

We shall use a plane polar coordinate system in the vertical plane of motion of the pendulum, with origin at the fixed point O, the centre of the circular motion. The forces on the particle are its weight $\mathbf{W}$ and the tension $\mathbf{T}$ due to the rod. We assume that the tension force is directed towards O, which is certainly the case when the pendulum is hanging vertically downwards (this assumption will be revisited later). The plane polar unit vectors $\mathbf{e}_r$ and $\mathbf{e}_\theta$, and a force diagram for the system, are shown in Figure 3.2.

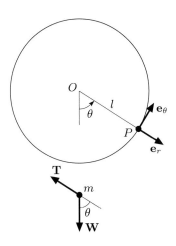

Figure 3.2

With respect to this coordinate system,

$$\mathbf{W} = (mg\cos\theta)\mathbf{e}_r - (mg\sin\theta)\mathbf{e}_\theta, \quad \mathbf{T} = -|\mathbf{T}|\mathbf{e}_r. \tag{3.1}$$

The acceleration of the particle is non-zero and is given by Equation (1.14):

$$\ddot{\mathbf{r}} = -l\dot{\theta}^2\mathbf{e}_r + l\ddot{\theta}\mathbf{e}_\theta. \tag{3.2}$$

Newton's second law applied to the particle gives

$$m\ddot{\mathbf{r}} = \mathbf{W} + \mathbf{T},$$

so, substituting from Equations (3.1) and (3.2), we obtain

$$-ml\dot{\theta}^2\mathbf{e}_r + ml\ddot{\theta}\mathbf{e}_\theta = (mg\cos\theta)\,\mathbf{e}_r - (mg\sin\theta)\,\mathbf{e}_\theta - |\mathbf{T}|\mathbf{e}_r.$$

Resolving in the $\mathbf{e}_r$-direction gives

$$-ml\dot{\theta}^2 = mg\cos\theta - |\mathbf{T}|. \tag{3.3}$$

Resolving in the $\mathbf{e}_\theta$-direction gives

$$ml\ddot{\theta} = -mg\sin\theta. \tag{3.4}$$

We concentrate first on integrating Equation (3.4) to obtain an expression for the rate of rotation $\dot{\theta}$. Multiplying Equation (3.4) by $\dot{\theta}/m$, we obtain

$$l\dot{\theta}\ddot{\theta} = -g\dot{\theta}\sin\theta. \tag{3.5}$$

By the Chain Rule,

$$\frac{d}{dt}(\dot{\theta}^2) = 2\dot{\theta}\ddot{\theta},$$

so Equation (3.5) can be rewritten as

$$\frac{d}{dt}(\tfrac{1}{2}l\dot{\theta}^2) = -g\sin\theta\frac{d\theta}{dt}.$$

Rewritten in the form $\ddot{\theta} = -\dfrac{g}{l}\sin\theta$, this is the undamped pendulum equation from *Unit 8*.

Integrating this equation with respect to time gives

$$\tfrac{1}{2}l\dot{\theta}^2 = -g\int \sin\theta\frac{d\theta}{dt}\,dt = -g\int \sin\theta\,d\theta = g\cos\theta + c.$$

The constant of integration c can be found, for example, in terms of the rate of rotation $\dot{\theta}_0$ of the particle at the lowest point of the path, where $\theta = 0$. This initial condition leads to

$$c = \tfrac{1}{2}l\dot{\theta}_0^2 - g,$$

so

$$\tfrac{1}{2}l\dot{\theta}^2 = g\cos\theta + \tfrac{1}{2}l\dot{\theta}_0^2 - g$$

and hence

$$\dot{\theta}^2 = \dot{\theta}_0^2 - \frac{2g}{l}(1 - \cos\theta).$$

When $\theta = 0$, we have $v_0 = l|\dot{\theta}_0|$, so the above equation becomes

$$\dot{\theta}^2 = \frac{v_0^2}{l^2} - \frac{2g}{l}(1 - \cos\theta). \tag{3.6}$$

In theory, this equation can now be integrated to find θ as a function of time t, but, in practice, the integral involved cannot be evaluated in terms of elementary functions. However, Equation (3.6) does permit us to calculate the speed $v = l|\dot{\theta}|$ of the particle at any point during its motion.

We can now use Equation (3.6) to substitute for $\dot{\theta}^2$ in Equation (3.3), to find the tension in the rod in terms of θ. We have

$$|\mathbf{T}| = mg\cos\theta + ml\dot{\theta}^2$$

$$= mg\cos\theta + \frac{mv_0^2}{l} - 2mg(1 - \cos\theta)$$

$$= \frac{mv_0^2}{l} + mg(3\cos\theta - 2). \tag{3.7}$$

In deriving this result we assumed that the tension force acting on the bob was directed towards O. Now we can say that this occurs when the right-hand side of Equation (3.7) is positive. This restriction needs to be kept in mind when applying Equation (3.7). We shall say more about this later, but for now we restate the result derived.

Tension in a pendulum rod

Consider a pendulum rod of length l, attached to a bob of mass m, which makes an angle θ with the downward vertical. If the bob has speed v_0 when $\theta = 0$, then the magnitude of the tension $|\mathbf{T}|$ in the pendulum rod is given by

$$|\mathbf{T}| = \frac{mv_0^2}{l} + mg(3\cos\theta - 2), \tag{3.7}$$

provided that the right-hand side is positive.

Let us now consider a slightly different pendulum, where the light model rod is replaced by a model string.

Exercise 3.1 _____

Consider the motion of a pendulum moving in a vertical plane, whose bob is attached to a fixed point by a model string. How, for low, high and intermediate speeds, is the motion of this new pendulum likely to differ from that of the original pendulum whose bob is attached to a fixed point by a light model rod?

_____

The answer to Exercise 3.1 emphasizes that Equations (3.6) and (3.7) only apply while the right-hand side of Equation (3.7) is positive. Depending on the nature of the pendulum rod, other phenomena might occur if the right-hand side of Equation (3.7) is negative.

*Exercise 3.2 _____

Consider the motion of a pendulum moving in a vertical plane, whose bob is attached to a fixed point by a model string.

(a) Show that if $v_0 > \sqrt{5gl}$, then the string never goes slack.

(b) If $v_0 = 2\sqrt{gl}$, find the angle θ for which the string goes slack.

_____

In Exercise 3.2(a) you saw that the string never goes slack if the speed v_0 of the pendulum bob at its lowest point is greater than $\sqrt{5gl}$. In this case, the pendulum bob performs complete revolutions in the same direction. It was also predicted, in Exercise 3.1, that the string would not go slack and the pendulum would perform oscillatory motion for certain lower speeds. So what is the condition on v_0 for the string to remain taut at lower speeds?

To answer this, look first at the tension in the string. From Equation (3.3) we have

$$|\mathbf{T}| = mg\cos\theta + ml\dot{\theta}^2, \tag{3.8}$$

and the right-hand side is positive for $-\frac{\pi}{2} < \theta < \frac{\pi}{2}$ (since $\cos\theta > 0$ on this interval, while $\dot{\theta}^2 \geq 0$ for any θ). So the string can never go slack before the bob reaches the horizontal.

Above the horizontal, $\cos\theta$ is negative. So, from Equation (3.8), we have

$$|\mathbf{T}| \leq ml\dot{\theta}^2.$$

So $|\mathbf{T}| = 0$ before $\dot{\theta} = 0$, i.e. the string becomes slack before the bob comes instantaneously to rest.

We know from Exercise 3.2(a) that the bob reaches the highest point of the circle if $v_0 > \sqrt{5gl}$. We have still to determine the initial speed so that the bob just reaches the horizontal.

Exercise 3.3 _____

Find an initial speed v_0 so that the pendulum bob just becomes horizontal.

_____

We have found that the model predicts the following.
(a) For $0 < v_0 \leq \sqrt{2gl}$, the bob oscillates back and forth with an amplitude of less than $\frac{\pi}{2}$.
(b) For $\sqrt{2gl} < v_0 < \sqrt{5gl}$, the bob travels initially in a circular path with the string taut, then at some angle between $\pi/2$ and π the string becomes slack and the bob falls under gravity as a projectile.
(c) For $\sqrt{5gl} \leq v_0$, the bob travels continuously in a circle.

A pendulum bob attached to a model rod will continue to oscillate in this case and will not become a projectile.

End-of-section Exercises

Exercise 3.4 _____

Consider a particle P of mass m, sliding on the outside of a fixed smooth sphere of radius R. Assume that the particle has started from the highest point of the sphere with an initial speed v_0 and that the radius from the centre of the sphere to the particle makes an angle θ with the upward vertical, as shown in Figure 3.3. Assume also that the particle's path lies in a vertical plane. If $v_0 = \sqrt{\frac{1}{2}gR}$, show that the particle leaves the surface of the sphere when $\theta = \arccos\frac{5}{6} \simeq 33.6°$.

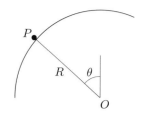

Figure 3.3

(*Hint*: When considering the motion of a particle in a vertical plane from an equilibrium position at the highest point on the sphere, measuring θ anticlockwise from the upward vertical is similar to measuring θ anticlockwise from the downward vertical in the case of a pendulum. Recall from *Unit 14* that a particle leaves a surface when the normal reaction of the surface on the particle becomes zero.)

Exercise 3.5 _____

A smooth hemispherical bowl of radius R, whose lowest point is at A, is fixed with its rim uppermost and horizontal. A particle of mass m is set in motion along the inner surface of the bowl towards A, so its subsequent motion is in a vertical plane through A. The particle is set in motion from a point at a vertical height $\frac{1}{2}R$ above A, with initial speed $\sqrt{gR}$.

(a) Show that the particle will just reach the top of the bowl.

(b) Find the magnitude of the normal reaction of the bowl on the particle when the particle is at a vertical height $\frac{2}{3}R$ above A.

Exercise 3.6 _____

On a fairground ride, the passengers are constrained to move at a non-uniform speed in a vertical circle. Passengers sit in carriages where the bases of the seats face into the centre of the circular motion. Sometimes the carriage carrying the passengers hangs vertically above the axis of rotation, and sometimes the carriage goes round and round in complete circles. Assume that the passengers and their carriage can be modelled as a particle of mass m. The particle is connected to the axis of rotation by a light model rod of length R, as shown in Figure 3.4. Assume also that the only forces acting on the particle are its weight and the tension force due to the rod.

(a) Show that

$$\dot{\theta}^2 = \frac{v_0^2}{R^2} - \frac{2g}{R}(1 - \cos\theta),$$

where θ is the angle the rod makes to the vertical (measured anticlockwise from the downward vertical, as shown in Figure 3.4) and v_0 is the speed of the particle at the lowest point of the circle.

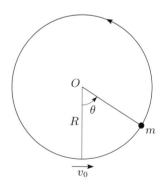

Figure 3.4

(b) Show that the particle will just reach the top of the circle if $v_0 = 2\sqrt{gR}$.

(c) Show that, when the particle executes complete circles, the passengers will not fall out, even if not constrained, provided that $v_0 > \sqrt{5gR}$. (Assume that the seats have sides, so that passengers cannot slip out of them sideways.)

4 Angular velocity and angular momentum

This section starts to look beyond circular motion to more general rotational motion. In this section we define two key quantities that will be useful in *Units 27* and *28*, which look at the motions of rigid bodies and planets. Subsection 4.1 defines the *angular velocity* of a particle. The magnitude of the angular velocity of a particle is the angular speed that we have been considering up to this point.

In *Unit 19* you were introduced to linear momentum and its conservation in the absence of external forces. You saw how the conservation of linear momentum could be used in the analysis of certain problems involving linear motion. For circular motion, and for rotational motion in general, the corresponding concept is *angular momentum*. Subsection 4.2 defines angular momentum for a particle and shows how it is linked to torques.

Linear momentum is defined both for a single particle and for an *n*-particle system in *Unit 19*.

4.1 Angular velocity

If a particle is moving in a circle or if a rigid body is rotating about a fixed axis, then the (angular) rate of rotation and the direction of the axis of rotation are of primary importance. These two quantities can be encapsulated by the vector $\boldsymbol{\omega}$, known as the *angular velocity*. The magnitude of $\boldsymbol{\omega}$ is the angular speed and the direction of $\boldsymbol{\omega}$ is defined to be along the axis of rotation in the sense given by the screw rule, i.e. in the direction in which a (right-handed) screw would move when turned in the direction of rotation (see Figure 4.1).

The rotation of rigid bodies is considered in *Unit 27*.

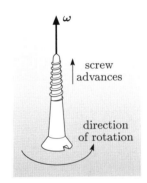

Figure 4.1

Definition

The **angular velocity** $\boldsymbol{\omega}$ of a particle moving in a circle, or of a rigid body rotating about a fixed axis, is a vector with magnitude equal to the angular speed and with direction along the axis of rotation in the sense given by the screw rule.

Example 4.1

The Earth rotates in an easterly direction once in a sidereal day (the rotation period with respect to the fixed stars, which is less than that with respect to the Sun by one part in 365.25), which is 23.9343 hours. Specify the angular velocity $\boldsymbol{\omega}$ of the rotation of the Earth.

Solution

The angular speed is

$$\omega = \frac{2\pi}{23.9343 \times 60 \times 60} \simeq 7.292 \times 10^{-5} \text{ rad s}^{-1}.$$

The direction of the angular velocity $\boldsymbol{\omega}$ is from the South Pole to the North Pole, as shown in Figure 4.2. ∎

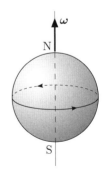

Figure 4.2

The direction of the angular velocity $\boldsymbol{\omega}$ is along the axis of rotation and is therefore perpendicular to the plane of motion. To be more specific about this direction, we use the usual right-handed system shown in Figure 4.3. Using the screw rule, the direction of the angular velocity vector $\boldsymbol{\omega}$ will be in the positive $\mathbf{k}$-direction if $\dot{\theta} > 0$ and in the negative $\mathbf{k}$-direction if $\dot{\theta} < 0$, as shown in Figure 4.4.

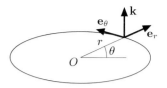

Figure 4.3

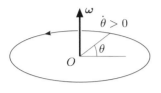 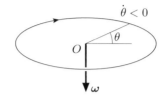

Figure 4.4

Therefore

$$\boldsymbol{\omega} = \begin{cases} \omega\mathbf{k} & (\dot{\theta} > 0) \\ -\omega\mathbf{k} & (\dot{\theta} < 0) \end{cases}$$

$$= \begin{cases} |\dot{\theta}|\mathbf{k} & (\dot{\theta} > 0) \\ -|\dot{\theta}|\mathbf{k} & (\dot{\theta} < 0) \end{cases}$$

$$= \dot{\theta}\mathbf{k}.$$

So the relationship $\boldsymbol{\omega} = \dot{\theta}\mathbf{k}$ holds, regardless of the direction of rotation.

The relationship also holds if there is no rotation, when $\dot{\theta} = 0$ and $\boldsymbol{\omega} = \mathbf{0}$.

We complete this subsection by establishing the link between the angular velocity $\boldsymbol{\omega}$ of a particle in circular motion and its velocity $\mathbf{v} = \dot{\mathbf{r}}$. For circular motion of radius R, we know from Equation (1.12) that $\mathbf{r} = R\mathbf{e}_r$, relative to the centre of the circle, and from Equation (1.13) that $\mathbf{v} = \dot{\mathbf{r}} = R\dot{\theta}\mathbf{e}_\theta$. We also know that $\boldsymbol{\omega} = \dot{\theta}\mathbf{k}$. Therefore

$$\boldsymbol{\omega} \times \mathbf{r} = \dot{\theta}\mathbf{k} \times R\mathbf{e}_r = R\dot{\theta}(\mathbf{k} \times \mathbf{e}_r) = R\dot{\theta}\mathbf{e}_\theta = \mathbf{v}.$$

You can check that $\mathbf{k} \times \mathbf{e}_r = \mathbf{e}_\theta$ by looking at Figure 4.3.

This result also holds if we take the origin to be anywhere on the axis of rotation. For then $\mathbf{r} = R\mathbf{e}_r + z\mathbf{k}$ for some z and

$$\boldsymbol{\omega} \times \mathbf{r} = (\dot{\theta}\mathbf{k}) \times (R\mathbf{e}_r + z\mathbf{k}) = \dot{\theta}\mathbf{k} \times R\mathbf{e}_r + \dot{\theta}\mathbf{k} \times z\mathbf{k}$$

$$= R\dot{\theta}(\mathbf{k} \times \mathbf{e}_r) = R\dot{\theta}\mathbf{e}_\theta = \mathbf{v}.$$

Recall from *Unit 4* that $\mathbf{k} \times \mathbf{k} = \mathbf{0}$.

Relationship between velocity and angular velocity

The velocity $\mathbf{v}$ of a particle moving in a circle with angular velocity $\boldsymbol{\omega}$ is

$$\mathbf{v} = \boldsymbol{\omega} \times \mathbf{r}, \tag{4.1}$$

where $\mathbf{r}$ is the position vector of the particle relative to an origin on the axis of rotation.

Exercise 4.1

A particle moves clockwise in a circle at a constant angular speed of $2\,\mathrm{rad\,s}^{-1}$.

(a) Find the angular velocity of the particle.

(b) If the position vector of the particle, relative to the centre of the circle, at a certain instant is $3\mathbf{i} + 4\mathbf{j}$, find its velocity at that instant both in terms of the Cartesian unit vectors $\mathbf{i}$ and $\mathbf{j}$, and in terms of the corresponding polar unit vectors $\mathbf{e}_r$ and $\mathbf{e}_\theta$.

4.2 Angular momentum

Consider a particle of mass m moving along a curve in space. This is illustrated in Figure 4.5.

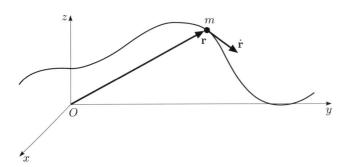

Figure 4.5

At time t the particle has position vector $\mathbf{r} = \mathbf{r}(t)$, velocity $\dot{\mathbf{r}} = \dot{\mathbf{r}}(t)$ and acceleration $\ddot{\mathbf{r}} = \ddot{\mathbf{r}}(t)$ relative to a fixed Cartesian coordinate system. The linear momentum of the particle is

$$\mathbf{p} = m\dot{\mathbf{r}}.$$

You saw in *Unit 19* that this is related to the force $\mathbf{F}$ acting on the particle according to the equation

$$\mathbf{F} = \dot{\mathbf{p}}, \tag{4.2}$$

which says that the rate of change of linear momentum of the particle is equal to the force acting on the particle.

This equation is Newton's second law $\mathbf{F} = m\ddot{\mathbf{r}}$ expressed in terms of linear momentum.

In *Unit 5* we quantified the turning effect of a force about a fixed point O by defining the torque $\boldsymbol{\Gamma}$ of the force about O as

$$\boldsymbol{\Gamma} = \mathbf{r} \times \mathbf{F}.$$

By analogy with the case of linear momentum, when analysing rotational motion it would be useful to have a quantity that plays the same role in relation to torques as linear momentum does to forces. So, by analogy with Equation (4.2), we should like the derivative of this quantity to equal the torque on the particle. A suitable quantity is

$$\boldsymbol{l} = \mathbf{r} \times \mathbf{p} = \mathbf{r} \times m\dot{\mathbf{r}},$$

since, using the rule for differentiating a cross product, we have

$$\dot{\boldsymbol{l}} = \frac{d}{dt}(\mathbf{r} \times m\dot{\mathbf{r}}) = (\dot{\mathbf{r}} \times m\dot{\mathbf{r}}) + (\mathbf{r} \times m\ddot{\mathbf{r}}) = \mathbf{r} \times m\ddot{\mathbf{r}} = \mathbf{r} \times \mathbf{F} = \boldsymbol{\Gamma}.$$

The cross product of parallel vectors is zero, so $\dot{\mathbf{r}} \times m\dot{\mathbf{r}} = \mathbf{0}$.

We call $\boldsymbol{l} = \boldsymbol{l}(t)$ the angular momentum of the particle about the fixed point.

Definition

For a particle that has linear momentum $\mathbf{p} = m\dot{\mathbf{r}}$ and position vector $\mathbf{r}$ relative to an origin O, its **angular momentum** $\boldsymbol{l}$ about O is

$$\boldsymbol{l} = \mathbf{r} \times \mathbf{p} = \mathbf{r} \times m\dot{\mathbf{r}}.$$

The SI units for the magnitude of angular momentum are $\mathrm{kg\,m^2\,s^{-1}}$.

As with torques, the angular momentum of a particle is dependent on the choice of origin O. Figure 4.6 illustrates this, where the vector $\boldsymbol{l} = \mathbf{r} \times m\dot{\mathbf{r}}$ represents the angular momentum relative to the origin O, while the vector $\boldsymbol{l'} = \mathbf{r'} \times m\dot{\mathbf{r}'}$ represents the angular momentum relative to the origin O'.

These vectors may differ in both magnitude and direction. (However, since both coordinate systems are static, the velocity of the particle is the same in each case, i.e. $\dot{\mathbf{r}} = \dot{\mathbf{r}}'$.)

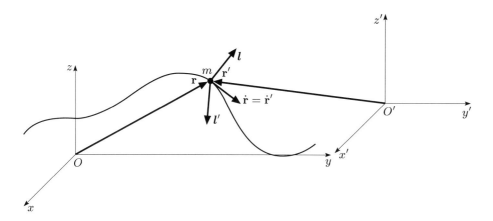

Figure 4.6

The fact that $\dot{\boldsymbol{l}} = \boldsymbol{\Gamma}$ is given a special name.

Torque law for a particle

The rate of change of a particle's angular momentum about a fixed point is equal to the applied torque about that point, i.e.

$$\dot{\boldsymbol{l}} = \boldsymbol{\Gamma}.$$

The **torque law** is fundamental to the study of rotating bodies.

Example 4.2

A particle of mass m, on which no forces act, moves with constant speed u parallel to the y-axis in the positive y-direction in the (x, y)-plane. At time $t = t_0$, its path intersects the x-axis at $x = b$ (see Figure 4.7). Calculate the magnitude and direction of the angular momentum of the particle with respect to the origin O.

Solution

The position of the particle in the coordinate system of Figure 4.7 is

$$\mathbf{r} = b\mathbf{i} + u(t - t_0)\mathbf{j},$$

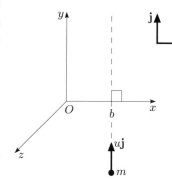

Figure 4.7

while the velocity is $\dot{\mathbf{r}} = u\mathbf{j}$. So, using $\mathbf{i} \times \mathbf{j} = \mathbf{k}$ and $\mathbf{j} \times \mathbf{j} = \mathbf{0}$, the angular momentum is

$$\boldsymbol{l} = \mathbf{r} \times m\dot{\mathbf{r}} = (b\mathbf{i} + u(t - t_0)\mathbf{j}) \times mu\mathbf{j} = bmu\mathbf{k}.$$

Thus, even though the vector $\mathbf{r}$ is changing continuously, the cross product $\mathbf{r} \times m\dot{\mathbf{r}}$ is a constant vector. Hence the angular momentum points along the positive z-axis and has magnitude bmu. ∎

Exercise 4.2

At a given time, a particle of mass 3 has position $\mathbf{i} + 2\mathbf{j}$ and velocity $2\mathbf{i} - \mathbf{j}$. What is its angular momentum about the origin of the coordinate system at this time?

All quantities are measured in SI units.

Example 4.3

A particle of mass m at position $\mathbf{r} = x\mathbf{i} + y\mathbf{j} + z\mathbf{k}$ moves in a circle, whose centre lies on the z-axis, with angular velocity $\boldsymbol{\omega} = \dot{\theta}\mathbf{k}$. Find the angular momentum $\boldsymbol{l}$ of the particle about the origin O in terms of x, y, z, $\dot{\theta}$, $\mathbf{i}$, $\mathbf{j}$ and $\mathbf{k}$.

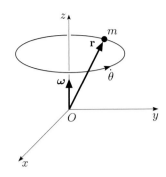

Solution

The motion of the particle is shown in Figure 4.8. By definition, we have $\boldsymbol{l} = \mathbf{r} \times m\dot{\mathbf{r}}$. From Equation (4.1), the velocity is

$$\dot{\mathbf{r}} = \boldsymbol{\omega} \times \mathbf{r} = \dot{\theta}\mathbf{k} \times (x\mathbf{i} + y\mathbf{j} + z\mathbf{k}) = \dot{\theta}(x\mathbf{j} - y\mathbf{i}).$$

It follows that

Figure 4.8

$$\begin{aligned}
\boldsymbol{l} = \mathbf{r} \times m\dot{\mathbf{r}} &= (x\mathbf{i} + y\mathbf{j} + z\mathbf{k}) \times m\dot{\theta}(x\mathbf{j} - y\mathbf{i}) \\
&= m\dot{\theta}(-xz\mathbf{i} - yz\mathbf{j} + (x^2 + y^2)\mathbf{k}). \quad \blacksquare
\end{aligned}$$

Example 4.3 demonstrates that, even for circular motion, the direction of the angular momentum $\boldsymbol{l}$ is *not*, in general, the same as the direction of the angular velocity $\boldsymbol{\omega}$. However, if the origin is at the centre of the circular motion, then the angular velocity and the angular momentum of the particle are in the same direction, since then $z = 0$ in Example 4.3 and $\boldsymbol{l} = m\dot{\theta}(x^2 + y^2)\mathbf{k} = mR^2\dot{\theta}\mathbf{k}$, where R is the radius of the circular motion.

These results hold even when $\boldsymbol{\omega}$ is not constant.

The relationship between angular velocity and angular momentum will be explored further in *Unit 27*.

*Exercise 4.3

A particle of mass m moves in the (x, y)-plane in a circle of radius R, whose centre is at the origin, with angular velocity $\boldsymbol{\omega} = \dot{\theta}\mathbf{k}$. Show that $|\boldsymbol{l}| = m|\mathbf{r}||\dot{\mathbf{r}}|$, where $\boldsymbol{l}$ is the angular momentum of the particle about the origin, $\mathbf{r}$ is its position relative to the origin and $\dot{\mathbf{r}}$ is its velocity.

Example 4.4

A pendulum bob of mass m is fixed to the origin O by a taut light string of constant length l. The bob swings to and fro in a vertical (x, y)-plane (see Figure 4.9). Use the torque law to derive the equation of motion of the bob.

Solution

Model the bob as a particle and the string as a model string. Use a plane polar coordinate system with origin at the centre of the motion, and let $\mathbf{k}$ be a unit vector pointing out of the page in Figure 4.9. The total force $\mathbf{F}$ acting on the particle is the sum of its weight $\mathbf{W}$ and the tension force $\mathbf{T}$ due to the string, i.e.

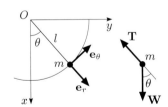

$$\mathbf{F} = \mathbf{W} + \mathbf{T},$$

Figure 4.9

where $\mathbf{W} = (mg\cos\theta)\mathbf{e}_r - (mg\sin\theta)\mathbf{e}_\theta$ and $\mathbf{T} = -|\mathbf{T}|\mathbf{e}_r$. The corresponding torque about O is

$$\begin{aligned}
\boldsymbol{\Gamma} = \mathbf{r} \times \mathbf{F} &= \mathbf{r} \times (\mathbf{W} + \mathbf{T}) \\
&= l\mathbf{e}_r \times ((mg\cos\theta)\mathbf{e}_r - (mg\sin\theta)\mathbf{e}_\theta - |\mathbf{T}|\mathbf{e}_r) \\
&= -(mgl\sin\theta)\mathbf{k}.
\end{aligned}$$

From Example 4.3, with $z = 0$ and $R = l$, the angular momentum of the particle about O is

$$\boldsymbol{l} = ml^2\dot{\theta}\mathbf{k}.$$

Hence, by the torque law, we have

$$\frac{d}{dt}(ml^2\dot{\theta}\mathbf{k}) = -(mgl\sin\theta)\,\mathbf{k}.$$

Differentiating, resolving in the **k**-direction and rearranging, we obtain the equation of motion

$$\ddot{\theta} = -\frac{g}{l}\sin\theta. \quad \blacksquare$$

This result is the same as that obtained by different means in *Unit 8* and in Section 3.

Exercise 4.4

The position of a particle of mass m at time t is given by

$$\mathbf{r}(t) = a\cos(\omega t)\mathbf{i} + a\sin(\omega t)\mathbf{j} + ut\mathbf{k},$$

where a, ω and u are constants. Write down expressions for the linear momentum of the particle, the force acting on the particle, the angular momentum of the particle about the origin O and the torque about O acting on the particle. Verify the torque law for the motion of the particle.

The most important special case for the torque law is the case when no resultant torque acts on a particle. In this case the torque law $\dot{\boldsymbol{l}} = \boldsymbol{\Gamma}$ reduces to $\dot{\boldsymbol{l}} = \mathbf{0}$ and so $\boldsymbol{l}$ is a constant vector. So if there is no resultant torque, then the angular momentum is constant. This is usually stated as the law of conservation of angular momentum, in the following form.

Law of conservation of angular momentum for a particle

If the total torque acting on a particle about a fixed point is zero, then the angular momentum of the particle about that point is constant. In other words, if $\boldsymbol{\Gamma} = \mathbf{0}$, then $\boldsymbol{l}$ is constant.

The total torque acting on a particle will be zero if the total force acting on the particle is zero, but this is not an especially interesting situation. More noteworthy is the case when the total force acting on a particle is directed towards a fixed point, which we can choose to be the origin. In this case the total torque about the origin is zero, as occurs in the following exercise.

*Exercise 4.5

Consider a particle moving around a circle at constant speed. Show that the total torque about the centre of the circle is zero.

Uniform circular motion is not the only interesting case where the total torque is zero. In *Unit 28* you will see that the total torque acting on a planet about the Sun is zero, and we shall use this fact to determine the orbits of the planets.

End-of-section Exercises

Exercise 4.6

In the film *The Wizard of Oz*, a house is swept up in a whirlwind. After a while, the whirlwind begins to dissipate and the house is subject to a decreasing torque. Although the house moves slowly towards the axis of the whirlwind, its motion is almost circular around this axis.

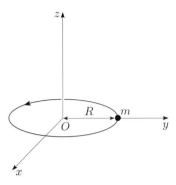

Model the house as a particle of mass m performing anticlockwise circular motion of radius R around a vertical z-axis in a horizontal (x,y)-plane, as shown in Figure 4.10. Model the decreasing torque by $\mathbf{\Gamma} = \Gamma_0 e^{-\alpha t}\mathbf{k}$, where Γ_0 and α are constants, t represents time and $\mathbf{k}$ is a unit vector in the positive z-direction.

Figure 4.10

(a) Find an expression for the angular speed of the particle in terms of the other variables and parameters. To what value does this angular speed tend as t increases?

(b) Suppose that we no longer ignore the motion towards the axis of the whirlwind and allow R to become smaller and smaller. How does this affect the angular speed? As R becomes smaller, does it remain valid to model the house as a particle?

Exercise 4.7

An electron is moving in a fixed plane in a uniform magnetic field. The total force on the electron is

$$\mathbf{F} = e\mathbf{B} \times \mathbf{v},$$

where e is a constant (the magnitude of the charge on the electron), $\mathbf{B}$ is a constant vector (the magnetic field vector) and $\mathbf{v}$ is the velocity of the electron.

All you need to know about magnetism to do this exercise is the quoted equation for the force on the electron.

Assume that the electron is moving in a circle of radius R with centre O so that the position vector of the electron is $\mathbf{r} = R\mathbf{e}_r$.

Let $\mathbf{k}$ be a unit vector normal to the plane of motion, with direction given by the screw rule, and let $\mathbf{B} = B\mathbf{k}$, where B is a constant.

(a) Show that the force $\mathbf{F}$ acts in the plane of motion.

(b) Determine the total torque on the electron and the angular momentum of the electron relative to O.

(c) Use the torque law to show that the angular speed of the electron is constant.

Outcomes

After studying this unit you should be able to:
- differentiate products of vector functions;
- understand and use the plane polar unit vectors $\mathbf{e}_r$ and $\mathbf{e}_\theta$;
- understand and use the expressions for position, velocity and acceleration for the circular motion of a particle in polar coordinates;
- understand and use angular velocity in the description of circular motion;
- relate the angular velocity to the velocity of a particle in circular motion;
- use plane polar unit vectors to solve mechanics problems involving uniform and non-uniform circular motion;
- understand and use Newton's law of universal gravitation;
- understand and use the concept of angular momentum for the motion of a particle;
- use the torque law to solve simple mechanics problems involving a single particle.

Solutions to the exercises

Section 1

1.1 (a) Differentiating, we find that
$$\dot{\mathbf{r}}(t) = -12\sin(4t)\mathbf{i} + 12\cos(4t)\mathbf{j},$$
$$\ddot{\mathbf{r}}(t) = -48\cos(4t)\mathbf{i} - 48\sin(4t)\mathbf{j}.$$

(b) The magnitude of the acceleration vector, $|\ddot{\mathbf{r}}(t)|$, is
$$\sqrt{(-48\cos(4t))^2 + (-48\sin(4t))^2}$$
$$= \sqrt{48^2(\cos^2(4t) + \sin^2(4t))} = 48.$$

(c) The acceleration vector can be written as
$$-16(3\cos(4t)\mathbf{i} + 3\sin(4t)\mathbf{j}) = -16\mathbf{r}(t).$$
So $\ddot{\mathbf{r}}(t) = -c\mathbf{r}(t)$, with $c = 16$.

1.2 The magnitude of the sideways force, towards the centre of the circle, exerted on the locomotive by the track is $|\mathbf{F}| = m|\mathbf{a}| = m\omega^2 R$. We have $m = 40\,\text{kg}$ and $R = 100\,\text{m}$. If one circuit is completed in $50\,\text{s}$, the angular speed is $\omega = 2\pi/50\,\text{rad}\,\text{s}^{-1}$. So the magnitude of the force is
$$40\left(\frac{2\pi}{50}\right)^2 100 \simeq 63.17.$$
So the magnitude of the sideways force exerted by the track on the locomotive is $63.17\,\text{N}$.

1.3 We write $\mathbf{f}$ and $\mathbf{g}$ in component form as
$$\mathbf{f} = f_1\mathbf{i} + f_2\mathbf{j} + f_3\mathbf{k}, \quad \mathbf{g} = g_1\mathbf{i} + g_2\mathbf{j} + g_3\mathbf{k},$$
so
$$\mathbf{f} \cdot \mathbf{g} = f_1 g_1 + f_2 g_2 + f_3 g_3.$$
Using the formula for differentiating the product of two scalar functions, we obtain
$$\frac{d}{dt}(\mathbf{f}\cdot\mathbf{g})$$
$$= \frac{d}{dt}(f_1 g_1) + \frac{d}{dt}(f_2 g_2) + \frac{d}{dt}(f_3 g_3)$$
$$= \left(\frac{df_1}{dt}g_1 + f_1\frac{dg_1}{dt}\right) + \left(\frac{df_2}{dt}g_2 + f_2\frac{dg_2}{dt}\right)$$
$$+ \left(\frac{df_3}{dt}g_3 + f_3\frac{dg_3}{dt}\right)$$
$$= \left(\frac{df_1}{dt}g_1 + \frac{df_2}{dt}g_2 + \frac{df_3}{dt}g_3\right)$$
$$+ \left(f_1\frac{dg_1}{dt} + f_2\frac{dg_2}{dt} + f_3\frac{dg_3}{dt}\right)$$
$$= \left(\frac{df_1}{dt}\mathbf{i} + \frac{df_2}{dt}\mathbf{j} + \frac{df_3}{dt}\mathbf{k}\right)\cdot(g_1\mathbf{i} + g_2\mathbf{j} + g_3\mathbf{k})$$
$$+ (f_1\mathbf{i} + f_2\mathbf{j} + f_3\mathbf{k})\cdot\left(\frac{dg_1}{dt}\mathbf{i} + \frac{dg_2}{dt}\mathbf{j} + \frac{dg_3}{dt}\mathbf{k}\right)$$
$$= \frac{d\mathbf{f}}{dt}\cdot\mathbf{g} + \mathbf{f}\cdot\frac{d\mathbf{g}}{dt},$$
as required.

1.4 Using the rule for differentiating the dot product of two vector functions,
$$\frac{d}{dt}(\mathbf{f}\cdot\mathbf{f}) = \frac{d\mathbf{f}}{dt}\cdot\mathbf{f} + \mathbf{f}\cdot\frac{d\mathbf{f}}{dt} = 2\mathbf{f}\cdot\frac{d\mathbf{f}}{dt}.$$

1.5

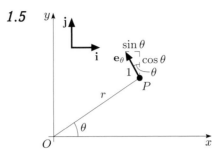

From the figure, the x-component of the unit vector $\mathbf{e}_\theta$ is $-\sin\theta$ and the y-component is $\cos\theta$. Hence
$$\mathbf{e}_\theta = (-\sin\theta)\mathbf{i} + (\cos\theta)\mathbf{j}.$$

1.6 Since $\mathbf{i}$ and $\mathbf{j}$ are themselves an orthogonal pair of unit vectors, we know from *Unit 4* that
$$\mathbf{i}\cdot\mathbf{i} = 1, \quad \mathbf{j}\cdot\mathbf{j} = 1, \quad \mathbf{i}\cdot\mathbf{j} = 0.$$
Hence
$$\mathbf{e}_r \cdot \mathbf{e}_r = ((\cos\theta)\mathbf{i} + (\sin\theta)\mathbf{j})\cdot((\cos\theta)\mathbf{i} + (\sin\theta)\mathbf{j})$$
$$= (\cos^2\theta)\mathbf{i}\cdot\mathbf{i} + (2\sin\theta\cos\theta)\mathbf{i}\cdot\mathbf{j} + (\sin^2\theta)\mathbf{j}\cdot\mathbf{j}$$
$$= \cos^2\theta + \sin^2\theta = 1.$$
Similarly,
$$\mathbf{e}_\theta \cdot \mathbf{e}_\theta = (-\sin\theta)^2 + (\cos\theta)^2$$
$$= \sin^2\theta + \cos^2\theta = 1,$$
$$\mathbf{e}_r \cdot \mathbf{e}_\theta = (\cos\theta)(-\sin\theta) + (\sin\theta)(\cos\theta)$$
$$= -\cos\theta\sin\theta + \sin\theta\cos\theta = 0.$$

1.7 Differentiating Equation (1.9) with respect to time using the Chain Rule, we have
$$\dot{\mathbf{e}}_\theta = (-\cos\theta)\dot{\theta}\mathbf{i} + (-\sin\theta)\dot{\theta}\mathbf{j}$$
$$= -\dot{\theta}((\cos\theta)\mathbf{i} + (\sin\theta)\mathbf{j}) = -\dot{\theta}\mathbf{e}_r,$$
using Equation (1.8).

1.8 Differentiating Equation (1.13) with respect to time (θ and $\mathbf{e}_\theta$ are functions of time) using the Product Rule, we obtain
$$\ddot{\mathbf{r}} = R\ddot{\theta}\mathbf{e}_\theta + R\dot{\theta}\dot{\mathbf{e}}_\theta,$$
which, by Equation (1.11), may be written as
$$\ddot{\mathbf{r}} = R\ddot{\theta}\mathbf{e}_\theta + (R\dot{\theta})(-\dot{\theta}\mathbf{e}_r) = -R\dot{\theta}^2\mathbf{e}_r + R\ddot{\theta}\mathbf{e}_\theta.$$

1.9 The radius of the circle is $R = 1$ and $\theta(t) = t^2$. Hence $\dot{\theta} = 2t$ and $\ddot{\theta} = 2$. Therefore the velocity of the particle is (from Equation (1.13))
$$\dot{\mathbf{r}} = R\dot{\theta}\mathbf{e}_\theta = 2t\mathbf{e}_\theta,$$
and the acceleration is (from Equation (1.14))
$$\ddot{\mathbf{r}} = -R\dot{\theta}^2\mathbf{e}_r + R\ddot{\theta}\mathbf{e}_\theta = -4t^2\mathbf{e}_r + 2\mathbf{e}_\theta.$$

Section 2

2.1 The minute hand of a clock makes one complete revolution (clockwise when viewed from the front of the clock) in 1 hour = 3600 seconds. So the fly's angular speed is

$$\omega = \frac{2\pi}{3600} \simeq 1.745 \times 10^{-3}\,\text{rad s}^{-1}.$$

The fly's speed is

$$v = R\omega = (0.5)\frac{2\pi}{3600} \simeq 8.727 \times 10^{-4}\,\text{m s}^{-1}.$$

The acceleration has magnitude

$$R\omega^2 = 0.5\left(\frac{2\pi}{3600}\right)^2 \simeq 1.523 \times 10^{-6}\,\text{m s}^{-2}.$$

2.2 Use a polar coordinate system with origin at the fixed end of the string, and let $\mathbf{k}$ be a unit vector pointing vertically upwards.

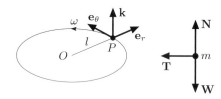

There are three forces acting on the particle: the tension force $\mathbf{T} = -|\mathbf{T}|\mathbf{e}_r$ due to the string, the normal reaction $\mathbf{N} = |\mathbf{N}|\mathbf{k}$ of the table on the particle and its weight $\mathbf{W} = -mg\mathbf{k}$. As the particle of mass m is in uniform circular motion with radius l and angular speed ω, the acceleration is

$$\ddot{\mathbf{r}} = -l\omega^2\mathbf{e}_r.$$

Applying Newton's second law gives

$$m\ddot{\mathbf{r}} = \mathbf{T} + \mathbf{N} + \mathbf{W},$$

so we have

$$-ml\omega^2\mathbf{e}_r = -|\mathbf{T}|\mathbf{e}_r + |\mathbf{N}|\mathbf{k} - mg\mathbf{k}.$$

Resolving in the $\mathbf{e}_r$-direction gives the required result,

$$|\mathbf{T}| = ml\omega^2.$$

2.3 Use a polar coordinate system in the plane of the table surface, with origin at the centre of the hole in the table, and let $\mathbf{k}$ be a unit vector pointing vertically upwards.

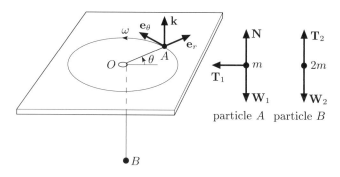

particle A particle B

First consider particle B. There are two forces acting on this particle: the tension force $\mathbf{T}_2 = |\mathbf{T}_2|\mathbf{k}$ due to the string and its weight $\mathbf{W}_2 = -2mg\mathbf{k}$.

As particle B is static,

$$\mathbf{T}_2 + \mathbf{W}_2 = \mathbf{0},$$

so we have

$$|\mathbf{T}_2|\mathbf{k} - 2mg\mathbf{k} = \mathbf{0}.$$

Hence, resolving in the $\mathbf{k}$-direction, we obtain

$$|\mathbf{T}_2| = 2mg.$$

Now consider particle A. There are three forces acting on this particle: the tension force $\mathbf{T}_1 = -|\mathbf{T}_1|\mathbf{e}_r$ due to the string, the normal reaction $\mathbf{N} = |\mathbf{N}|\mathbf{k}$ of the table on the particle and its weight $\mathbf{W}_1 = -mg\mathbf{k}$. Applying Newton's second law to particle A gives

$$m\ddot{\mathbf{r}} = \mathbf{T}_1 + \mathbf{N} + \mathbf{W}_1,$$

so we have

$$-m\frac{v^2}{R}\mathbf{e}_r = -|\mathbf{T}_1|\mathbf{e}_r + |\mathbf{N}|\mathbf{k} - mg\mathbf{k}.$$

Resolving in the $\mathbf{e}_r$-direction gives

$$|\mathbf{T}_1| = \frac{mv^2}{R}.$$

Since we have a model string and a smooth hole, $|\mathbf{T}_1| = |\mathbf{T}_2| = 2mg$ and so we obtain

$$v^2 = 2gR.$$

It follows that the constant speed of particle A is

$$v = \sqrt{2gR} = \sqrt{2 \times 9.81 \times 0.4} \simeq 2.80\,\text{m s}^{-1}.$$

2.4 Use a polar coordinate system in the plane of the surface of the disc, with origin at the centre of the disc, and let $\mathbf{k}$ be a unit vector pointing vertically upwards.

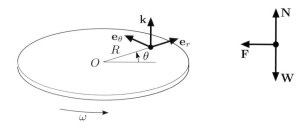

If the disc rotates through one complete revolution every two seconds, then its angular speed is

$$\omega = 2\pi/2 = \pi\,\text{rad s}^{-1}.$$

The forces acting on the particle are its weight $\mathbf{W} = -mg\mathbf{k}$, the normal reaction $\mathbf{N} = |\mathbf{N}|\mathbf{k}$ from the disc and the friction force $\mathbf{F}$. The direction of $\mathbf{F}$ is in the horizontal plane of the disc.

Since the particle stays at the same point on the disc, at a distance R, say, from the centre, it performs uniform circular motion. Hence its acceleration is

$$\ddot{\mathbf{r}} = -R\omega^2\mathbf{e}_r.$$

Applying Newton's second law to the particle, we obtain

$$m\ddot{\mathbf{r}} = \mathbf{W} + \mathbf{N} + \mathbf{F},$$

so we have

$$-mR\omega^2\mathbf{e}_r = -mg\mathbf{k} + |\mathbf{N}|\mathbf{k} + \mathbf{F}.$$

Since the friction force is in the horizontal plane, resolving in the $\mathbf{k}$-direction gives

$$|\mathbf{N}| = mg.$$

Hence we can deduce that

$$\mathbf{F} = -mR\omega^2\mathbf{e}_r,$$

so the friction force is directed towards the centre of the disc and has magnitude

$$|\mathbf{F}| = mR\omega^2.$$

If the particle is to remain static (relative to the disc), we must have

$$|\mathbf{F}| \le \mu|\mathbf{N}|,$$

which, from the expressions above for $|\mathbf{F}|$ and $|\mathbf{N}|$, and from $\omega = \pi$ and $\mu = \frac{1}{2}$, leads to

$$R \le \frac{\mu g}{\omega^2} = \frac{g}{2\pi^2} \simeq 0.497\,\text{m}.$$

Thus the maximum possible distance of the toy from the centre of the roundabout is about $0.5\,\text{m}$.

2.5 Applying Newton's second law to the planet, we obtain

$$-mR\omega^2\mathbf{e}_r = -\frac{GmM}{R^2}\mathbf{e}_r.$$

Hence

$$\omega = \sqrt{\frac{GM}{R^3}}.$$

So the period of the planet in its orbit is

$$T = \frac{2\pi}{\omega} = 2\pi\sqrt{\frac{R^3}{GM}}.$$

It follows that

$$T^2 = \frac{4\pi^2}{GM}R^3,$$

that is,

$$T^2 \propto R^3.$$

(This result is generalized in *Unit 28*.)

2.6 Use a polar coordinate system in the horizontal plane of the particle's motion, with origin at the centre of its circular path, and take $\mathbf{k}$ to be a unit vector pointing vertically upwards. Let R be the radius of the circular path. The only forces acting on the particle are its weight $\mathbf{W}$ and the tension force $\mathbf{T}$ due to the rod.

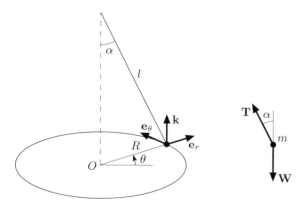

Applying Newton's second law to the particle, we have

$$-mR\omega^2\mathbf{e}_r = \mathbf{W} + \mathbf{T},$$

where $\mathbf{T} = -(|\mathbf{T}|\sin\alpha)\mathbf{e}_r + (|\mathbf{T}|\cos\alpha)\mathbf{k}$ and $\mathbf{W} = -mg\mathbf{k}$.

(a) Resolving in the $\mathbf{k}$-direction gives

$$0 = -mg + |\mathbf{T}|\cos\alpha,$$

so the tension in the rod is $|\mathbf{T}| = mg/\cos\alpha$.

(b) Resolving in the $\mathbf{e}_r$-direction gives

$$-mR\omega^2 = -|\mathbf{T}|\sin\alpha.$$

Substituting for $|\mathbf{T}|$ from the result in part (a), dividing through by m and rearranging, we obtain

$$\omega = \sqrt{\frac{g\sin\alpha}{R\cos\alpha}}.$$

We are asked for ω in terms of g, l and α, so we note that $R = l\sin\alpha$ and hence that the angular speed is $\omega = \sqrt{g/(l\cos\alpha)}$. Rearranging gives $\cos\alpha = g/(l\omega^2)$, so $\alpha = \arccos(g/(l\omega^2))$.

2.7 Use a plane polar coordinate system in the horizontal plane of particle P's motion, with origin at the centre of its circular path, and take $\mathbf{k}$ to be a unit vector pointing vertically upwards. Let R be the radius of the circular path. The forces acting on particle P are its weight $\mathbf{W}_1$, and the tension forces $\mathbf{T}_1$ and $\mathbf{T}_2$ due to the rods PA and PD, respectively. The forces acting on particle D are its weight $\mathbf{W}_2$, the tension force $\mathbf{T}_3$ due to the rod DP and the normal reaction $\mathbf{N}$ of the shaft on the particle.

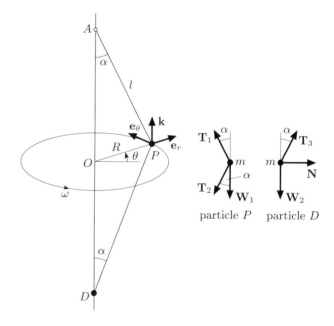

particle P particle D

Applying Newton's second law to particle P gives

$$-mR\omega^2\mathbf{e}_r = \mathbf{W}_1 + \mathbf{T}_1 + \mathbf{T}_2, \tag{S.1}$$

where $\mathbf{T}_1 = -(|\mathbf{T}_1|\sin\alpha)\mathbf{e}_r + (|\mathbf{T}_1|\cos\alpha)\mathbf{k}$, $\mathbf{W}_1 = -mg\mathbf{k}$ and $\mathbf{T}_2 = -(|\mathbf{T}_2|\sin\alpha)\mathbf{e}_r - (|\mathbf{T}_2|\cos\alpha)\mathbf{k}$.

For fixed ω and α, particle D is in equilibrium, so

$$\mathbf{W}_2 + \mathbf{T}_3 + \mathbf{N} = \mathbf{0}. \tag{S.2}$$

(a) We want to find $|\mathbf{T}_1|$ and $|\mathbf{T}_2| = |\mathbf{T}_3|$. Resolving Equations (S.1) and (S.2) in the $\mathbf{k}$-direction gives

$$0 = -mg + |\mathbf{T}_1|\cos\alpha - |\mathbf{T}_2|\cos\alpha,$$

$$-mg + |\mathbf{T}_2|\cos\alpha = 0$$

(since $\mathbf{N}$ is horizontal and so has no $\mathbf{k}$-component).

Hence $|\mathbf{T}_2| = |\mathbf{T}_3| = mg/\cos\alpha$ and $|\mathbf{T}_1| = 2mg/\cos\alpha$. where $\mathbf{W}_2 = -mg\mathbf{k}$ and $\mathbf{T}_3 = -\mathbf{T}_2$ (by Newton's third law).

(b) Resolving Equation (S.1) in the $\mathbf{e}_r$-direction gives
$$-mR\omega^2 = -|\mathbf{T}_1|\sin\alpha - |\mathbf{T}_2|\sin\alpha.$$
Substituting the values found in part (a) for $|\mathbf{T}_1|$ and $|\mathbf{T}_2|$, and using $R = l\sin\alpha$, we obtain
$$-m(l\sin\alpha)\omega^2 = -\frac{3mg\sin\alpha}{\cos\alpha},$$
so $\omega = \sqrt{3g/(l\cos\alpha)}$ and $\alpha = \arccos(3g/(l\omega^2))$.

2.8 (a) Using Equation (2.10) with $\mu = 1.3$, the maximum speed with which the car can follow a circular path of radius $R = 10$ is $\sqrt{\mu Rg} = \sqrt{1.3 \times 10 \times 9.81} \simeq 11.29$. So the maximum speed here is about $11.29\,\mathrm{m\,s}^{-1}$.

(b) Rearranging Equation (2.10) with $v = 15$, the condition to avoid slipping is
$$R \geq \frac{v^2}{\mu g} = \frac{15^2}{1.3 \times 9.81} \simeq 17.64.$$
So the radius of the roundabout needs to be at least $18\,\mathrm{m}$.

(c) We use the same condition as in part (b), but with $\mu = 0.65$. So we need $R \geq 35.29$.

In this case, the roundabout needs a minimum radius of about $36\,\mathrm{m}$.

2.9 If $v^2 \leq \mu Rg$, then the numerator in inequality (2.13) is negative, which makes the right-hand side negative since the denominator is positive. For any angle α between 0 and $\pi/2$ the tangent is positive, so any angle α satisfies inequality (2.13). The vehicle would not slip even when $\alpha = 0$, i.e. no banking is necessary for the vehicle not to slip.

Example 2.2 looked at the situation of having no banking, and the condition for the car to negotiate the corner without slipping was found to be exactly the same, $v^2 \leq \mu Rg$.

(Inequality (2.13) for the minimum angle of banking gives a negative minimum value of $\tan\alpha$. This is, in fact, meaningful. A negative value of α between 0 and $-\pi/2$ corresponds to banking facing away from the centre of the circle — an 'adverse camber' — and inequality (2.13) then gives the greatest angle of adverse camber on which the car can be driven without slipping sideways.)

2.10 (a) Starting from inequality (2.14),
$$-v^2 + Rg\tan\alpha \leq \mu Rg + \mu v^2\tan\alpha, \qquad (2.14)$$
we rearrange it to make $\tan\alpha$ the subject, obtaining first
$$Rg\tan\alpha - \mu v^2\tan\alpha \leq v^2 + \mu Rg.$$
So the possible angles of banking are given by
$$\tan\alpha \leq \frac{\mu Rg + v^2}{Rg - \mu v^2}. \qquad (\text{S.3})$$
The condition $\mu v^2 < Rg$ ensures that the right-hand expression gives a positive value for $\tan\alpha$, so a solution for α is between 0 and $\frac{\pi}{2}$.

(If $\mu v^2 \geq Rg$, the car can drive on *any* angle of banking — even vertical — without slipping downwards.)

(b) Substituting the numeric values from Example 2.3(b) into inequality (S.3) gives
$$\tan\alpha \leq \frac{0.4 \times 500 \times 9.81 + 80^2}{500 \times 9.81 - 0.4 \times 80^2} \simeq 3.57.$$
So $\alpha \leq 1.30$, and the maximum angle of banking on which the car can be driven without slipping is about $74°$.

2.11 Use a plane polar coordinate system in the horizontal plane of the particle's motion, with origin at the centre of the circular motion, and take $\mathbf{k}$ to be a unit vector pointing vertically upwards. The radius of the uniform circular motion of the particle is $R + l\sin\alpha$. The forces on the particle are its weight $\mathbf{W}$ and the tension force $\mathbf{T}$ due to the string.

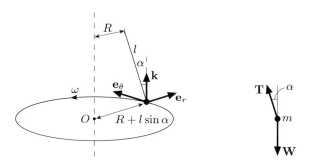

Applying Newton's second law to the particle gives
$$-m(R + l\sin\alpha)\omega^2\mathbf{e}_r = \mathbf{W} + \mathbf{T},$$
where $\mathbf{T} = -|\mathbf{T}|\sin\alpha\,\mathbf{e}_r + |\mathbf{T}|\cos\alpha\,\mathbf{k}$ and $\mathbf{W} = -mg\mathbf{k}$. Resolving in the $\mathbf{e}_r$- and $\mathbf{k}$-directions gives
$$-m(R + l\sin\alpha)\omega^2 = -|\mathbf{T}|\sin\alpha,$$
$$0 = -mg + |\mathbf{T}|\cos\alpha,$$
so $|\mathbf{T}| = mg/\cos\alpha$.
Substituting for $|\mathbf{T}|$ gives the equation of motion
$$m(R + l\sin\alpha)\omega^2 = mg\tan\alpha.$$
Hence, dividing through by $m\omega^2$, we have
$$\frac{g}{\omega^2}\tan\alpha = R + l\sin\alpha.$$

2.12 Use a plane polar coordinate system in the vertical plane of the particle's motion, with origin at the centre of the uniform circular motion. We measure the angle θ of rotation anticlockwise from the downward vertical through the origin. The forces on the particle are its weight $\mathbf{W}$ and the reaction $\mathbf{S}$ due to the seat.

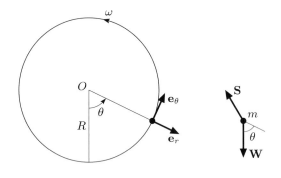

(a) Applying Newton's second law to the particle gives
$$-mR\omega^2\mathbf{e}_r = \mathbf{W} + \mathbf{S},$$
where $\mathbf{W} = (mg\cos\theta)\mathbf{e}_r - (mg\sin\theta)\mathbf{e}_\theta$ and $\mathbf{S} = S_r\mathbf{e}_r + S_\theta\mathbf{e}_\theta$.

Resolving in the $\mathbf{e}_r$- and $\mathbf{e}_\theta$-directions gives
$$-mR\omega^2 = mg\cos\theta + S_r,$$
$$0 = -mg\sin\theta + S_\theta,$$
so the radial component of $\mathbf{S}$ is $S_r = -mR\omega^2 - mg\cos\theta$ and the tangential component is $S_\theta = mg\sin\theta$.

(b) For a passenger to remain in a seat without constraint, the component vector of the reaction force S that is normal to the surface of the seat (i.e. $S_r\mathbf{e}_r$) must represent an inward force. Since $\mathbf{e}_r$ points outwards, we require that $S_r < 0$, i.e. $-mR\omega^2 - mg\cos\theta < 0$, which, on dividing through by m and rearranging, gives $R\omega^2 + g\cos\theta > 0$. This needs to hold for all θ. The least value of $\cos\theta$ is -1 (at the top of the ride), so the condition becomes $R\omega^2 - g > 0$, which we can rearrange to give $\omega > \sqrt{g/R}$. Thus the minimum angular speed for which unconstrained passengers will not fall out is $\omega = \sqrt{g/R}$.

2.13 Use a plane polar coordinate system in the horizontal plane of the surface of the table, with origin at the fixed point, and take $\mathbf{k}$ to be a unit vector pointing vertically upwards. The forces on the particle are its weight $\mathbf{W}$, the normal reaction $\mathbf{N}$ of the table and the spring force $\mathbf{H}$. Let R be the length of the spring.

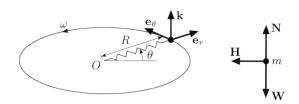

Applying Newton's second law to the particle, we have
$$-mR\omega^2\mathbf{e}_r = \mathbf{W} + \mathbf{N} + \mathbf{H},$$
where $\mathbf{W} = -mg\mathbf{k}$, $\mathbf{N} = |\mathbf{N}|\mathbf{k}$ and $\mathbf{H} = -k(R - l_0)\mathbf{e}_r$. Resolving in the $\mathbf{e}_r$-direction gives
$$-mR\omega^2 = -k(R - l_0),$$
so the length of the model spring is
$$R = \frac{kl_0}{k - m\omega^2}.$$
(Since $R > 0$, we must have $k - m\omega^2 > 0$, that is, $\omega < \sqrt{k/m}$.)

2.14 Use a plane polar coordinate system in the horizontal plane of particle A's motion, with origin at the centre of the circular motion, and take $\mathbf{k}$ to be a unit vector pointing vertically upwards. The forces on particle A are its weight $\mathbf{W}_1$ and the tension force $\mathbf{T}_1$ due to the string. The forces on particle B are its weight $\mathbf{W}_2$ and the tension force $\mathbf{T}_2$ due to the string.

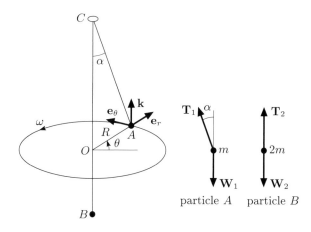

particle A particle B

Applying Newton's second law to particle A gives
$$-mR\omega^2\mathbf{e}_r = \mathbf{W}_1 + \mathbf{T}_1, \qquad (S.4)$$
where $\mathbf{T}_1 = -(|\mathbf{T}_1|\sin\alpha)\mathbf{e}_r + (|\mathbf{T}_1|\cos\alpha)\mathbf{k}$ and $\mathbf{W}_1 = -mg\mathbf{k}$.

Since particle B is in equilibrium, we have
$$\mathbf{W}_2 + \mathbf{T}_2 = \mathbf{0}, \qquad (S.5)$$
where $\mathbf{W}_2 = -2mg\mathbf{k}$ and $\mathbf{T}_2 = |\mathbf{T}_2|\mathbf{k}$.

(a) Resolving Equations (S.4) and (S.5) in the $\mathbf{k}$-direction gives
$$0 = -mg + |\mathbf{T}_1|\cos\alpha,$$
$$-2mg + |\mathbf{T}_2| = 0,$$
so $|\mathbf{T}_1| = mg/\cos\alpha$ and $|\mathbf{T}_2| = 2mg$. But $|\mathbf{T}_1| = |\mathbf{T}_2|$, so $mg/\cos\alpha = 2mg$, giving $\cos\alpha = \frac{1}{2}$ and $\alpha = \frac{\pi}{3}$.

(b) Resolving Equation (S.4) in the $\mathbf{e}_r$-direction gives
$$-mR\omega^2 = -|\mathbf{T}_1|\sin\alpha,$$
so, using $|\mathbf{T}_1| = mg/\cos\alpha$ and $\alpha = \frac{\pi}{3}$, we have
$$\omega = \sqrt{\sqrt{3}g/R}.$$

2.15 To find the upper speed limit, start from inequality (2.12), which gives the condition needed for the car not to slip up the banking:
$$v^2 - Rg\tan\alpha \le \mu Rg + \mu v^2\tan\alpha. \qquad (2.12)$$
Rearranging this to make v the subject gives
$$v^2 - \mu v^2\tan\alpha \le \mu Rg + Rg\tan\alpha$$
$$v^2 \le Rg\frac{\mu + \tan\alpha}{1 - \mu\tan\alpha}.$$
Note that $1 - \mu\tan\alpha$ is positive for the given data. The largest value of the speed v is given by
$$v^2 = 400 \times 9.81\left(\frac{0.45 + \tan 35°}{1 - 0.45\tan 35°}\right),$$
that is,
$$v \simeq \sqrt{6590} \simeq 81.18.$$

To find the lower speed limit, start from inequality (2.14), which gives the condition for the car not to slip down the banking:
$$-v^2 + Rg\tan\alpha \le \mu Rg + \mu v^2\tan\alpha. \qquad (2.14)$$

Proceeding as before, we rearrange the inequality to find the speed:

$$\mu v^2 \tan\alpha + v^2 \geq Rg\tan\alpha - \mu Rg$$

$$v^2 \geq Rg\frac{\tan\alpha - \mu}{\mu\tan\alpha + 1}.$$

So the minimum speed is given by

$$v^2 = 400 \times 9.81\left(\frac{\tan 35° - 0.45}{0.45\tan 35° + 1}\right),$$

that is,

$$v = \sqrt{746.6} \simeq 27.32.$$

So the car can be driven without skidding at between about $28\,\mathrm{m\,s^{-1}}$ and $81\,\mathrm{m\,s^{-1}}$.

2.16 The forces on the motorcycle (modelled as a particle) are its weight $\mathbf{W}$, the normal reaction of the cylinder wall $\mathbf{N}$ and the friction force $\mathbf{F}$, as shown.

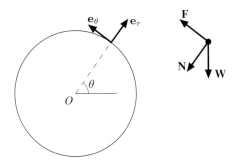

If m is the mass of the motorcycle, then Newton's second law gives

$$\mathbf{N} + \mathbf{W} + \mathbf{F} = m\ddot{\mathbf{r}}. \tag{S.6}$$

Now we model the forces. First note that the cylinder wall can only 'push' on the motorcycle, it cannot 'pull' it towards the wall. So we have $\mathbf{N} = -|\mathbf{N}|\mathbf{e}_r$.

The friction force is in the tangential direction, i.e. $\mathbf{F} = F\mathbf{e}_\theta$.

(To drive round the loop at a constant speed, the motorcycle engine must drive the wheels in such a way that the friction force is as shown in the above force diagram (otherwise there would be a non-zero resultant force component in the tangential direction and the motorcycle's speed would drop). In the left-hand half of the circle the force diagram is reversed and the friction force reverses direction.)

Suppose that the speed of the motorcycle is v, then its acceleration $\ddot{\mathbf{r}}$ is $-(v^2/R)\mathbf{e}_r$, with $R = 8$.

Resolving Equation (S.6) in the $\mathbf{e}_r$-direction gives

$$-|\mathbf{N}| - mg\sin\theta + 0 = -m\frac{v^2}{R}.$$

Thus

$$|\mathbf{N}| = m\left(\frac{v^2}{R} - g\sin\theta\right). \tag{S.7}$$

Since $|\mathbf{N}|$ is the magnitude of a vector, it must be non-negative. So the right-hand side of Equation (S.7) must be positive, i.e. we must have $v^2 \geq gR\sin\theta$ for all values of θ. The largest value taken by $\sin\theta$ is 1 (when $\theta = \frac{\pi}{2}$, i.e. when the motorcycle is at the top of the cylinder).

So the speed must satisfy

$$v \geq \sqrt{gR} = \sqrt{9.81 \times 8} \simeq 8.859.$$

Thus the slowest speed at which the motorcyclist can ride without coming away from the cylinder wall is about $9\,\mathrm{m\,s^{-1}}$.

2.17 (a) A force diagram and Newton's second law (Equation (S.6)) for the motorcycle are given in the previous solution. If the motorcycle is moving at a constant speed, the acceleration tangential to the circle is zero. Resolving Equation (S.6) tangential to the circle (in the $\mathbf{e}_\theta$-direction), we obtain

$$0 - |\mathbf{W}|\cos\theta + F = 0,$$

so

$$F = |\mathbf{W}|\cos\theta = mg\cos\theta. \tag{S.8}$$

(b) As in Solution 2.16, we also have

$$|\mathbf{N}| = m\left(\frac{v^2}{R} - g\sin\theta\right). \tag{S.7}$$

To avoid slipping, $|F| \leq \mu|\mathbf{N}|$ (with $\mu = 0.8$). So, from Equations (S.8) and (S.7), we need

$$|mg\cos\theta| \leq \mu m\left(\frac{v^2}{R} - g\sin\theta\right) \tag{S.9}$$

for all values of θ between 0 and 2π.

We can rearrange inequality (S.9) as

$$\mu\sin\theta + |\cos\theta| \leq \frac{\mu v^2}{gR}.$$

Using the hint, the largest value taken by either $\mu\sin\theta + \cos\theta$ or $\mu\sin\theta - \cos\theta$ is $\sqrt{\mu^2 + 1}$, so we need

$$\frac{\mu v^2}{gR} \geq \sqrt{\mu^2 + 1},$$

that is,

$$v^2 \geq gR\sqrt{1 + \frac{1}{\mu^2}}.$$

With $R = 8$ and $\mu = 0.8$, we need

$$v \geq \sqrt{gR\sqrt{1 + \frac{1}{\mu^2}}} \simeq 11.21.$$

So, to avoid slipping, the motorcyclist needs to go faster than calculated in Exercise 2.16, say $12\,\mathrm{m\,s^{-1}}$ at least.

Section 3

3.1 For low speeds, both pendulums will oscillate gently back and forth about the stable equilibrium position. For very high speeds, both will move in a circle around the fixed point. For intermediate speeds, the original pendulum will perform large oscillations or will circle around the fixed point, but the new pendulum will behave in this way only while the string stays taut (when the bob is above the level of the fixed point). If the speed is not high enough to keep the string taut, then the only force acting on the bob will be its weight, and the bob will behave like a projectile until the string becomes taut once more.

3.2 **(a)** Provided that

$$|\mathbf{T}| = \frac{mv_0^2}{l} + mg(3\cos\theta - 2) > 0,$$

the string will not go slack. Dividing by m and rearranging, we obtain

$$v_0^2 > gl(2 - 3\cos\theta).$$

The greatest value of $gl(2 - 3\cos\theta)$ occurs when $\cos\theta = -1$, giving $v_0^2 > 5gl$ and $v_0 > \sqrt{5gl}$. So the string never goes slack if the speed v_0 of the pendulum bob when $\theta = 0$ is greater than $\sqrt{5gl}$ (in which case the bob performs complete revolutions).

(b) If $v_0 = 2\sqrt{gl}$, then, from Equation (3.6), we have

$$\dot\theta^2 = \frac{4g}{l} - \frac{2g}{l}(1 - \cos\theta) = \frac{2g}{l}(1 + \cos\theta),$$

so $\dot\theta = 0$ only when $\cos\theta = -1$, i.e. when $\theta = \pi$. So the bob will reach the top of the circle unless the string goes slack first. We know from part (a) that, for the string never to go slack, we must have $v_0 > \sqrt{5gl}$. Therefore, since $2\sqrt{gl} < \sqrt{5gl}$, we know that the string must go slack before the bob comes momentarily to rest.

To see when the string goes slack, substitute $v_0 = 2\sqrt{gl}$ into Equation (3.7) to obtain

$$|\mathbf{T}| = 4mg + mg(3\cos\theta - 2) = mg(3\cos\theta + 2) = 0.$$

So the string goes slack when $3\cos\theta + 2 = 0$, which gives $\cos\theta = -2/3$. In the range $-\pi \le \theta \le \pi$, this gives $\theta \simeq \pm 2.3$ rad $\simeq \pm 132°$. So the string goes slack when the pendulum makes an angle of approximately $42°$ above the horizontal.

3.3 The condition for the pendulum bob just to reach the horizontal is $\dot\theta = 0$ at $\theta = \pm\frac{\pi}{2}$. So, from Equation (3.6), we find that

$$0 = \frac{v_0^2}{l^2} - \frac{2g}{l}.$$

Hence $v_0 = \sqrt{2gl}$.

3.4 Use a plane polar coordinate system in the vertical plane of the particle's motion, with origin at the centre of the sphere. The forces acting on the particle are its weight $\mathbf{W}$ and the normal reaction $\mathbf{N}$ of the sphere.

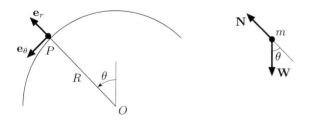

As suggested by the hint, the analysis of this situation is similar to that for the pendulum, with $\mathbf{T}$ replaced by $-\mathbf{N}$, $\mathbf{W}$ replaced by $-\mathbf{W}$ and l replaced by R, so we can make use of the results obtained for the pendulum at the beginning of Section 3.

With respect to the chosen coordinate system, we have

$$\mathbf{W} = -(mg\cos\theta)\,\mathbf{e}_r + (mg\sin\theta)\,\mathbf{e}_\theta, \quad \mathbf{N} = |\mathbf{N}|\mathbf{e}_r.$$

The acceleration of the particle is

$$\ddot{\mathbf{r}} = -R\dot\theta^2\mathbf{e}_r + R\ddot\theta\mathbf{e}_\theta.$$

Applying Newton's second law to the particle gives

$$m\ddot{\mathbf{r}} = \mathbf{W} + \mathbf{N},$$

so we have

$$-mR\dot\theta^2\mathbf{e}_r + mR\ddot\theta\mathbf{e}_\theta$$
$$= -(mg\cos\theta)\,\mathbf{e}_r + (mg\sin\theta)\,\mathbf{e}_\theta + |\mathbf{N}|\mathbf{e}_r.$$

Resolving in the $\mathbf{e}_r$-direction gives

$$-mR\dot\theta^2 = |\mathbf{N}| - mg\cos\theta,$$

so, rearranging this equation and using the appropriately amended version of Equation (3.6) with $l = R$, we have

$$
\begin{aligned}
|\mathbf{N}| &= mg\cos\theta - mR\dot\theta^2 \\
&= mg\cos\theta - \frac{mv_0^2}{R} - 2mg(1 - \cos\theta) \\
&= mg(3\cos\theta - 2) - \frac{mv_0^2}{R}.
\end{aligned}
$$

For $v_0 = \sqrt{\frac{1}{2}gR}$, we have

$$|\mathbf{N}| = mg(3\cos\theta - 2) - \tfrac{1}{2}mg = mg(3\cos\theta - \tfrac{5}{2}).$$

The particle will leave the surface when $\mathbf{N} = \mathbf{0}$, i.e. when $3\cos\theta - \frac{5}{2} = 0$, which gives

$$\theta = \arccos\tfrac{5}{6} \simeq 0.59 \; (\simeq 33.6°).$$

3.5 Use a plane polar coordinate system in the plane of motion of the particle, with origin at the centre of the circular motion. The forces acting on the particle are its weight $\mathbf{W}$ and the normal reaction $\mathbf{N}$ of the bowl. Let θ be the angle between the radius to the particle and the downward vertical, measured anticlockwise from the vertical, and let h be the vertical height of the particle above A.

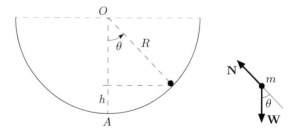

The analysis of this situation is identical to that for the pendulum at the beginning of Section 3, with $\mathbf{T}$ replaced by $\mathbf{N}$ and l by R.

(a) From Equation (3.6) we have

$$v^2 = v_0^2 - 2gR(1 - \cos\theta), \qquad (\text{S.10})$$

where v_0 is the speed of the particle at A and $v = R\dot\theta$ is its speed at angle θ. Initially we have $h = \frac{1}{2}R$, $v = \sqrt{gR}$ and $\cos\theta = (R - h)/R = \frac{1}{2}$, giving

$$gR = v_0^2 - 2gR \times \tfrac{1}{2},$$

so $v_0^2 = 2gR$. Hence Equation (S.10) becomes

$$v^2 = 2gR\cos\theta. \qquad (\text{S.11})$$

The speed at the top of the bowl, where $\theta = \pm\frac{\pi}{2}$, is thus zero, showing that the particle just reaches this level.

(b) From Equation (3.3) we have

$$|\mathbf{N}| = mg\cos\theta + mR\dot\theta^2.$$

From Equation (S.11) we have

$$\dot\theta^2 = v^2/R^2 = (2g\cos\theta)/R,$$

so

$$|\mathbf{N}| = mg\cos\theta + 2mg\cos\theta = 3mg\cos\theta.$$

(We could, alternatively, have obtained this expression for $|\mathbf{N}|$ by use of Equation (3.7) with $v_0^2 = 2gR$ and $l = R$.)

With $h = \frac{2}{3}R$, we have $\cos\theta = (R - h)/R = \frac{1}{3}$, so $|\mathbf{N}| = mg$, i.e. the magnitude of the normal reaction when $h = \frac{2}{3}R$ is mg.

3.6 Use a plane polar coordinate system in the vertical plane of the particle's motion, with origin at the centre of the circular motion.

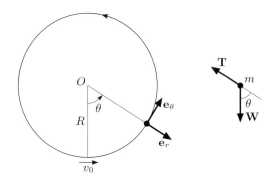

This situation is identical to that of the pendulum at the beginning of Section 3, except that here we denote the length of the rod by R rather than l.

(a) As in Section 3, we have Equation (3.6), i.e.

$$\dot\theta^2 = \frac{v_0^2}{R^2} - \frac{2g}{R}(1 - \cos\theta).$$

(b) For the particle just to reach the top of the circle, we must have $\dot\theta = 0$ when $\cos\theta = -1$. So, from part (a), this means we must have $v_0^2/R^2 - 4g/R = 0$, which gives $v_0 = \sqrt{4gR}$. So the particle will just reach the top of the circle if $v_0 = \sqrt{4gR} = 2\sqrt{gR}$.

(c) The ride executes complete circles if $v_0 > 2\sqrt{gR}$ (from part (b)). Passengers will not need constraints provided that the component of the reaction force of the seat on the passenger normal to the seat remains non-zero. This component force is of the same magnitude as the tension force in the rod, which, from Equation (3.7), is given by

$$|\mathbf{T}| = \frac{mv_0^2}{R} + mg(3\cos\theta - 2).$$

As in Section 3, $|\mathbf{T}|$ is greater than zero for all angles θ, provided that $v_0 > \sqrt{5gR}$. Since $\sqrt{5gR} > 2\sqrt{gR}$ both conditions are satisfied if $v_0 > \sqrt{5gR}$, i.e. the ride executes complete circles without the need for constraining the passengers if $v_0 > \sqrt{5gR}$.

Section 4

4.1 (a) Since the motion is clockwise, θ is decreasing during the motion, so $\dot\theta = -2$ and the particle's angular velocity is

$$\boldsymbol\omega = \dot\theta\mathbf{k} = -2\mathbf{k}.$$

(b) From Equation (4.1), the particle's velocity is

$$\mathbf{v} = \boldsymbol\omega \times \mathbf{r} = -2\mathbf{k} \times (3\mathbf{i} + 4\mathbf{j}) = 8\mathbf{i} - 6\mathbf{j}.$$

Since the radius of the circular path is $\sqrt{3^2 + 4^2} = 5$, the velocity is also given by

$$\mathbf{v} = \dot{\mathbf{r}} = R\dot\theta\mathbf{e}_\theta = 5 \times (-2)\mathbf{e}_\theta = -10\mathbf{e}_\theta.$$

Alternatively, we have

$$\mathbf{v} = \boldsymbol\omega \times \mathbf{r} = -2\mathbf{k} \times 5\mathbf{e}_r = -10\mathbf{e}_\theta.$$

4.2 By definition, the angular momentum is

$$\boldsymbol{l} = \mathbf{r} \times m\dot{\mathbf{r}} = (\mathbf{i} + 2\mathbf{j}) \times 3(2\mathbf{i} - \mathbf{j})$$

$$= (-3\mathbf{i} \times \mathbf{j}) + (12\mathbf{j} \times \mathbf{i}) = -15\mathbf{k}.$$

4.3 We know, from the text just before the exercise, that $\boldsymbol{l} = mR^2\dot\theta\mathbf{k}$, so $|\boldsymbol{l}| = mR^2|\dot\theta|$. We also know, from Section 1, that $\mathbf{r} = R\mathbf{e}_r$ and $\dot{\mathbf{r}} = R\dot\theta\mathbf{e}_\theta$, so $|\mathbf{r}| = R$ and $|\dot{\mathbf{r}}| = R|\dot\theta|$. Hence we have

$$m|\mathbf{r}||\dot{\mathbf{r}}| = m \times R \times R|\dot\theta| = mR^2|\dot\theta| = |\boldsymbol{l}|.$$

4.4 The position of the particle is

$$\mathbf{r} = a\cos(\omega t)\,\mathbf{i} + a\sin(\omega t)\,\mathbf{j} + ut\mathbf{k}.$$

Hence the linear momentum of the particle is

$$\mathbf{p} = m\dot{\mathbf{r}} = m(-a\omega\sin(\omega t)\,\mathbf{i} + a\omega\cos(\omega t)\,\mathbf{j} + u\mathbf{k}).$$

Therefore the force acting on the particle is

$$\mathbf{F} = \dot{\mathbf{p}} = -ma\omega^2(\cos(\omega t)\,\mathbf{i} + \sin(\omega t)\,\mathbf{j}).$$

The angular momentum of the particle about the origin O is

$$\boldsymbol{l} = \mathbf{r} \times m\dot{\mathbf{r}}$$

$$= (a\cos(\omega t)\,\mathbf{i} + a\sin(\omega t)\,\mathbf{j} + ut\mathbf{k})$$
$$\quad \times m(-a\omega\sin(\omega t)\,\mathbf{i} + a\omega\cos(\omega t)\,\mathbf{j} + u\mathbf{k})$$

$$= mau(\sin(\omega t) - \omega t\cos(\omega t))\mathbf{i}$$
$$\quad - mau(\omega t\sin(\omega t) + \cos(\omega t))\mathbf{j}$$
$$\quad + ma^2\omega(\cos^2(\omega t) + \sin^2(\omega t))\mathbf{k}$$

$$= mau(\sin(\omega t) - \omega t\cos(\omega t))\mathbf{i}$$
$$\quad - mau(\cos(\omega t) + \omega t\sin(\omega t))\mathbf{j} + ma^2\omega\,\mathbf{k}.$$

The torque about O acting on the particle is

$$\boldsymbol\Gamma = \mathbf{r} \times \mathbf{F}$$

$$= -(a\cos(\omega t)\,\mathbf{i} + a\sin(\omega t)\,\mathbf{j} + ut\,\mathbf{k})$$
$$\quad \times ma\omega^2(\cos(\omega t)\,\mathbf{i} + \sin(\omega t)\,\mathbf{j})$$

$$= ma\omega^2(ut\sin(\omega t)\,\mathbf{i} - ut\cos(\omega t)\,\mathbf{j})$$

$$= mau\omega^2 t(\sin(\omega t)\,\mathbf{i} - \cos(\omega t)\,\mathbf{j}).$$

To verify the torque law, we need to check that $\dot{l} = \Gamma$. We have

$$\dot{l} = mau(\omega\cos(\omega t) - (\omega\cos(\omega t) - \omega^2 t\sin(\omega t)))\mathbf{i}$$
$$- mau(-\omega\sin(\omega t) + (\omega\sin(\omega t) + \omega^2 t\cos(\omega t)))\mathbf{j}$$
$$= mau\omega^2 t(\sin(\omega t)\,\mathbf{i} - \cos(\omega t)\,\mathbf{j})$$
$$= \Gamma,$$

as required.

4.5 Choose the origin to be the centre of the circle. Let ω be the (constant) angular speed of the particle and m be its mass. Let R be the radius of the circular motion.

Using Equation (2.2), the total force acting on the particle is $-mR\omega^2\mathbf{e}_r$. So the total torque about the origin is given by

$$\Gamma = \mathbf{r} \times \mathbf{F},$$
$$= \mathbf{r} \times (-mR\omega^2\mathbf{e}_r),$$
$$= \mathbf{0}, \text{ since } \mathbf{r} \text{ and } \mathbf{e}_r \text{ are parallel.}$$

So the total torque about the centre of the circle is zero.

4.6 (a) Let $\boldsymbol{\omega} = \dot{\theta}\mathbf{k}$ be the angular velocity of the particle. From Subsection 4.2, the angular momentum is $\mathbf{l} = mR^2\dot{\theta}\mathbf{k}$. The torque law gives $\dot{l} = \Gamma$, so we have

$$mR^2\ddot{\theta}\mathbf{k} = \Gamma_0 e^{-\alpha t}\mathbf{k}.$$

Resolving in the $\mathbf{k}$-direction and rearranging, we obtain

$$\ddot{\theta} = \frac{\Gamma_0}{mR^2}e^{-\alpha t}.$$

Integrating, we obtain

$$\dot{\theta} = -\frac{\Gamma_0}{\alpha mR^2}e^{-\alpha t} + c.$$

Taking $t = 0$ when the house is first picked up by the whirlwind so that $\dot{\theta}(0) = 0$, we have $c = \Gamma_0/(\alpha mR^2)$ and hence

$$\dot{\theta} = \frac{\Gamma_0}{\alpha mR^2}(1 - e^{-\alpha t}).$$

So the angular speed is

$$\omega = |\dot{\theta}| = \frac{\Gamma_0}{\alpha mR^2}(1 - e^{-\alpha t}).$$

As $t \to \infty$, $\omega \to \Gamma_0/(\alpha mR^2)$.

(b) Assuming that the model remains valid for decreasing R, as R becomes smaller, ω becomes larger and larger without limit. However, as R becomes smaller, the distance from the centre of mass of the house to the axis of the whirlwind gets smaller and smaller. Eventually some parts of the house will coincide with this axis and the particle model will no longer be valid because the dimensions of the house can no longer be neglected.

4.7 (a) We are given $\mathbf{r} = R\mathbf{e}_r$, so $\mathbf{v} = R\dot{\theta}\mathbf{e}_\theta$. Now substitute into the given formula for $\mathbf{F}$:

$$\mathbf{F} = e\mathbf{B} \times \mathbf{v}$$
$$= eB\mathbf{k} \times R\dot{\theta}\mathbf{e}_\theta$$
$$= -eBR\dot{\theta}\mathbf{e}_r.$$

This has no $\mathbf{k}$-component, so $\mathbf{F}$ acts in the plane of motion.

(b) The total torque about O is

$$\Gamma = \mathbf{r} \times \mathbf{F} = R\mathbf{e}_r \times (-eBR\dot{\theta}\mathbf{e}_r) = \mathbf{0}.$$

The angular momentum about O is

$$\mathbf{l} = \mathbf{r} \times m\mathbf{v} = R\mathbf{e}_r \times mR\dot{\theta}\mathbf{e}_\theta = mR^2\dot{\theta}\mathbf{k}.$$

(c) By the torque law, $\dot{l} = \Gamma$, so, from part (b), we have

$$\frac{d}{dt}(mR^2\dot{\theta}\mathbf{k}) = \mathbf{0}.$$

Since both m and R are positive constants, we must have $\ddot{\theta} = 0$. Therefore $\dot{\theta}$ is constant, and so is the angular speed.

Index